The postwar Royal Navy carrier force at its peak: HMS *Victorious*, *Ark Royal* and *Hermes* steam in company, December 1960. Erect jet blast deflectors are visible at both catapults of *Victorious*, with the new generation of aircraft represented by Scimitars, the old by four Sea Venoms. Of the other four modern carriers, *Eagle* was then in dockyard hands for her reconstruction, the light carriers *Albion* and *Bulwark* were both commando carriers (refitted, respectively, February 1961–August 1962 and 1959–January 1960), and the light carrier *Centaur* was refitting for further carrier service (completed May 1961). *Conway Picture Library*

NORMAN FRIEDMAN

CARRIER AIR POWER

Drawings by John Roberts

The Rutledge Press
New York, New York

Contents

ACKNOWLEDGEMENTS

This book could never have been written without the assistance of many friends, particularly John Lewis, Norman Polmar (who as usual disclaims responsibility for the result), David Lyon of the National Maritime Museum, David K Brown (who very kindly permitted me access to portions of his forthcoming history of the Royal Corps of Naval Constructors), Antony Preston, Charles Haberlein, Larry Sowinski, Chris Wright, Arthur D Baker III and Richard Anderson. For assistance in obtaining aircraft data I am indebted to Dr William Armstrong of the Naval Air Systems Command, to H J 'Schonie' Schoenberg and his staff at the Grumman History Center, and to J D Brown of the Naval Historical Section of the Ministry of Defence. Mrs Susan Weidner of the US Naval Sea Systems Command assisted me in obtaining official plans and sketches of several US carriers, and Giorgio Giorgerini of *Almanacco Navale* provided official data on the abortive Italian carrier *Aquila*. For photographs I am grateful to Robert Carlisle of the Photojournalism Branch, US Navy, to Lon Nordeen of McDonnell Douglas, and to all the individuals and organisations acknowledged in the photo captions. Others have asked to remain anonymous; that does not decrease my debt to them. Uncredited photos are US Navy Official. My friends have, among other things, helped me to avoid some of the pitfalls which come of an inadequate knowledge of aerodynamics. The corrections are due to them, and the errors remaining are my own responsibility. Above all, this book could never have been written without the constant encouragement and assistance of my wife Rhea, particularly in some of the historical research. I hope it justifies her patience.

Norman Friedman

Introduction

Aircraft carriers are surely the most impressive, and at the same time the most controversial, manifestations of sea power. Over a history of more than sixty years they rose from experiments conducted even before 1914 to a position of significance in several interwar navies, and to pre-eminence during and after World War II. They assumed a major role in US, British, and French nuclear war planning, and at the same time their roles expanded to embrace helicopter amphibious assault. Now the carrier's role and even its existence are in question. The immense cost of conventional carriers has pushed Britain out of the practice of operating them, and it seems likely that France will follow. To many, the small V/STOL carrier is all the sea-based air capability that any rational navy can afford, and the United States is alone in espousing the large strike carrier. However, even as this is written, it appears that the US monopoly on new carrier construction will soon end; the Soviets appear to be preparing their own carrier, reflecting their own distinctive concepts of naval warfare. When it appears later this decade, there will once more be two carrier forces at least partly orientated towards mutual attack, as in the Pacific before 1945. Until then, the primary role of Western carriers will continue to be power projection, and their design and mode of operation will continue to be shaped by that role.

The carrier may be the last capital ship, the last type of ship which can assure free use of the sea by denying it to an enemy's warships while itself surviving their attacks. It succeeded the battleship because, like many other new types (such as the torpedo-boat and the submarine) it could destroy a battleship, and unlike them it could survive attacks and, indeed, protect friendly shipping over a wide area. It could also expand the reach of sea power to include attacks on inland targets by its own aircraft, and so survived the demise of hostile naval powers in 1945. Since then its chief enemies have been political, a combination of advocates of economy and advocates of land-based air power. Capital ships are extremely expensive, which is why relatively few navies can maintain enough of them to achieve sea control. However, it is not clear that there is any alternative in sight, and the Western Alliance is held together by the sea – and by the Alliance's control of that sea.

Carriers have a flexibility quite unique among warships. Ships of very similar appearance and physical characteristics may be operated in very different ways, with very different air groups and for very different ends – even in the same navy. For example, the difference between an *Essex* class carrier operated as a CVS (ASW support carrier) in the Far East and her sister operated as a limited attack carrier off Vietnam lay largely in aircraft, weapons, and operational doctrine. Thus any study of carriers must emphasize the aircraft and the tactical role assigned them. In addition, carriers, perhaps more than other types of ships, depend for their effectiveness on relatively minor fittings, such as catapults, arresting gear,

elevators and magazine arrangements. Again, two very similar ships operated differently will have very different capabilities, even aircraft capacities. Carrier operating practice, moreover, explains why one navy might adopt an innovation like the armored flight deck whereas the same system would be quite unacceptable to another, and why it might impose quite different penalties on a third.

A carrier is inherently far more manpower-intensive than any other type of surface ship, so that differences in training and morale may far outweigh the physical differences between two carriers. Men arm the aircraft on a carrier's flight deck, and men prepare those aircraft for flight. Men perform the maintenance which keeps them flying, and indeed one or two men fly each airplane – where not too many more than one or two are required to control the main battery of say, a missile boat or even a frigate armed with Exocet or Harpoon. Although considerable efforts have been made to automate many carrier functions previously performed by hand, the quality of deck crews remains supremely important.

As a concomitant, carriers require extremely large complements, partly proportional to the size of their air groups. Thus small navies have found it difficult merely to man such large ships, and as jet aircraft were introduced found it unprofitable to operate what were for them large ships with quite limited offensive qualities, ie operating small numbers of aircraft at great cost. For his part the carrier designer feels pressure to provide more and more space per man, to make a ship of fixed dimensions more comfortable for each of a larger number of men. In all Western navies there has been an accelerating pressure towards greater habitability since World War II as more and more prosperous civilian economies have attracted the large numbers of skilled technicians each warship and, doubly, each carrier requires.

Although carriers did not grow to provide greater habitability, to some extent their growth has improved conditions on board. In particular, the smaller carriers were so cramped internally that some maintenance work had to be done on the flight deck rather than in the hangar, as larger aircraft were introduced after World War II. The same ship required a permanent deck park, and aircraft deteriorated as they rode the flight deck in all weather. Although the permanent deck park was a feature of US practice even well before World War II, its maintenance implications became apparent only well after the war, as the rising cost of each airplane required that it be kept serviceable for much longer periods. More maintenance in turn had the human price of more hours per skilled man. With the US Navy operating almost under war conditions from 1950 onwards, time out of port increased sharply and the cost, in men re-enlisting, of maintenance in port (while most men enjoyed liberty) was considerable. In this sense the money spent on the much larger postwar carriers was well worthwhile, although the effect of their size on crew morale cannot be gauged. Moreover, as they were ultimately stretched to their limits to accommodate aircraft which the smaller ships could not operate, they, too, ultimately became uncomfortable. US carrier dimensions have been maintained almost constant since the *Forrestals*, while complements have risen enormously: one of the minor dramas of carrier design is the continuing attempt to resolve this inherent conflict.

There are other aspects to the personnel problem. Pilots require ready rooms with easy access to the flight deck. In *Essex* class carriers they were just under the flight deck on the gallery deck, and many pilots died when Kamikazes crashed through the thin wooden flight deck. When the same ships were rebuilt, the ready rooms were relocated under the armored hangar deck, and the ships show a characteristic enclosed escalator leading from ready rooms up to the flight deck, to avoid fatiguing the pilots unneccessarily. On an even subtler level, in all carriers there is the issue of how many ready rooms to provide: one per squadron with limited seating and some cramping, or fewer, with some squadrons sharing. This totally invisible detail may determine in part the number of aircraft the carrier can put into the air simultaneously, since it will determine the number of pilots who can be briefed simultaneously.

For the purpose of this book, an aircraft carrier is a ship whose main battery consists solely, or at least primarily, of aircraft or helicopters which it can launch and retrieve in mid-ocean, and whose operations it can sustain for an extended period. Thus aviation fuel stowage and maintenance facilities are essential elements of carrier characteristics, quite as much as flat decks or catapults. Indeed, the mere presence of a flat deck suited for, say, V/STOL operation, does *not* make a ship a carrier. This characterization includes helicopter carriers, but excludes the seaplane carriers and tenders which formed an important naval catagory even after the Second World War. It leaves on the borderline many 'air capable ships' whose helicopters (and, in future, probably V/STOLs) form adjuncts to their primary batteries.

In keeping with this restriction, this book is concerned primarily with the carrier as her design is fixed by her aircraft, and continues the theme of *Battleship Design and Development* and *Modern Warship Design and Development* in its concern for warship design as an attempt to resolve a wide variety of policy and technical conflicts. It differs in emphasizing the interaction of alternative naval strategies with the design of the carrier weapon, the airplane, and the airplane-related features of the carrier, rather than the more universal issues of hull design and seakeeping. In those terms most carriers were not too different from battleships, although they did not require heavy side armor and they did not have to accommodate such heavy concentrated weights as barbettes and turrets. As in the earlier books, the argument in this one reflects a bias towards US practice, due to the author's access to a wide range of US design and policy studies. Moreover, the United States built the great majority of all postwar carriers, and strongly influenced British and French practice in their own designs. Should the Soviet Union indeed build a conventional (non-V/STOL, albeit probably nuclear-powered) carrier during the 1980s, as now appears likely, it will presumably display an independent point of view. However, even a Soviet designer will have to confront the same basic conflicts as his counterpart in the West.

1. Elements of Compromise

All warships represent a compromise, but the compromises reflected in the design of an aircraft carrier are particularly complex. One series of choices implicit in the design concerns the air group which is the carrier's main battery. In practice the carrier has proven remarkably flexible in aircraft operations; for example, she may operate five generations of quite different aircraft over her career, with little alteration in her structure to show for all of that evolution. Even so, the choice of naval aircraft imposes minimum limits on such features as the flight and hangar decks, and the latter in turn impose limits on naval aircraft development. On the other hand, like any other warship, the carrier represents conventional naval architectural choices, such as the choice of hull form, which in turn affect air operations. There are also other choices, trade-offs between hull and aviation qualities. For example, when the British Admiralty chose to build an armored (flight deck) carrier in 1936, it implicitly accepted a much reduced air group. In many carriers of the World War II and earlier periods, conscious choices were made between carrier self-defense weapons, such as heavy guns, and aviation features such as unobstructed flight decks.

Very crudely, the need to operate specific types of aircraft sets a lower limit on acceptable carrier size, either through requirements on the flight deck itself or through requirements to stow and service aircraft. Seakeeping is also an important consideration. For example, when the US General Board considered a proposal for a 10,000-ton protected carrier in 1939, it observed that the 14,000-ton *Ranger* pitched excessively in Pacific Ocean swells and so could not be relied upon in all weather. The upper limit on carrier, as on other warship, size is generally set by cost, either directly, or through limits imposed by existing dockyard and port facilities. For example, through 1946 US carriers were limited by a requirement to be able to transit the Panama Canal; even the *Midways*, designed in 1942, were intended to meet this requirement, given a project for enlarging the locks. The Panama Canal limit was abandoned only when it proved impossible to incorporate in carriers designed to operate a new generation of heavy attack aircraft; in this case the lower limit set by aircraft exceeded the upper limit previously deemed essential. Even the large new carriers, however, were limited by the dimensions of existing Navy graving docks; they were designed so as to be able to enter certain docks on both coasts even in a grossly overloaded (badly damaged) state.

LIMITATION BY TREATY

Until 1939 there were also the effects of the naval treaties. The Washington Treaty of 1922 limited new carriers to 27,000 tons and also limited the total size of the carrier forces which the naval powers could maintain. However, it also permitted the reconstruction of up to two capital ships per signatory as carriers, providing that their displacement did not exceed 33,000 tons. At this time aircraft made such minimal demands on flight deck space that successful

Perhaps the primary compromise of carrier design is between the lengths and deck areas required for hangars and flight deck, and the tonnage available on the basis of international agreement or cost. The Royal Navy and the Imperial Japanese Navy both adopted double hangars to increase aircraft stowage, and in early carriers both adopted auxiliary flight decks: fighters stowed in the upper hangar could take off over the short flight deck at the bows, the longer conventional flight deck being reserved for torpedo and spotter-reconnaissance aircraft. The double-deck arrangement is visible here aboard HMS *Courageous*, as is the pronounced rise in the principal flight deck forward of the island, intended to help slow down landing aircraft. *Conway Picture Library*

carriers could easily be built on as little as 10,000 tons. By the accident of the existence of suitable hulls for conversion, the United States, Great Britain, and Japan each obtained two rather large carriers, and at least the US and Japanese Navies began to experiment with the type of mass carrier attacks which proved so successful during World War II.* At least in the US Navy, the experience with large carriers, whose size was at first regretted (as it limited the number of smaller carriers which could be built within the treaty limit), showed the value of large air groups and so led to the construction of further large carriers. In the case of Japan, the overall treaty limit was so largely consumed by the two ex-capital ships that the Japanese chose to restrict their next to less than 10,000 tons; she became the smallest Japanese fleet carrier, the *Ryujo*.

For the US Navy, the effect of the total tonnage limit was also temporarily to favor the smallest possible carrier. In 1926 the US Navy equated flight deck area with air-

---

*The British ships were *Courageous* and *Glorious;* at the time of the Washington Conference the Royal Navy was unique in already possessing three more converted carriers, *Argus, Eagle* and *Furious*, as well as one purpose-built ship, *Hermes*.

plane operating capacity; on this basis the smaller the individual carriers, the larger their total operating capacity. The *Lexington* and *Saratoga* were still under construction, so that there was no real experience with large as against small carriers. Thus when the Bureau of Construction and Repair proposed a 13,000-ton type, of which five could be built under the Treaty, and General Board approved it; it became the smallest US carrier, the *Ranger*, and proved far to small to be effective during World War II.* The 20,000-ton *Yorktown* type was adopted instead, but after two had been built there remained about 15,000 tons under the Treaty and, rather than waste this tonnage, the General Board eventually bought *Wasp* as a modified *Ranger*.

The 1930 London Treaty did not alter matters, but between 1930 and 1934 Great Britain sought to reduce the maximum tonnage of warships in all catagories, in hopes of reducing the cost of new construction. She looked toward a 22,000-ton limit on carriers – which was applied to the new *Ark Royal* design. In fact a 23,000-ton unit limit, and no limit on total carrier tonnage, was adopted in the next, and final, naval treaty (London, 1936). The only carriers affected were the new British armored flight deck type, as the United States built only a repeat *Yorktown* (*Hornet*) during this period, and Japan was not bound by the treaty system.

SMALL vs LARGE CARRIERS

After the demise of the treaty system, there remained the more fundamental limits on cost and dockyard facilities. There are two quite different aspects of cost. A smaller ship is always far less expensive than a larger one, so that if only a fixed number of ships of minimum capability is sought (eg to be able to cover a large number of stations), then the smallest ship is the most economical. However, a carrier has a considerable fixed 'overhead' which is almost independent of its size. For example, in the 1950s US proponents of large attack carriers argued that any attack carrier required a fixed minimum fighter force for self-defense. The same carrier required a fixed electronic system, and a fixed minimum level of aircraft maintenance shops. *Per aircraft embarked*, a larger carrier would be less expensive, and, moreover, would be able to field a larger attack aircraft group. The larger carrier would also be able to stow more fuel and more ordnance per aircraft, so that in sustained operations it would require less frequent replenishment, which in turn would reduce the number of underway replenishment ships needed by the fleet as a whole. This type of argument has been used to show that even if all conventional aircraft are replaced by VTOLs, and thus all conventional flight deck requirements foregone, a 95,000-ton carrier is still a less expensive way *per plane* to deploy such aircraft.

Vulnerability is the other side of this argument. Carriers are often characterized as floating volcanoes, waiting to erupt: before the advent of jets, the mechanism of their destruction was gasoline for the air group; now, with non-explosive jet fuel, it is the mass of aviation ordnance. In each case, aircraft on deck are little more than bombs

HMS *Hermes* was the first carrier laid down as such, although postwar economies delayed her completion until well after that of the Japanese *Hosho*. She was of cruiser size and was intended to operate with the Grand Fleet cruisers; the minimal demands on flight deck area made by the aircraft of the day meant that she was an entirely reasonable proposition at the time. *MoD(N)*

awaiting their detonators. A large carrier can be armored, and it can be given considerable structural protection against fire and against underwater explosion. If indeed it can survive hits that will destroy a smaller carrier, then the logic of the large carrier is reinforced. However, in an era of anti-ship missiles and tactical nuclear weapons, it is sometimes suggested that any carrier which can be found can be hit and destroyed: safety lies only in dispersal.

This is hardly a new idea. It was generally accepted before World War II that a carrier was inherently highly vulnerable, that its only defense was the active defense of its fighters and the pre-emptive attack of its bombers. Dispersal might ensure the survival of a large fraction of a carrier force under attack. On the other hand, it would reduce the impact of carrier attacks, and it could be argued that several carriers operating in company might mutually reinforce fighter screens. Certainly recent estimates of the chances of carrier task forces successfully attacking Soviet bases bear out the value of concentration, and of large air groups, hence large carriers.

FIXED BATTERIES

Most carriers have been armed with conventional surface-ship weapons as well as airplanes: guns, now missiles, even (as designed) torpedoes. In early carriers an important motive for armament was the fear that the carrier might be surprised by heavy surface ships when unable to operate her aircraft. Carriers generally had cruiser speed, and were armed with cruiser weapons. HMS *Eagle* and the USS *Lexington* and *Saratoga* would have had, as well, torpedoes to act as 'equalizers' in case they were surprised by battlecruisers, but in the event none was so fitted. The German *Graf Zeppelin* was to have had a battery of 5.9in guns with which to repel hostile destroyer attacks, a decision made on the basis of prewar German exercises with destroyer flotillas. By World War II such weapons had generally been abandoned on the theory that they were too expensive in aviation qualities; however, as late as 1941 the US Navy seriously considered a new carrier armed with 8in guns, a predecessor design, in fact, of the *Midway*.

On the other hand, anti-aircraft weapons persist to the present. There is always a trade-off between such weapons and flying capabilities, since they must have clear sky arcs and therefore they must impose on the flight deck. For example, in the US *Yorktown* class the gun battery was originally arranged to provide for the maximum width of flight deck, with weapons fore and aft of it. As flight deck

*Given the treaty limit on her size, *Ranger* could not be armored against surface or air attack, nor could she be given sufficient speed to combine tactically with other US carriers, which were designed for about 32kts. She did participate in the North African invasion and then in a joint US–British carrier raid on Norway, but in 1944 was relegated to training, her 5in guns removed as weight compensation for a catapult. The alternative, blistering to retrieve stability, was rejected as too expensive. Prior to the outbreak of war, carrier commanders had complained of her pitching and rolling in Pacific swells, which limited the proportion of the time she could launch aircraft; presumably the provision of a catapult (which had other unfortunate consequences) would have solved this particular problem.

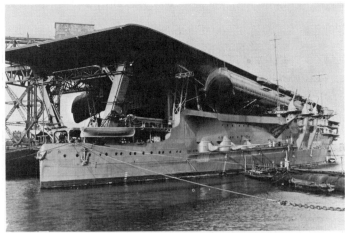

Carrier armament originally had to take into account both air and surface threats: of the three major carrier-building navies, the Royal Navy alone did not arm its first modern carriers with the heavy anti-ship guns permitted under the Washington Treaty. The Japanese carrier *Kaga*, seen here as completed in 1928, shows both batteries: 8in guns in casemates, as well as three twin 4.7in anti-aircraft guns sponsoned out from the hull to improve their fields of fire. Also visible is the Japanese answer to the problem of smoke disposal, a long smoke pipe discharging near the stern. The upper edge of *Kaga*'s thick armor belt, a legacy of her battleship origin, is visible beneath the sponson supports. Radio presented yet further problems, since good range required an antenna well above the water, the supports for which would interfere with flight deck operations. Most navies adopted hinged masts, two of which are visible in the upright position. *By courtesy of Norman Polmar*

British prewar carrier doctrine emphasized the gun as a means of self-defense; the armored flight deck was originally conceived as a means of protecting aircraft struck below in anticipation of air attack. Thus the Royal Navy was willing to adopt very heavy anti-aircraft batteries even at the expense of flight deck space, a choice emphasized by the forward port 4.5in guns in this September 1950 photograph of HMS *Indefatigable*. *Conway Picture Library*

length became more important, the design changed, with the guns mounted alongside in cut-outs. The *Essex* was considered an improvement from the *aviation* point of view, in that cuts on the starboard side of the flight deck were avoided; at the same time the 5in battery was increased by mounting eight guns in twin gunhouses fore and aft of the island. To some extent this increase reflected the decline of the belief that carrier fighters would suffice to destroy all incoming attackers. American defensive batteries reached their peak in the *Midways*, in which a compromise between sky arcs and encroachments on the flight deck was reached: all eighteen 5in/54 guns were mounted on the hangar deck level alongside the flight deck, leaving a cone above the ship essentially unprotected. Contemporary British practice, as in the *Ark Royal* and then in the armored carriers, was orientated more heavily towards guns, and the Royal Navy was willing to sacrifice flight deck area to large twin gunhouses.

Postwar, the old issue of maximum aircraft operating capacity became over-powering , particularly as the guns required large crews for maintenance and operation, and thus competed on another level with the air group. Moreover, it was not at all clear that light anti-aircraft weapons would be able to deal with jet attackers. The United States did mount many 5in and 3in guns aboard converted *Essex* class carriers but these were gradually eliminated, partly to compensate for continuous additions of topweight. The evolution of the *Forrestal* class was more striking. The design began with a combination of 5in automatic guns and a new 3in/70. However, it was limited, for political reasons, to 59,000 tons, and the guns were first to go. The ships entered service with eight 5in/54, and the forward gun sponsons limited ship speed in heavy weather, as they were relatively close to the water and created amounts of spray, which absorbed engine power. Since US naval strategy valued the ability to operate in heavy weather in areas such as the Norweigian Sea and the Formosa Strait, all of the forward guns – half the total battery – were removed. Later ships in the class, armed

▲ In some cases the requirements of air and surface action conflicted directly. The American light carriers of the *Independence* class were originally designed to carry single 5in guns fore and aft, and the name-ship of the class, shown here, actually did. However, it was soon concluded that a carrier in company with numerous surface escorts would be more subject to air than to surface attack, and after a short time the single guns were replaced by quadruple 40mm anti-aircraft weapons.

The *Midways*, completed at the end of World War II, were fitted with what was probably the heaviest anti-aircraft battery of any carrier: eighteen 5in/54 in single mounts at hangar deck level, as well as twenty-one quadruple Bofors guns and numerous 20mm weapons. The unusual position of the heavy weapons was originally chosen merely to clear the flight deck but by 1945 was seen, too, as a means of protecting the unarmored hangar deck from Kamikazes. *Midway*, photographed here in May 1947, still shows her wartime configuration, as well as a wartime-type air group including numerous SB2C Helldivers, with Corsair fighters forward. The small white objects under the Helldivers' wings are ▼ APS-4 radars.

with the Terrier surface-to-air missile, had their batteries located entirely aft.

The issue remains. Current US air defense practice envisages a layered defense, in which most attackers (at least in theory) fall victim to fleet fighters at long range, or to escort-fired surface-to-air missiles at medium range. However, it is conceded that some attackers must leak through, and against this eventuality current US carriers are armed with a combination of the Sea Sparrow Point Defense Missile System (in one of several variants) and the Phalanx close-in weapon system – plus deceptive ECM and

chaff launchers. None of these fittings is very heavy, and none takes up much space, although it can be argued that the warning radar for Sea Sparrow must of necessity interfere with the mass of other, aviation-related, carrier radars, given the constricted space available on the carrier island. However, the primary load imposed by current carrier defensive weapons is in manpower, primarily for maintenance and for reloading. That is probably why the Seacats were removed from HMS *Ark Royal*: they were judged not worth the maintenance troubles they brought.

On the other hand, defensive weapons have a considerable psychological value. For example, by the end of World War II the US Navy was convinced that the 20mm cannon was virtually useless. Yet such weapons were to have been incorporated in the reconstructed *Essex* class carriers; as one officer put it, there is considerable morale value in being able to shoot back at attackers, even if that shooting turns out to be pointless. There is apparently considerable sentiment in the US Navy that any ship as large as a carrier should be able to do *something* if she is approached by a hostile craft, say a sampan with a bazooka aboard. That explains in part the retention of four 5in guns aboard the *Forrestal*s, and it also explains the serious consideration given, from time to time, to placing lightweight 5in guns aboard later carriers. What it hardly explains is how a capital ship normally screened by at least three destroyers would find herself in just that situation – but that type of logic is irrelevant, given the feeling of nakedness that the complaint reveals.

AIRPLANE CAPACITY

There are two sides of aircraft operation. The first is the number of aircraft the carrier can operate effectively at any one time. Before and during World War II, for example, the standard US carrier tactic was the deck-load strike, in which the flight deck was filled with warming-up aircraft, all of which were flown off. Thus the area of the flight deck became the measure of aircraft operating

In the last two decades the gun has lost most of its value as an anti-aircraft weapon, and in many cases has been sacrificed in favor of flight deck extension and strengthening. US amphibious assault carriers were an exception: their 5in guns were considered useful for shore bombardment. This is USS *Valley Forge* as LPH8, May 1964, still carrying two of her former four twin 5in/38 and two single shielded 5in/38 (of her original four) in sponsons. All of her lighter weapons, useful only for anti-aircraft fire, have been landed, and her air group has been replaced by Marine Corps CH-34 helicopters.

As an offensive weapon, the carrier had to accommodate large attack aircraft. Here *Lexington* recovers a Martin T4M-1 torpedo-bomber; earlier arrivals parked forward have been folded to permit compact parking. The smaller aircraft are probably a mix of F3B-1 fighters and O2U-2 scouts. Wind screens in the lowered position are visible amidships; note also the forward elevator, with the tail of the 'T' shape closed off, and the Loening amphibian perched outboard abaft the island. US practice was always to move landing aircraft into a deck park near the bows, then 'respot' them aft for another take-off; however, aircraft could be flown off over the stern, the carrier backing down to provide wind-over-deck, and until 1944 US carriers were fitted with arresting gear forward. The reversible flight deck had the additional merit of survivability: even if one end of the deck were disabled, the air group could still use the other. *By courtesy of Larry Sowinski*

British prewar practice did not contemplate deck parking upon landing, and British carriers were designed with their forward elevators *well* forward, so that a landing airplane could be struck below while the next landed. *Courageous* shows both elevators (lifts) down, their cross shape evident, and a wind screen erected before her upper hangar opening onto the small flight deck forward. *Conway Picture Library*

Modern aircraft crowd the flight deck of even the largest carriers. *Ark Royal*, shown here in June 1976, was the largest carrier built in Britain, but she was designed for the era of 30,000lb propeller-driven strike bombers. A Buccaneer may weigh as much as twice that. Parked forward are three US Navy guests, two A-7s and an A-6 of Carrier Air Wing 1 (fin code 'AB'); behind them are a Buccaneer and a Gannet airborne early warning aircraft, recognizable by its double-folded wing, with a Phantom and more Buccaneers in the background and also right aft. By this time the increased demands of her aircraft had entirely deprived the 'Ark' of shipboard defensive weapons (her former gun sponsons have been faired over and plated in), and the ultimate effect of such demands was to transfer as many carrier functions as possible to other ships of the task group. On *Ark Royal*'s flight deck is a large Sea King ASW helicopter, which encroaches upon the limited space for strike and air defense aircraft; when the Royal Navy planned its new carriers from about 1959 onwards, it hoped to move ASW helicopters to specialist escort carriers, the predecessors of the current *Invincible* class. The massive projection forward is part of a large steam catapult installed during a 1967–70 refit, which enabled her to operate Phantoms and Buccaneers. *HMS Ark Royal/Royal Navy*

capacity, within limits set by aircraft endurance and the tempo of landings and take-offs. The other measure of operating capacity is the ability of the carrier to sustain air operations, and that depends, first, on her capacity for aircraft fuel and aviation ordnance. Over a longer period it depends upon her ability to maintain her aircraft and their electronics. The latter has become more and more important since it began with aircraft radios during World War I. For example, although a carrier might not be expected to do more than mount a limited series of strikes against a defended target, she would have to maintain a continuous Combat Air Patrol (CAP) consisting of several jet fighters and an airborne early warning aircraft, in postwar US practice. Both are radar-equipped, and both require constant attention, and a constant supply of shop facilities and spare parts – and technicians.

The flight deck itself limits the size of the effective air group. Before the advent of the current angled deck, it was standard to divide the flight deck into a launching area forward, a deck park, and a landing area abaft the safety barrier which protected the deck park from aircraft missing the arresting gear wires. The length of the launching

area was defined, before World War II, by the distance the lightest aircraft would have to roll before becoming airborne, given a wind-over-deck (WOD) generated by a combination of ship motion and the prevailing wind. During the latter part of the war it became common for ships to catapult off the first aircraft, until a sufficiently clear space was reached for rolling take-offs, which were quicker than the catapult and hence better liked. This change in practice in itself increased the number of aircraft which could be operated at the same time. In addition, there was a change in deck park procedure. Prewar practice was for the air group to fly off as a unit, and to be recovered as a unit. The time taken to launch and recover the entire air group had to be deducted from its endurance and hence from its effective range. Moreover, some problems arose in fitting CAP into this flight-deck cycle. Late in the war, when carriers made sustained strikes against shore targets, it became common to fly off half the air group at one time, recover the other half, then rearm and launch when the first half returned. This practice minimized the time the carrier had to spend steaming into the wind, which might be blowing towards the strike area.

British practice was very different, and had different consequences for carrier design. Where in the US case the hangar was largely used for maintenance and for the storage of non-operational aircraft, the Royal Navy considered it the storage area for the entire group when the latter was not in the air. For example, until well into the war it was standard British practice to strike each landing airplane below before landing the next, whereas the US Navy merely rolled a landing aircraft forward over the retracted barrier, and reset the barrier for the next landing. Although British carriers had very fast elevators, their landing rate was far more leisurely than that of the US Navy, a point well known among prewar British naval aviators. In part, the acceptance of this low rate of operation reflected British carrier tactics which, unlike those of the US and Japanese Navies, did not contemplate mass attacks. The British view of the importance of the hangar as a means of protecting relatively flimsy aircraft when

not in flight may have been in part a survival of World War I experience, when floatplanes not stowed in steam-heated hangars would become sodden as to be unable to rise from the water due to the extra weight. There may also have been an acute awareness of the flimsiness of many of the adapted Royal Air Force land types the Navy had to use, as well as of the difficulty of obtaining replacements for damaged aircraft. In any case, to the Royal Navy aircraft operating capacity was hangar capacity. On a ship of limited length, the only way to increase it was to adopt a second hangar under the original one, with all of the delays that implied for elevator operations. The double hangar was first adopted in the British carriers *Courageous* and *Glorious,* with a short take-off deck for fighters built out of a lower hangar; this system was copied by the Japanese Navy in its two large carrier conversions, *Akagi* and *Kaga*. It was also a feature of the abortive German *Graf Zeppelin*, the initial design of which was heavily influenced by that of the *Courageous*. Even after the demise of the lower flight deck, the double hangar system was an efficient way of combining large hangar capacity with a relatively short hull. This solution was adopted for the 1935 *Ark Royal* (and, indeed, for the next *Ark Royal*) as well as for several of the later armored carriers. In effect the *Illustrious* traded her second hangar for an armored flight deck.

Japanese practice roughly paralleled that of the Royal

Even ships not subject to major refit in the postwar decade showed the effects of weight growth associated with the new aircraft: this is USS *Midway* in February 1955, moored at Manila, with most of her starboard 5in guns already removed. Visible on deck are Skyraiders aft, with Banshee jet fighters lining the port side of the flight deck and swept-wing Cougars on the starboard side forward. By this time *Midway* was considered marginal at best as a jet carrier; a few months later she entered Puget Sound Navy Yard for SCB-110 reconstruction.

Navy, in that operating capacity was equated with hangar capacity, and double-decked hangars were employed to increase it. For example, *Ryujo* was designed as a 'minimum carrier', with a single hangar, her length determined by the capability of available arresting gear. When the Naval Staff decided that she had an insufficient air group, a second hangar was added above the first. In view of the use of hangar stowage, it seems somewhat surprising in retrospect that few Japanese naval aircraft had wings which folded completely, so that great ingenuity was required to achieve maximum stowage. A very limited deck park, generally twelve aircraft, was employed in wartime.

During World War II the Royal Navy was forced to increase the size of many of its air groups to increase the number of fighters. The US deck park system had to be adopted – albeit somewhat reluctantly, as shown by the continuing interest in double hangars in the *Ark Royal*. In some escort carriers aircraft were actually too large either for the elevators or for the hangar, and so had to ride

The sheer size of a modern carrier makes for considerable flexibility. For example, in November 1963 a Lockheed Hercules (C-130) was flown onto and off the attack carrier *Forrestal*; in view of its size, no other aircraft were left on deck, and the ship's flight deck layout is particularly visible. By this time *Forrestal* and her sisters had had their forward battery of 5in guns removed to reduce resistance in heavy weather; the after port weapons are just visible. The non-standard dotted line down the center of the flight deck was presumably a guide for the C-130 pilot, who seems just barely to have missed clipping the carrier's island.

permanently on deck, and the Merchant Navy operated semi-carriers (MAC-ships) with no hangars at all.

A new factor entered with the advent of jet aircraft. Jets required very long take-off rolls and so would have to be catapulted. Moreover, they had very short endurance, which limited effective air group size. That is, an airplane with a one-hour endurance is unlikely to be useful as part of a sixty-airplane strike for which the average take-off interval is a minute and the average landing interval is forty seconds. It is necessary either to limit the air group or to change tactics – and flight decks. At first the US Navy

did the former, but the day was saved by the invention of the angled deck, which permitted simultaneous launch and landing of aircraft. An angled deck also provides an aircraft park in which aircraft can be rearmed and refueled, but its size is determined far more by aircraft characteristics than by the size of the air group. In theory, the flight deck can work continuously, sending out a stream of aircraft. Alternatively, aircraft can go in groups, to achieve some of the advantages of concentration at the expense of total numbers over time.

In each case it is not the size of the flight deck alone which determines carrier capability, but rather a combination of flight deck dimensions and ship speed, for wind-over-deck. In the case of a jet carrier catapult capacity determines the maximum weight of aircraft which can be launched at a given WOD. For a steam catapult, that in turn depends to a large extent upon available boiler power, in effect upon a trade-off between the loss of speed due to continuous catapulting and the loss of catapult power.

Catapult power also depends upon the length available: the catapult can only apply acceleration up to the capacity of airplane and pilot, so to achieve a given speed it needs a minimum distance. Similarly, an arresting gear can apply only so much deceleration to an airplane; it, too, requires a minimum distance in which to work.

In contrast to big-gun capital ships, carrier designs require trade-offs in length, internal arrangement and internal volume. For example, in a modern carrier the combination of arresting gear run-out and catapult length sets a minimum limit on flight deck length. In earlier ships with axial (non-angled) decks, the critical quantities were landing length (including run-out), deck park length and take-off length, and their magnitudes depended on carrier operating practice and on the characteristics of the carrier aircraft. Length of course also affects hydrodynamic performance, in that it determines the speed-to-length ratio which is an important factor in determining the power required to attain a given speed.

INTERNAL ARRANGEMENTS
A carrier differs from virtually all other warship classes in the degree to which different elements of her internal arrangement interact. The earliest such consideration was smoke disposal: a high-powered steam plant produces a considerable volume of smoke, which has to be discharged without creating such turbulence above the flight deck as to make landing impossible. In the earliest British carriers complex systems of ducting through the after part of the hangar were tried, generally with unfortunate consequences: the hangar became uninhabitable *and* smoke rose aft. One solution was the now familiar island superstructure, with a conventional funnel offset to starboard, to raise the stream of smoke well above the flight deck. However, the island itself created some problems, and most aviators much preferred a flush-deck carrier with either no island at all or at worst a very small one. They prevailed in the Japanese Navy, and in the US Navy decided – at least at first – the design of the *Ranger*, with six folding uptakes aft. Japanese practice, as perfected in the 1930s, was to carry smoke up to flight deck level abaft the island, and exhaust it downwards so as to avoid interference with flight deck operations; Japanese carriers which were built with islands had their funnels angled outboard for similar reasons. By way of contrast to Japanese practice, US escort and light fleet carriers, which had very small islands and virtual flush decks, employed small deck-side uptakes, apparently without any difficulties.

The island exists for much more than the uptakes. When the *Yorktown* class were being designed in 1931, the Bureau of Aeronautics wanted a flush-deck design like that of the *Ranger*, but it proved impossible to design efficient folding uptakes for the high power (150,000shp) contemplated. Quite soon Aeronautics was willing to accept a conventional island superstructure, as it was found essential to provide a raised platform for flight control ('pri-fly' in US parlance). In wartime and postwar design an island superstructure was essential for radar and communications. For example, the original design for the US CVL (the light cruiser conversion) had no island; however, the ship required air and surface search radar. That in turn required a mast, and efficient navigation required a small bridge. The structure then being designed for escort carriers was adopted.

When the enormous carrier *United States* was designed in 1946–48, there was renewed interest in a flush-deck configuration. She was to operate very large aircraft, and it was considered essential that she be capable of launching several simultaneously. By deleting (or at least minimizing) the island, her designers could provide catapults sponsored out to port and starboard; in fact ultimately she had two catapults in her waist and two more in her bow, for simultaneous launch of two bombers and two fighters. That in turn revived the issue of smoke disposal, which afflicted both the *United States* design and its successor, the *Forrestal*; it was solved only by the invention of the angled deck with the consequent return of the island. During the super-carrier design smoke disposal was so severe a problem that nuclear power seemed the only solution.

The flight deck arrangement is reflected in the layout of the rest of the ship. For example, the uptakes consume considerable volume between boilers and flight deck. The more compact the machinery the less volume lost – but the more vulnerable the ship to single underwater hits in her engines and fire rooms. On the other hand long horizontal runs of uptake are themselves a source of vulnerability, carrying water from one flooding compartment to another. Since the *Essex* class of 1940, US carriers have adopted *en échelon* and unit arrangements of machinery; in current ships, an auxiliary machinery space separates two pairs of combined turbine and boiler rooms. The advent of nuclear power greatly simplifies matters, since there need no longer be any direct connection between island location and machinery space location, nor need the machinery spaces be concentrated to reduce uptake runs. In the *Enterprise* the reactor plant was quite massive and relatively concentrated, but by the time the current *Nimitz* was designed it was possible to power a carrier with only two reactors, which in turn could be widely separated within her hull to reduce sharply the probability of crippling damage by only a few hits.

Hangar configuration must reflect both the location of elevators on the flight deck and the location of magazines far below, as generally bomb elevators open onto the hangar deck or decks; depending upon their operating practice, navies vary as to whether these ammunition hoists also open onto the flight deck. Since World War II, elevator configuration has also reflected a division of the hangar deck into fire-tight bays, with at least one elevator serving each.

There is also a fundamental choice in hangar and flight deck structure, between a design in which the flight deck is the upper flange of the hull girder, and so is a strength deck, and one in which it is no more than a superstructure superimposed on the hull. Before and during World War II the Royal Navy espoused the former, the US Navy the latter practice. British carriers had enclosed hangars, the structure around the hangar well containing maintenance shops. The flight deck thus became the upper flange of the ship girder, and the hangar walls became part of its longitudinal structure. Advantages included lower stresses in the hull, since the hull girder was deeper; it also became easier to isolate hangar fires, using a combination of fire curtains and salt water sprays, as introduced in HMS *Eagle*. In its interwar carrier designs the Royal Navy was particularly concerned with fire hazards (including aviation gasoline stowage) because of its unfortunate experiences of magazine explosion during World War I. Finally, the enclosed hangar had 'environmental' advantages for a navy operating very largely in cold, wet weather. The hangar/maintenance space could be kept tolerably warm and, in addition, corrosion damage to aircraft – which, due to political and financial circumstances, were difficult to replace – could be limited, when they were stowed within it. When the Royal Navy did decide to provide protection for its aircraft, in the *Illustrious* and later classes, the enclosed hangar was well suited to this requirement, as side armor was necessary to protect aircraft against cruiser fire.

COMPARATIVE INBOARD PROFILES (SIMPLIFIED) OF SELECTED AIRCRAFT CARRIERS

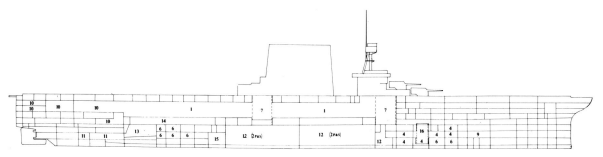

LEXINGTON (as designed 1922)

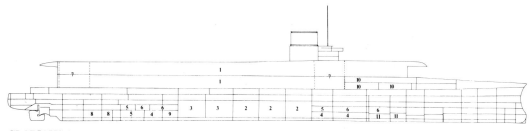

GLORIOUS (as reconstructed 1930)

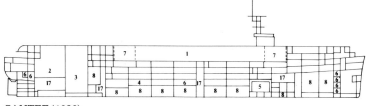

HIRYU (1935)

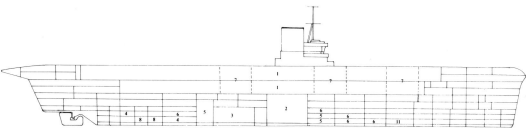

ARK ROYAL (1937)

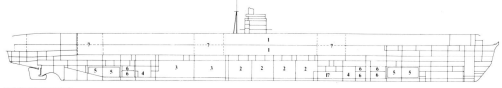

SANTEE (1939)

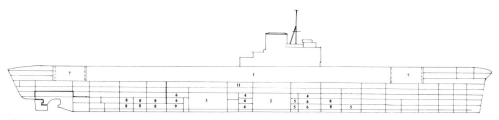

FORMIDABLE (1939)

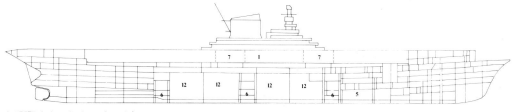

AQUILA (as designed 1941)

Scale 1: 1700 approx

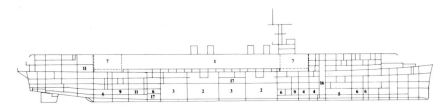

INDEPENDENCE (1942)

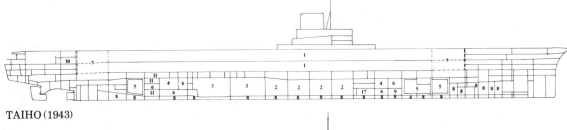

TAIHO (1943)

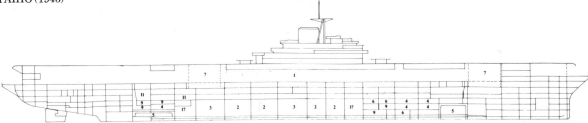

RANDOLPH (1944)

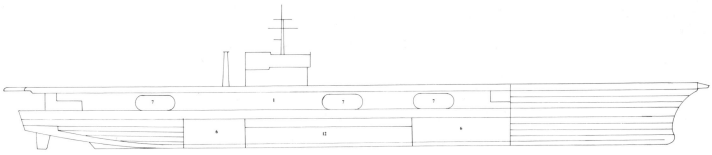

JOHN F KENNEDY (1967)

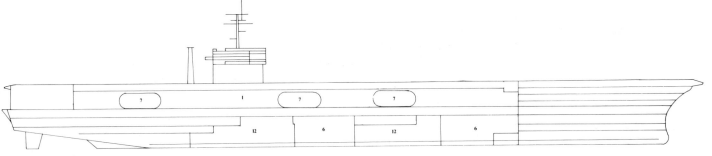

NIMITZ (1972)

The balance of the volumes in carriers has shifted considerably over time: recent ships such as the *Nimitz* show larger and larger magazines whereas, with the passing of piston-engined aircraft, aviation fuel need no longer be stowed in protected spaces. In contrast to US practice, the Royal and Imperial Japanese Navies equated hangar volume with aircraft capacity, leading to extensive use of double-level hangars, even in ships with relatively small air groups. Even when large amounts of topweight were consumed in armored flight decks, the Japanese provided their *Taiho* with two hangars. However, HMS *Formidable*, of the *Illustrious* class, shows only a single hangar: in effect her designers traded air group size for passive protection against dive-bombing. Finally, the relative inefficiency of hulls converted from other configurations is evident in such ex-capital ships as the *Lexington* and *Glorious*. In the ex-tanker *Santee* much of the final displacement was consumed by ballast, not evident here.

KEY
1 Hangar
2 Boiler room
3 Engine room
4 Bomb magazine
5 Aviation fuel stowage
6 Magazine
7 Aircraft elevator
8 Oil fuel stowage
9 Aircraft and ship small-arms magazine
10 Aircraft repair and maintenance facilities
11 Torpedo magazine
12 Machinery space
13 Main motor rooms (in *Lexington*) forward motor rooms abreast after magazine spaces)
14 Reserve aircraft stowage
15 Main control room
16 Bomb elevator
17 Auxiliary machinery room

Although the size of the carrier's hangar does not determine the size of her air group, its dimensions, particularly its height, do limit the types of aircraft the carrier can operate. This is the 25ft high hangar deck of the nuclear carrier *Enterprise*, September 1964; work is proceeding on a pair of Vigilante (A-5) strategic bombers in the foreground, and Crusaders and Skyhawks are in the background. The 'AE' tail fin code identified the Carrier Air Group (6), the 'A' prefix indicating Atlantic – Sixth (Mediterranean) Fleet in this case. Although none of the aircraft visible came close to needing the full depth of the hangar, that would not have been the case with airborne early warning aircraft owing to their high radomes.

In US carriers the hangar was an open structure which could be enclosed by rolling shutters. One advantage of the open structure was that aircraft engines could be run up inside the hangar, thus permitting the carrier to launch a larger strike consisting of her normal deck load plus aircraft from the hangar. There were problems: the flight deck incorporated expansion joints and had to be reinforced considerably as aircraft weight increased. When it was armored, in the *Midway* class, the problem of support became far more severe, due to much increased flight deck weight; at the same time stresses on the hull itself increased, since the depth of the hull girder was less than it would have been had the flight deck been incorporated as a structural member. Hull stress, particularly in rough weather, became a serious problem for the *Essex*s postwar, as the US Navy began to operate more routinely in Arctic waters. Thus proposals for the reconstruction of the *Essex* class ASW carriers (1968) to assure their operation through the 1980s included the provision of a new flight deck which *would* act as a member of the hull girder. As for protection of the hangar proper, in the 1945 revision of the official Characteristics (Staff Requirements) of the *Midway* class, it was suggested that in effect the row of single 5in gun mounts on either side of the hangar would tend to keep Kamikazes from penetrating the otherwise open structure.

Japanese practice was midway between the two: generally the flight deck was not a strength deck, but on the other hand the hangar or hangars were enclosed by shops. The trade-off is in volume as well as structural weight and strength: in the Royal and Japanese Navies aircraft were stowed in the hangars, and indeed superimposed hangars were often necessary. Any intrusion into these spaces was, therefore, to be avoided. Moreover, if the hangars were fully enclosed, it was possible to tolerate hangar decks quite close to the waterline without fear of flooding, at least in the undamaged condition. In US practice, on the other hand, the effective freeboard of the carrier was the freeboard of her hangar deck. This remains the case on current designs, since the hangar is open to water entering the large elevator openings. On the other hand, the most important freeboard issue in seakeeping is freeboard at the bow, and the system of enclosing US carriers forward to form 'hurricane bows' has largely overcome the wetness of wartime designs, particularly the *Midway*s.

Speed costs below-decks volume, which in a carrier is both in short supply and largely devoted to those factors which increase the *endurance* of the carrier air group. In standard US practice, for example, an attack carrier has, within her armored internal box, her engines and her magazines. Non-inflammable aviation fuel presents no problem, as it fills torpedo protection spaces and can be traded off against ship fuel oil capacity in a non-nuclear carrier. However, magazine volume is a major issue, as aircraft bomb loads grow. The volume problem is only aggravated by the introduction of low-drag bombs which cost more volume per unit weight, and by missiles which require less dense stowage, not to mention special checkout facilities and shops. In carriers designed to operate piston-engined aircraft ordnance demands were less pressing, but on the other hand explosive aviation gasoline

(avgas) had to be stowed within the armored box, often surrounded by sea water. There was, of course, constant pressure to increase gasoline stowage as aircraft performance improved and aircraft engine appetites grew stronger.

There are also volume conflicts above the armored box. Modern aircraft carriers devote a growing proportion of their hangars to maintenance shops and spare parts stowage; the squeeze is so bad that in the *Nimitz* class the large sponson supporting the angled deck has been taken over for shop space. Hangar height is determined by the requirements of aircraft maintenance, and contributes to problems of topweight, given the size and weight of the flight deck and the requirements that both it and the hangar deck be dry under most sea states. A subtler squeeze is personnel. All of those shops require trained technicians, and more and more are needed with each increase in avionics or weapon sophistication. They in turn require housing and messing facilities, and although this might not have been an issue in a ship with perhaps 1500 men aboard, it is complex indeed when the complement is more than 5000.

The personnel squeeze has affected the US Navy particularly severely. All current US carriers are directly descended from the *Forrestal* design of 1950, which in its day was considered quite spacious for about 3800 men. Shops and stowage ate into the accommodating space, while at the same time the complement, including the air group, rose to about 5000. Meanwhile, with the end of the draft, the Navy has found the recruiting and retention of qualified technicians more and more difficult – particularly given the unpleasant working conditions of overcrowded ships. Men are, in effect, yet another drain on the internal volume of a hull already at the limits of dockyard facilities; it seems very unlikely that future US carriers

In early US carriers, hangar dimensions dwarfed the aircraft accommodated: this is the newly completed *Lexington*, her hangar filled with Curtiss F6C-3 fighters of VF-5. Later carriers had deep overhead girders from which spare aircraft could be hung; it was standard practice to carry up to 25 per cent spares to make up for battle and operational losses. Given aircraft hung overhead, hangars had to be very deep, with a standard 17ft 6in clearance – which in turn was reflected in such US aircraft as the F4U Corsair, with considerable height when folded.

will grow substantially beyond the current size, or that their air groups will be so substantially reduced as to relieve the problem. The only real hope is improved reliability, particularly in electronic systems. To some extent electronic equipment which can automatically diagnose faults is a step in this direction.

Much the same squeeze of personnel and ammunition appears in other modern surface ships, but they have a way out: more superstructure can be built up, within the limits set by stability. A carrier, on the other hand, is sharply limited by her flight deck. Because she is designed primarily to operate aircraft, the aviators can quite reasonably demand that any structure above the flight deck be minimized, if not eliminated entirely, as at one time was proposed. Perhaps the greatest counter-example is presented by British carriers, which historically have incorporated immense islands supporting, for example, elaborate communications gear and radar. US practice has always been to forego such equipment rather than enlarge the island, ie in effect to size the island first and then later to decide what can go onto it, after the minimum demands of ship control and air control have been met.

HULL DESIGN REQUIREMENTS

Even the size and form of the carrier's hull is a matter of considerable compromise. Carriers tend to be long, for high speed, but that length must be balanced by a considerable depth of hull girder, for strength, and by a considerable freeboard, for dryness; the latter depends not upon the freeboard itself but rather upon the ratio of freeboard to length. All of this is quite standard, except that in a carrier the uppermost (flight) deck must generally be broken to admit elevators, which weaken it as a strength deck. Until the *Forrestal* class, the United States solved this problem by taking the hangar deck as the strength deck; the flight deck was a light structure incorporating expansion joints and it did not contribute to overall hull strength. The British and Japanese practice was to make the flight deck the strength deck. This was probably predicated on the practice of totally enclosing the hangars within the hull, surrounding them by shop spaces; US policy, by way of contrast, was to close off the hangar only by light rolling shutters. When the latter were opened, aircraft on the hangar deck could be warmed up before rising to the flight deck for launch.

The abortive *United States* and the *Forrestal* were so long that the hangar deck could no longer supply sufficient strength; the flight deck had to be the strength deck. To some extent the American design problem was simplified by the adoption of deck-edge elevators throughout, but then there remained the major structural problem of limiting stress around the large openings made by the elevators. This was not the only problem. For example, there was a maximum angle acceptable between catapult and ship centerline, as too great an angle would amount to a break in the strength deck. The net consequence of this limit was that although the original Characteristics for the *Forrestal* required a capacity to catapult four aircraft simultaneously, two catapults (on the sponson) had to be placed so close that at best an aircraft could sit on one while the other fired.

Presumably the size of a centerline elevator in a carrier whose flight deck is her strength deck is limited by structural considerations, but that in turn implies a limitation on the size of aircraft which she can operate, which may be more critical than that imposed by her speed, or her catapult capacity, or her flight deck layout. On the other hand, as the Royal Navy pointed out in the 1960s, an elevator on the flight deck can be operated in seas which entirely preclude the operation of deck-edge elevators.

There is another side to carrier length: maneuverability. Carriers generally turn into the wind to launch and recover their aircraft. The smaller their turning circles, the less distance lost per turn, if the wind is opposite to the general direction of the carrier force. This was considered particularly important before World War II when carrier operation often included frequent launch and recovery of scouts and patrolling aircraft, and it militated against maximum length. Maneuverability was also of course important in operations in company with escorts, but it is no longer emphasized: the escorts, which must be at least as handy as the carrier, conform to her movements. One related issue, important in US practice before World War II, was the ability to steam astern at high speed. By the mid-1930s it was common US practice both to launch and to recover aircraft over both bow and stern.

The design of the hull is also shaped by requirements for passive and active protection. Weight must be found for armor, and volume for the anti-torpedo systems which protect by absorbing the blow of an underwater explosion. Generally, armor requirements are stated in the form of a required probability that specified bombs and rockets will be excluded from the vitals deep in a ship. Much of the protection is afforded by the massive structure of the ship, as any weapon penetrating to, for example, a magazine must pass through several bulkheads – which are, however, there for structural rather than protective reasons. As large as a carrier is, she still does not afford vast margins for extra protective weight. Thus the designer must calculate the effect of all of that structure before adding specialized internal armor, and he must attempt to achieve some balanced level of protection over the vitals: machinery, magazines and, in earlier ships, aviation gasoline stowage. In recent years a new threat has emerged: where bombs and rockets might strike almost vertically, a cruise missile is likely to approach almost horizontally. It is, moreover, provided with a powerful shaped charge capable of penetrating a thickness of armor greater than its diameter. In addition, the momentum of the cruise missile may carry it through the hole it makes, and unexpended fuel will be a fire hazard. Such a weapon may be a direct threat to the carrier in that it may be able to penetrate to a magazine. Protective measures, such as means of preventing the mass detonation of the magazine even in the event of a hit, have their own costs, not merely fiscal but also in the capacity of the magazine and in the ease and rapidity of transfer from magazine to aircraft, ie on the net offensive power of the carrier.

The underwater volume of the hull must accommodate magazines, machinery, and, in some ships, gasoline stowage, all within the side protective system. The machinery may be spread out to reduce the probability that the ship will lose all power after a single lucky hit, but that reduces space for magazines. Magazine volume in turn determines much of the striking power of the carrier. There may be, for example, a trade-off between the length the magazines occupy (ie the probability that a hit randomly located along the length of the ship will penetrate to a magazine) and their height: a magazine extending above the waterline is, of course, far more vulnerable than one entirely under water.

The choice of machinery presents additional trade-offs. In the United States the usual debate is between advocates of nuclear power and those who feel that nuclear endurance is illusory, since the carrier must replenish her stocks of aviation fuel, ordnance, and spare parts at intervals far shorter than those that conventional propulsion would enforce. As in so many other features of carrier operation, part of the issue is the way the carrier is to be used. For example, in the 1950s the US carrier force was designed primarily to launch nuclear strikes deep in Soviet and satellite territory. Carriers would run in at high speed (which gave them immunity from submarine attack), reach launch positions, launch their aircraft, move on, recover, and then launch again. A few consecutive strike days would exhaust the nuclear munitions aboard the carrier, but on the other hand nuclear weapons were expensive and there was no interest in placing many more aboard, or in forward areas for replenishment. Nuclear power provided more sustained high speed for both the carrier and her escorts, if the latter were nuclear; otherwise the carrier herself could accommodate fuel for the escorts. The longer the high-speed run, the farther from the target the carrier force might be able to slow down to a normal cruising speed. The high-speed dash in and out was a countermeasure against attack by Soviet land-based bombers.

This kind of hit-and-run raid remained attractive even after the carriers gave up their strategic attack mission. For example, before Vietnam one of the principal carrier missions was support of amphibious operations. This involved a few days of carrier strikes, after which the Marines would have secured a sufficient beach-head to land their own aircraft, and the carriers would be able to withdraw. Again, it could be argued that high-speed carrier endurance would be extremely valuable, as the carriers would be constrained only by their munitions and aircraft fuel capacities, not by any need to withdraw to fuel. Moreover, they would not have to transit toward the target area at less than full speed, which again would provide some immunity from the only important open-ocean threat, the submarine.

Conversely, in Vietnam, carriers typically conducted intensive operations for several days at a time, withdrew to replenish, and then returned to the flight line. It could be argued that ship fuel capacity was only a minor factor in such operations, and that the expense of nuclear plants might well be foregone in order to keep up the number of carriers – and their aviation capabilities. Part of this argument was that carrier transit speed to the operating area was of little import, and certainly was no longer any protection from submarines in an era of numerous fast nuclear submarines and, moreover, numerous submarines armed with long-range missiles. Thus a carrier task force is now limited in its transit speed by its need to maintain sonar watch. For example, the abortive US CVV design, for a smaller non-nuclear carrier, called for a trial speed of less than 30kts, for the first time since the prewar *Ranger*.

Peacetime transit speeds may not be affected by sonar consideration, and nuclear plants do permit a carrier to remain in a crisis area with minimal support. Since Vietnam the principal role of the US carrier force has been to provide US tactical air power in crisis areas in which the United States has no land bases and no existing forces; the latest example is the Indian Ocean. In such areas the carrier must maintain the potential for high-intensity strikes, but in practice it operates at a low level, protecting itself with its fighters and its ASW aircraft. Its endurance, then, is determined almost entirely by its steaming endurance – and that is the unique advantage of a nuclear plant. If, as some believe, crises such as that in Iran are likely to become more frequent even as general war is not much more probable, then such peacetime operating endurance may come to be a dominant advantage.

A nuclear plant is expensive, and it may impose a considerable minimum size on a carrier which might otherwise be smaller and less expensive, given some set of operational requirements. One cannot avoid wondering, for example, whether the French would now have an operational helicopter carrier had they not decided to provide their PH75 with a nuclear power plant. The question, then, is not only the mode of operation of the carrier but also the relative costs imposed by her air group, her air group endurance (in, for example, shops and maintenance personnel), and a suitable nuclear plant.

For some years the USS *Enterprise*, the first US nuclear aircraft carrier, was the world's largest. Here she is shown newly completed, carrying two of the most impressive naval aircraft of the early 1960s, the F-4 Phantom II and the A-5 Vigilante supersonic strategic bomber. In 1962, when this photograph was taken, the US carrier force was gradually being shifted from the strategic to the tactical role, currently symbolized by the A-6 Intruder and the A-7 Corsair II. Neither had yet entered service, and this photograph shows their functional predecessors, the A-1 Skyraider and the A-4 Skyhawk, one of the latter sitting on one of the two waist catapults. Also visible, aft, are a pair of E-1B Tracers and several F-8 Crusader day air superiority fighters.

2. Aircraft at Sea 1918-1945

An aircraft carrier has two possible roles. It operates aircraft in company with a moving naval force at sea, far from land bases, and it can move high-performance aircraft within range of a shore or inland target beyond the reach of similar land-based aircraft, given available bases. In the first role the emphasis is on timeliness. Although the fleet may be within range of land-based aircraft, the latter are unlikely to arrive soon enough to affect the issue. Alternatively, they may be unable to arrive in sufficient numbers, carrying sufficient weapons. Furthermore, coordination between a force at sea and a distant land base is difficult at best, and even modern aircraft may be affected by bad weather at their base. The only way to avoid these difficulties would be a kind of standing patrol over or near a fleet, and that would be extremely costly in aircraft, if it were practicable. These factors remain as important now as when they led to the invention of the aircraft carrier during World War I.

Perhaps the most prominent examples of this role in current carrier operation are combat air patrol (CAP) for fleet air defense and ASW patrol flown from a carrier to help protect a moving force. Earlier examples include reconnaissance (the original carrier role), artillery spotting, and attack on enemy warships as part of a general naval engagement. It is worthwhile, further, to draw a distinction in carrier and in carrier air group design between roles requiring continuous operation of aircraft (such as CAP) and roles requiring only a few massive efforts, as in strikes against an enemy fleet during a limited battle.

The second basic carrier role remains important even in an era of long-range aircraft. Against tactical targets, the issue is either bomb tonnage delivered per unit time, or else time available to the attacking aircraft for loitering over the target area, eg for close air support of ground forces. In the latter case, the closer the air base (or carrier) to the target area, the more time the tactical airplane can spend over it. In the former, the further the airplane has to fly before and after its strike, the smaller its bomb load, or perhaps the lower its penetration speed and hence the less its chance of survival. Attacks from greater ranges generally require either larger aircraft, or more aircraft, or both, to deliver the same tonnage of bombs. Longer flying time has its cost as well; it causes losses through damage which would not be fatal, given a closer base at which to land. Even non-battle accidents become more serious. In recent years the development of more and more efficient means of in-flight refueling has sometimes been advanced as an argument in favor of the use of distant land bases in place of carrier task forces. However, even with aerial refueling, land-based tactical aircraft remain subject to the disadvantages of very long range flying, not to mention the additional vulnerabilities associated with their tanker force.

As in the case of the first role, there are many variations on this theme, perhaps the most unusual being the use of carrier-borne helicopters for 'vertical envelopment' assaults. There is also an important distinction between the hit-and-run raid and steady bombardment, with important consequences for carrier design, such as the requirements for aircraft fuel and ordnance. Carrier operations through much of World War II emphasized the short, intense raid. Ordnance tables prepared for carriers designed before World War II generally provide for only a few sorties by the carrier air group. For example, it was British practice to provide 1½ torpedoes per torpedo-bomber, one load of 500lb SAP bombs per aircraft, and three loads of 250lb SAP per aircraft. On the other hand, American carrier operations off Korea and Vietnam were continuous; carriers withdrew from the operating area only as they exhausted fuel and ammunition, and the less frequent the withdrawal the more efficient the operation. This type of operation explains in part the very large magazine space provided for recent US carriers.

In effect, the carrier is a far more efficient means of deploying air power at a great distance than is a system of land bases. However, the radius over which a carrier is effective is itself limited by the capability of her air group. The carrier cannot be everywhere at once, and cannot respond rapidly to a very distant emergency, a point emphasized by recent US experience in emergencies in the Indian Ocean. Carriers based at Subic Bay in the Philippines required as much as ten days to steam to the crisis area off the Straits of Hormuz. Long-range land-based aircraft can respond far more quickly, although they cannot remain on station for extended periods (at least, as compared to a surface ship). This type of timeliness is of little value in a political crisis, but it does permit a land-based airplane to attack a distant ship or submarine detected by some long-range sensor.

That is the role of US P-3 Orions and Soviet 'Badgers'. The US P-3 force exists very largely to attack submarines whose positions are revealed by long-range sensors such as the SOSUS bottom-moored sonar system. The 'Badger' force is designed to attack surface ships whose presence is detected by the Soviet Ocean Surveillance System (SOSS). During World War II, German and Italian land-based torpedo- and dive-bombers proved extremely effective against Allied naval and merchant shipping, particularly where, as in the Mediterranean, they were present in large enough numbers to overwhelm the small number of carrier-borne interceptors present. Perhaps significantly, the same Italian land-based aircraft proved quite ineffective in direct support of the Italian fleet. The latter tried to create its own carrier force during the war, even though previously it had preferred to depend upon land-based aircraft, which in a narrow sea such as the Mediterranean would always be within reach of their targets.

SHIPBOARD AVIATION IN WORLD WAR I

Carrier missions are reflected in the composition of carrier air groups. Thus, the British 'semi-carriers' of World War I

▲ HMS *Furious*, the first fast British carrier, in her final World War I form (1918), with a landing-on deck aft and a flying-off deck forward. The large net abaft the funnel was intended as a safety barrier. However, the air currents created by her funnel made landing-on aft impossible, and the first successful landings were made on her foredeck. In her sole offensive operation, the raid on Tondern, aircraft flew off but had to land in the water alongside on their return. *Furious* was rebuilt postwar as a flush-decker, and her half-sisters *Courageous* and *Glorious* became the first really modern British carriers. *Conway Picture Library*

HMS *Argus*, converted from an Italian liner, was the prototype of the modern carrier, with her flush deck permitting both landing-on and taking-off. She was completed just too late for World War I, and in 1939 ▼ was assigned to trade protection duty. *Conway Picture Library*

operated first reconnaissance, then reconnaissance and fighter aircraft. Reconnaissance was their most valuable service, particularly in elucidating the enemy formation early in a battle. Without an airborne observer, the fleet was nearly blind, given the limited vision of surface scouts and the usual fog, mist and smoke. Thus Admiral Jellicoe's great achievement at Jutland was his correct perception of the disposition of the High Seas Fleet, based on fragmentary surface reports. Ironically, the High Seas Fleet was spotted by a seaplane launched by HMS *Engadine*, one of the three original seaplane carriers, but although its message reached the carrier it never reached Jellicoe. The significance accorded aerial observation is evident in the standard Grand Fleet disposition of the time: *Engadine* was to operate with the scouting screen of light cruisers, so that she would not have to fall back out of the fleet as she stopped to launch and retrieve floatplanes.

The fighters were the obverse side of reconnaissance. They were to deny to the Germans the advantage represented by their large fleet of Zeppelins. The latter were intended for long-range scouting over the North Sea. For the German fleet they were to provide the sort of strategic intelligence the British obtained by radio analysis; for example, in August 1916 it was a Zeppelin report which permitted the German High Seas Fleet to avoid a trap set by the British Grand Fleet. In addition, a Zeppelin loitering above the scene of a battle could provide the sort of tactical intelligence the British sought from their own shipborne aircraft.

Another reconnaissance function was spotting. Although the heavy gun was the undisputed primary naval weapon, in practice its range was limited by the

HMS *Eagle*, converted from a battleship hull under construction for Chile, introduced the modern island configuration. She ran flying trials in 1920 even though she was still incomplete, as shown here, without her forefunnel, her characteristic tripod mast and the extreme forward end of her flight deck. Completion was delayed until 1924. Of the two aircraft on deck, the larger appears to be a Sopwith Cuckoo and the smaller a Parnall Panther. *Conway Picture Library*

The classical prewar role of the Fleet Air Arm was to 'find, fix and strike', ie to find the enemy fleet, to 'fix' it by slowing it down enough to permit the slower British fleet to come into range, and then to assist the fleet in the ultimate gunnery battle. TSR (torpedo-spotter-reconnaissance) aircraft, like these 810 and 820 Sqn Blackburn Sharks warming up on board *Courageous* (about 1936), could carry out all three roles, including spotting the fall of shot for the battle fleet. The Shark itself served only briefly, being superseded by the Swordfish in 1938; it was the last of a series of Blackburn torpedo-bombers which included the single-seat Dart and the Ripon and Baffin. The airplanes with uncowled engines waiting further aft are 810 Sqn Baffins. *By courtesy of Richard L Ward*

range at which the fall of shot could be observed, or 'spotted'. Aircraft could, then, greatly extend the effective range of shellfire, particularly if the objectives were hidden by land or smoke. Naval aircraft proved effective both in the Dardanelles and in the destruction of the German cruiser *Konigsberg* by the Rufiji Estuary in July 1915. By the end of World War I spotting was done by Grand Fleet reconnaissance planes, and it was well understood that fighters would be necessary to permit the spotters to work undisturbed, as well as to protect the Fleet from enemy spotters.

Fleet aircraft could also attack an enemy directly, using torpedoes. The Royal Navy experimented with torpedoes dropped from floatplanes as early as the Fall of 1914, and British floatplanes made successful attacks in the Dardanelles the following year. However, torpedo planes could

not accompany the fleet until the advent of the true aircraft carrier. Soon after the first such ship, HMS *Argus*, had been ordered in 1916, Commodore Murray Sueter, the Admiralty's Superintendent of Aircraft Construction, asked Sopwith to produce a carrier-borne torpedo-bomber, which became the Cuckoo. Admiral David Beatty, commander of the Grand Fleet, was sufficiently impressed to plan a 200-plane raid on the German fleet in harbor, for early 1918. His program included the conversion of several additional merchant hulls to aircraft carriers, and it was ultimately rejected partly because the Cuckoo's 19in torpedo could not sink a capital ship and partly because the large, fast merchant ships in question were urgently needed elsewhere. Even so, the torpedo-bomber became a major element of British naval thinking.

BRITISH POLICY BETWEEN THE WARS

The Royal Navy thought, throughout the interwar period, in terms of carriers fully integrated with the battle fleet; the primary naval weapon would continue to be the heavy gun, but aircraft would both protect the fleet and support its operations. At the end of World War I this philosophy seemed to imply the construction of specialist carriers. One, HMS *Hermes*, was intended specifically to work in the cruiser scouting line; she would carry 25 reconnaissance machines. In addition, flying-off and landing-on decks were added to the cruiser *Vindictive*, which retained part of her cruiser armament; she would carry 6 reconnaissance and 2 fighter aircraft. The ex-battlecruiser *Furious*, the largest of the converted carriers, was assigned 14 reconnaissance and 6 fighter aircraft. Offensive air power was limited to two carriers, the *Argus* with 20 and the new *Eagle* with 23 torpedo-bombers. Aircraft were also carried by many capital ships and light cruisers: Grand Fleet air doctrine of August 1918 required that each capital ship be fitted to launch two aircraft from runways atop turrets, and for at least two light cruisers in each squadron to be so fitted. As scouts, the battlecruisers would each operate two reconnaissance aircraft, although as of the end of the war each generally operated one reconnaissance and one fighter airplane. Each battleship division was to be able to operate independently, which meant one reconnaissance plane and one fighter for the flagship and the relief flagship, and two fighters each for the other two ships in the division. The light cruisers were too small to operate reconnaissance aircraft, but their fighters were equipped with radios and, according to a contemporary US report, 'have pilots sufficiently expert to send radio messages while flying the plane. These machines are therefore capable of assisting in reconnaissance work'.

Only the carriers could retrieve aircraft, and to some extent it was expected that aircraft launched from other ships would land aboard them. In addition, Grand Fleet aircraft were fitted with flotation bags, and attempts were made to modify their landing gear to make for easier ditching.

This lavish establishment, which replaced the earlier series of 'semi-carriers', was clearly beyond British means for the interwar period. Yet many of its features remained. For example, carriers built and converted (*Glorious*, *Courageous*) through the 1920s were all designed to operate fleet float- or seaplane reconnaissance aircraft, in effect to serve as their tenders as part of the battle fleet; this continued the notion that the carrier would service aircraft launched by the capital ships. Reconnaissance in support of the fleet was often cited as the single most important function of the Fleet Air Arm, and indeed in 1937 the Admiralty issued a Specification (S.23/37) for a specialized carrier airplane which might shadow an enemy fleet. The emphasis on reconnaissance also showed in the designs of strike (torpedo-spotter-reconnaissance, TSR) and even fighter-reconnaissance (FR, by virtue of a second seat for an observer) aircraft.

It was the Royal Navy's great misfortune that all of its aircraft were transferred to the new Royal Air Force on 1 April 1918. At that time the Royal Naval Air Service actually operated far more aircraft, including land-based types, than the Royal Flying Corps, and many of its officers were quite air-minded, as witness Admiral Beatty's ambitious plans for carrier air strikes. Carrier operations had advanced from experiments to integration with the main fleet. However, with the formation of the separate Royal Air Force many of the naval aviators transferred to the new service. This is not to deny the Royal Navy's

continuing interest in carriers – indeed, until well into the 1930s it operated the largest carrier fleet in the world – but its ships were all handicapped by their World War I origin: the combination of operating procedure (perhaps conditioned by difficulties in replacing deteriorated aircraft) and hulls originally designed for other purposes made for aircraft complements far below those accommodated by ships of similar or lesser displacement in the US Navy.

Above all, the Royal Navy continued through the interwar period to consider the battleship the principal element of sea power. This was hardly a unique concept, but in the Royal Navy it implied that the carriers would be used largely to support a battle-line engagement, since it seemed unlikely that carrier aircraft could themselves sink the enemy's battle line. The US and Japanese Navies tended to agree that battleships could survive air attack, as long as they were properly handled, but also to feel that such survival might be irrelevant as long as the enemy carriers were not dealt with first. They tended to separate carrier operations from the battle line, and such a distinction made it easy to abandon the battle line concept entirely when it was shown that airborne weapons could indeed sink modern capital ships.

From a political point of view, the Royal Navy's loss of control over the design of aircraft reduced sharply its ability to obtain modern types, and perhaps even its perception of the possibilities inherent in modern aircraft, particularly in the immediate prewar period. Historians differ as to the extent to which the Admiralty lost financial control over aircraft procurement, and hence the extent to which a non-Navy-minded Air Ministry could avoid the development of appropriate naval aircraft. It seems likely, however, that in the absence of a large body of senior aviators within the Royal Navy, comparable perhaps to the US Bureau of Aeronautics, even formal fiscal authority would have had little impact. During the interwar period much of

---

HMS HERMES (as built, 1920s)

The profile shows *Hermes* at load water line; when fully loaded she trimmed excessively by the bow – hence the rise in the boot topping forward. The latter, combined with the flat flight deck, produces the optical illusion that the flight deck slopes down slightly toward the bow. Note that the wind scoop (21) was fitted to keep funnel gases clear of the foretop.

KEY
1 Aircraft elevator
2 Observation platform
3 Fixed slope (provided for original longitudinal arrester wire system)
4 Wireless masts
5 Arresting wires
6 2pdr pompom
7 Safety nets
8 Palisade
9 Hinged transverse bridge
10 Telescopic mast
11 Hinged DF mas
12 Wind screen
13 Rails for wind screen
14 5.5in director
15 4in AA gun
16 5.5in control position
17 AA control position
18 Type 71 W/T receiver
19 Type 71 W/T transmitter
20 RU petrol tank
21 Wind scoop (port and starboard)
22 Hangar
23 Fireproof curtain
24 Overhead aircraft runway
25 Oil fuel
26 Central store
27 Dynamo

MIDSHIP SECTION   PLAN OF HANGAR DECK

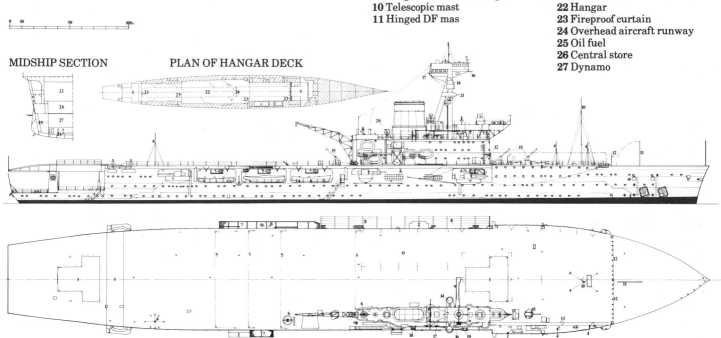

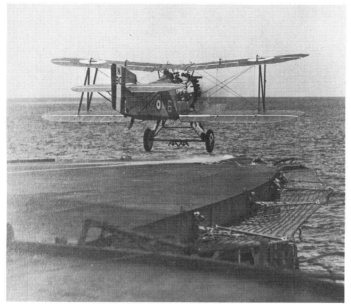

The Fairey Flycatcher, shown here, was the principal carrier fighter of the Fleet Air Arm from 1923 to 1934 and, indeed, the only FAA fighter between 1924 and 1932. It was so light that it could take off from the 60ft auxiliary (lower) flight decks of *Furious*, *Glorious* and *Courageous*; in fact, it was flown from short platforms atop the turrets of capital ships, the predecessors of the later catapults. The Flycatcher was succeeded by the Hawker Nimrod, a naval equivalent of the Hawker Fury; it was symbolic of British interest in two-seat fighters that although the contemporary Osprey was designed to a 1926 Specification, the Fury was a private venture, not sanctioned until Specification 16/30 was drafted around it. *Fleet Air Arm Museum*

the development of aircraft stemmed not from a perception of tactical or strategic requirements but rather from the logic of a rapidly advancing aeronautical technology. On the other hand, in its other branches the Royal Navy dealt with mature technologies: it could formulate operational and strategic requirements to drive their development. In some important ways, the situation of aircraft between wars mirrored that of battleships at the turn of the century, when the development of the dreadnought type was driven not by some larger strategic plan but by the feeling that advancing gunnery and propulsion technology would force some such revolution, no matter what the larger concepts might be. Without a large internal aviation community, the Royal Navy could not take full advantage of the interwar aviation revolution, nor, perhaps, could it fully appreciate the postwar revolution of jet aircraft and nuclear weapons.

THE PROBLEM OF THE FLEET FIGHTER

In the period just after World War I it was assumed that the fleet would steam preceded by a scouting line of light cruisers (the 'A–K line'), followed up by the battlecruisers and then by the main body of the fleet. Carriers bearing reconnaissance and torpedo aircraft would steam just astern of the cruisers, their aircraft scouting up to 135 miles ahead of the fleet and 50–100 miles on either side. Once contact was made it would be maintained, and torpedo aircraft on these carriers would be able to slow the enemy fleet so as to bring it to action. Enemy carriers might also be an object of an early strike; by the late 1930s it was acknowledged that 'the fleet deprived of carriers will be unable to undertake any further major fleet operation in the face of an enemy who has carriers at his disposal'. Carriers operating with the battle line itself would furnish spotting aircraft as well as fighters to protect the spotters and to deny the enemy air spotting. Since spotting was a prerequisite for effective very long range shellfire, such operations might be decisive. In addition, torpedo-bombers might attack the enemy battle line during the gunfire phase of the engagement. Merely forcing battle-

ships out of precise formation would ruin their long-range fire, which by the 1920s was typically concentrated among several ships, all controlled by a single officer, often all firing at a target beyond the horizon.

There was some confusion as to the proper role of the fighter. At first, it was to secure the air over the battle, at least to the extent of rendering enemy spotting impossible. Fighters might also escort the torpedo strike, and in addition they might neutralize enemy carriers by strafing and bombing their vulnerable flight decks, particularly if they could achieve surprise. Fighter defense of the fleet against enemy attack was far less certain, before the days of radar warning. There was also a certain ambivalence: if the torpedo-bombers could generally penetrate enemy defenses, surely an enemy could expect to penetrate the fleet's? This view echoed the contemporary belief that bombers would always be able to penetrate land-based fighter defenses, and may reflect the Air Ministry's influence on the fleet. Another important influence was exercised by the Gunnery Branch, which had enormous prestige throughout the interwar period. For example, in the early 1930s it was believed that the 2pdr multiple pom-pom, coupled with a specialized director, would make air attack on a concentrated fleet at sea an extremely unprofitable exercise. The physical embodiment of this view was the design of the armored flight deck carrier (*Illustrious* class) in which the hangar was armored precisely so that aircraft could be struck below during an air attack. Indeed, when the unarmored carrier *Ark Royal* was attacked soon after the outbreak of war in 1939, her Skua fighters, drained of their explosive avgas, were placed below out of harm's way in her hangar.

The evolution of British naval fighters reflected these problems. At first naval fighters were very similar to their land-based cousins, high performance single-seaters such as the popular Fairey Flycatcher, the fleet fighter from 1923 through 1932. The Flycatcher rarely operated out of sight of its carrier, and there was no question of its pilot performing much navigation. Its successor, the Hawker Nimrod, did have a long range and was, moreover, intended to operate well out of sight of its carrier. Official doctrine held that a pilot could not be relied upon to navigate over long distances, particularly in poor weather; a flight of three two-seat Ospreys was attached to each twelve-airplane fighter squadron, the other nine being single-seat Nimrods. Unfortunately the two aircraft differed sufficiently in performance that they could not combine effectively, and some squadrons were equipped entirely with Ospreys. The two-seater did have the great advantage of suitability for reconnaissance, given its second crewman; in 1934 the Naval Staff considered the FR (fighter-reconnaissance) type so versatile that it was 'probably the correct fighter type for *all* Fleet work'. That year a Specification was issued for the next naval fighter, a two-seater with a dive-bombing capability (FDB), which became the Blackburn Skua. No companion Specification for a single-seat high-performance interceptor was issued. To some extent the Navy's preference for two-seat aircraft may have stemmed from the status within the Service of the Observer Branch, which included many of the most senior Navy aircrew; pilots of similar seniority were, before the re-absorption of the Fleet Air Arm by the Navy, RAF officers.

The Skua is often described as an unsuccessful attempt to combine in one airplane the features of two very contradictory types, the fighter and the dive-bomber. In its time, however, it would appear to have been a perfectly logical consequence of Admiralty policy concerning Fleet Air Arm tactics. By the mid-1930s British naval fighters were in effect strike support aircraft designed to accom-

The Gloster Sea Gladiator was bought on an emergency basis in March 1938. In 1937 the Admiralty had approached the Air Ministry to suggest which aircraft, either in service or under development, would be suited for conversion to naval use; the results were the two interim fighters, the Gladiator and the Fulmar. Gladiator modifications were limited to strengthening for an arrester hook, the hook proper, an Admiralty radio, and an airspeed indicator reading in knots. The aircraft illustrated is the third production RAF Gladiator I. *Fleet Air Arm Museum*

pany the torpedo-bombers attacking enemy battleships. Their primary role was twofold: attack on enemy anti-aircraft weapons, particularly those aboard screening ships; and neutralization of enemy carrier aircraft, preferably by strafing them while they remained on their flight decks. In each case machine-gun fire was likely to be more effective than conventional bombing, given the ability of the target ship to escape damage by radical maneuvering. Only with the advent of the dive-bomber could bomb hits be assured. Even then the tactic was confined to attacks on lightly armored ships: the bombs still did not attain sufficient terminal velocities to penetrate the protective decks of capital ships. The Osprey and even the Swordfish could dive with light bombs carried underwing, and in effect the Skua carried the Osprey's light bombing role further by providing a crutch for a heavier under-fuselage weapon. It would appear, then, that to the Royal Navy dive-bombing attack on enemy carrier decks and screening ships was a natural extension of fighter-attack doctrine, rather than an attempt to combine in a single aircraft two incompatible roles. The major air superiority role of the fleet fighter, denial of reconnaissance and spotting to an enemy fleet, would not require very high performance.

It can be argued, too, that the Royal Navy's apparent denial of the potential threat of land-based bombers was largely a matter of the Navy's belief that anti-aircraft

Given the tactics of the prewar Fleet Air Arm, high fighter performance was relatively unimportant. The fighter was a strike escort, disabling enemy carriers and anti-aircraft screening ships while the torpedo-bombers attacked the enemy battleships. In this context, it was not surprising that the fleet fighter of the late 1930s, the Blackburn Skua, was more effective as a dive-bomber than as a conventional air-to-air fighter. A fighter-caliber machine gun was manned by the observer/navigator/gunner in the rear cockpit and light bomb racks were fitted underwing; the main bomb was a 500-pounder carried on a crutch under the fuselage. *Fleet Air Arm Museum*

The very rapid development of aero-engines and airframe technology in the late 1930s left aircraft like the Skua well behind. In 1938 the Admiralty ordered the Fairey Fulmar as an interim fighter, pending the development of a fully satisfactory two-seat fleet fighter to accompany the new Barracuda strike aircraft. The Fulmar was immediately available because it was a modified version of an existing light bomber prototype; however, unlike the Skua, it was incapable of dive-bombing. In practice it operated as a fleet defense fighter rather than as a strike escort, given the early warning provided by radar. *Fairey Aviation Ltd by courtesy of Ian Huntley/Richard L Ward*

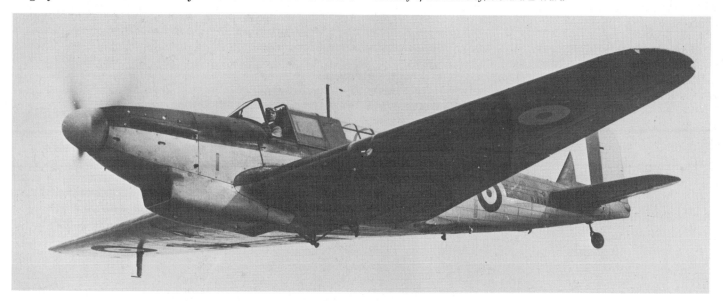

Electronics transformed the tactics of the Fleet Air Arm and made the high-performance single seat interceptor not merely practical but extremely desirable. Here a Seafire IIC, one of the highest-performance British naval aircraft of its time, takes off past the electronics-laden island of the fleet carrier *Indomitable*, March 1943. The electronic homing beacon (Type 72) housed in the masthead 'dustbin' made the second crewman unnecessary for navigation back to the carrier, while the long-range air search set, one antenna for which is visible on the short main-mast, made fighter interception of approaching attackers practicable. The other antennas visible on the carrier's island are a surface search set in the 'lantern' before the bridge, and several gunnery sets above it. The Seafire itself was extemporized, and was not entirely suited to carrier operations; in particular its weak, narrow-track undercarriage caused more losses than did enemy action. *Conway Picture Library*

guns would be the primary fleet anti-air defense. Indeed, fleet fighters would have almost no role at all against an enemy without carriers, since they would not be needed to destroy the enemy's flight decks, although they might still be valuable in the strike support role against enemy screening units. In this light the policy shift in which dive-bombing was associated with torpedo attack in the Barracuda (designed to a 1937 Specification) would seem to mark a shift in the role of the naval fighter, and indeed perhaps an attempt further to increase the potential strike power of the carrier by reducing the need for numbers of fighter-bombers.

The late 1930s were a period of rapid, even violent, development, particularly of high-performance aircraft and their engines. By 1938 the Skua, not yet in service, was obsolescent, largely because of the rapid advance in aero-engine technology which had produced the Merlin, and with it the new RAF interceptors. The Admiralty ordered two interim types, the existing Gloster Gladiator biplane and an adaptation of a two-seat light bomber prototype, which became the Fairy Fulmar, the true successor to the Skua and the Osprey. At the same time work began to frame a Specification for a more satisfactory two-seat naval fighter, to be powered by the more potent Griffon engine then already in prospect; it became the Firefly. In effect, the purchase of the Gladiator reflected an Admiralty desire to achieve the performance it expected of the

Fulmar, at the cost of the operational flexibility represented by the second seat. There seems to have been little expectation that any naval fighter would have to face large numbers of land-based aircraft, because by the late 1930s the Royal Navy still appears to have believed that fighter defense of naval formations would be futile no matter what the performance of the defending aircraft. Nor was this a totally theoretical conclusion: it had been tested again and again in fleet exercises.

With the outbreak of war and, incidentally, with the advent of radar early warning which transformed the interception problem, the Admiralty began to press for a high-performance single-seat interceptor. To some extent, too, this change of heart may be traceable to the success of a pilot-operated homing aid, the Type 72 'dustbin', then entering service. In any case the Admiralty requests led to design work on a folding-wing Spitfire, which in January 1940 was expected to enter service the following October. The Admiralty bought the US Wildcat (then designated Martlet) as an interim measure, and after several Hurricanes landed aboard the carrier *Glorious* it was able to obtain hooked Hurricanes as well. A Specification was issued for a specialized naval interceptor, which became the Blackburn Firebrand – and which did not enter service until the end of the war. By that time the folding-wing Spitfire, dropped in March 1940, had reappeared as the Seafire, the standard wartime British-built naval interceptor.

Ultimately the rationale for high-performance naval interceptors was that the prewar image of the role of the fighter had been entirely incorrect. Rather than engage an enemy fleet, the Royal Navy's carriers found themselves engaging large numbers of high-performance land-based bombers. Radar made fighter interception not only practicable but a standard tactic, and high performance was now mandatory. The Martlet, about to enter service, was clearly near its peak possible performance, and the Admiralty therefore asked for the fastest British fighter, the Spitfire; permission to procure the Sea Spitfire was

◀ The Fairey IIIF (a Mk I is shown) was the standard Fleet Air Arm spotter-reconnaissance aircraft of the late 1920s and early 1930s, before the type merged with the torpedo-bomber. There was no arrester hook, the Royal Navy having abandoned arresting gear entirely by the late 1920s, and armament consisted of a fixed Lewis gun forward and a flexible one aft, supplemented by up to 500lb of bombs underwing. The IIIF was the last in a very long series of Fairey III biplanes which began in 1917; between 1928 and 1936 IIIFs served aboard every British carrier and, in floatplane form, aboard many capital ships and cruisers. *Fleet Air Arm Museum*

The Blackburn Ripon had sufficient range to require an observer/navigator in a second seat, and thus was the first British multi-seat torpedo-bomber. It served from 1929 to 1934, and enjoyed roughly twice the radius of action of its predecessor, the Blackburn Dart. Ripon IIs are ▼ shown. *Fleet Air Arm Museum*

first granted in the Fall of 1941. The Sea Hurricane functioned as an interim interceptor pending its development.

STRIKE AIRCRAFT

The Fleet Air Arm's choice of its primary offensive weapon, the torpedo, was based largely on the Royal Navy's continuing belief in the battleship. Where US and Japanese naval aviators regarded the carrier as their primary target, their British contemporaries continued to

The Fairey Swordfish, although archaic by US or Japanese standards, fitted precisely the Fleet Air Arm doctrine of the mid-1930s, in which spotting and fleet shadowing were quite as important as the actual attack; moreover, there was reason to suspect that the highly maneuverable Swordfish would evade defensive fire while achieving surprise against defensive fighters. The Swordfish also proved extremely adaptable to the very small escort carriers and merchant aircraft carriers with which the Royal Navy fought the Battle of the Atlantic. This early production example lacks the radar and rocket racks of later marks. *Fleet Air Arm Museum*

The Barracuda was much maligned, partly because its low priority condemned it to underpowering. It combined torpedo-bombing, dive-bombing and reconnaissance in a single airframe; visible here are the large dive flaps underwing and the windows for observation. *Conway Picture Library*

concentrate on the battleship. This choice was particularly apt in a European context, given the absence of carriers in the two major potential adversaries the British faced, the German and Italian navies. Thus, where a properly placed bomb might well disarm a carrier by smashing her flight deck, the Royal Navy had to look for a weapon which would damage or sink a heavily armored warship. An armor-piercing bomb dropped from high altitude might well penetrate, but it would be unlikely to hit a maneuvering warship; that left only the torpedo, despite its many deficiencies. Even if a torpedo did not sink a capital ship, it would probably exact a speed penalty which would permit the relatively slow British battle line to close to decisive gunnery range. That was certainly the role of the Swordfish which attacked the *Bismarck* in 1941, for example. Given its emphasis on torpedo attacks, the Fleet Air Arm developed a steep diving approach which, like dive bombing, minimized exposure of the attacker to anti-aircraft fire. The ability to control an attacking airplane in a dive, required for such tactics, did provide British torpedo-bombers such as the Swordfish and the later Barracuda with a secondary shallow dive-bombing capability.

The torpedo-bomber, too, was affected by the Admiralty's preference for a navigator for long-range operation. Thus the Ripon of 1929, which had roughly twice the radius of action of its predecessor, the Dart, required a second seat for an observer/navigator; this seat in turn conferred a secondary reconnaissance capability on the airplane. Given the limited capacity of British carriers (and, moreover, the very limited willingness of the Air Ministry and the Treasury to countenance a large Fleet Air Arm), multi-role aircraft were particularly attractive. Thus by 1935 the previous mixture of types had been shaken down to a combination of TSRs and fighters. The TSR concept itself, which combined the former three-seat spotter with the torpedo-bomber into a new three-seat aircraft, the Swordfish, was a means of increasing the striking power of the carrier without increasing the size of its air group, by providing as many aircraft as possible with torpedoes.

A visit to the United States in 1931 by a British naval officer introduced the Royal Navy to the possibilities of dive-bombing: hence the development of the Skua. To some extent the Gunnery Branch militated against dive bombing by its faith in the 2pdr; to some extent, too, the Air Ministry appears to have been unwilling to provide an effective sight. In any case, the successor to the Skua was a pure fighter. On the other hand, the new multi-purpose attack aircraft, the Barracuda, was intended for dive- as well as torpedo-bombing; it was generally designated TBR, torpedo-bomber-reconnaissance. By this time the spotting role was being relegated to cruisers and capital ships, and the TSR concept could be dropped.

One peculiarity of British naval air policy at this time was the attempt to use cruiser catapult aircraft to balance off the limited numbers of carrier aircraft prior to the end of the 'treaty period'. Thus in 1930 TSR aircraft had been specified for the *Leanders*, and in 1933 the Osprey, an FR type, was adopted for cruisers. It could contribute to fleet air defense and so free limited carrier space for offensive aircraft. The performance limitations implicit in catapult operation were not quite so crippling as might otherwise be imagined, since the fleet fighters would generally be attacking enemy spotters of limited performance. Clearly, catapult aircraft were of limited value in any case, and with the end of the treaty limits on total carrier tonnage it was proposed in 1936 that all naval aircraft ultimately operate from carriers. Until that could be implemented the cruisers would surrender their fighter role and would instead take over the reconnaissance and spotting role, a decision reflected in the adoption of the Walrus as the standard cruiser aircraft.

As war approached, the carrier mission of fleet air defense, as compared to reconnaissance and torpedo attack, became more and more important, particularly as the Admiralty contemplated operations in Far Eastern waters liberally supplied with Japanese naval air stations as well as with Japanese carriers. On the other hand, in European waters, where the immediate threat lay, the principal task would remain torpedo attack on capital ships. It appears that the Admiralty hoped to build up a new fleet for the Far East, perhaps with very different air groups; the carriers and aircraft it designed before the outbreak of war were intended primarily for the European theatre.

Throughout the interwar period the Admiralty was concerned with a very different carrier function as well: trade defense, by which it meant the security of merchant shipping in the face of surface commerce raiders. It was widely believed that submarines would be limited to the area around the British Isles, and in any case that they could be countered by sonar- or asdic-equipped sloops. Large commerce raiders were another matter. In 1939, for example,

Even late in World War II, the Royal Navy continued to adapt contemporary RAF fighters to its needs in order to obtain sufficient performance to counter the latest German land-based aircraft. The Hawker Sea Fury, the standard postwar carrier-borne propeller-driven fighter, was adapted from a lightweight fighter which was not produced for the RAF owing to the decision to employ only jets. These Sea Furies of 805 Squadron fought in Korea; they are shown preparing for take-off aboard HMS *Theseus*. Sea Furies remained in front-line service from 1947 until 1954, sharing light carrier decks with Fireflies, eight of which are visible right aft. *By courtesy of Chris Thomas/Richard L Ward*

both of the smallest carriers, *Hermes* and *Eagle*, were assigned to distant waters with exclusively torpedo-bomber air groups. The earlier *Argus* had been proposed for conversion to similar duties as early as 1937, and indeed the Admiralty had planned for some time the conversion of suitable merchant ships into emergency trade protection carriers. Fighters played no part in these plans, as it was tacitly assumed that enemy aircraft would not be able to attack in mid-ocean.

That belief proved incorrect, as the Germans both obtained bases on the European coast and began to operate very long range attack aircraft, primarily Fw 200s. Trade protection now included fighter support, and indeed the latter became far more important than an ability to counter surface raiders. The first converted merchant ships, the escort carriers, were considered above all fighter carriers. Only somewhat later did it become apparent that the German seizure of bases on the Atlantic also opened up the prospect of large mid-ocean submarine attacks; now the new small carriers turned to ASW as much as to fighter warfare, and their air groups came to include torpedo planes.

THE FLEET AIR ARM IN WORLD WAR II

Wartime developments continued the prewar themes. By the time the prototype 1940 interceptor, the Blackburn Firebrand, flew in 1942, the Royal Navy had several equivalents available, and it decided to recast the new fighter as a single-seat torpedo strike aircraft. This decision accorded to some extent with British interest in very high

speed torpedo delivery, in which the torpedo would spend most of its trajectory in the air, giving its target the minimum chance of evasion. The Firebrand was not a dive-bomber, although it could carry a 2000lb bomb in place of the torpedo. It was envisaged as effective in formation attacks, led by a multi-seat aircraft which would navigate and conduct a radar search for the target. Thus the Firebrand became part of a larger British program for strike aircraft formulated in 1943.

The single-seater would be effective only in clear weather; in bad weather the Royal Navy wanted a second man for radar navigation. The airplane carrying him would necessarily sacrifice performance, but on the other hand it might have greater range. Although it might often benefit from escorting fighters, it would require a rearward-firing defensive armament for self-protection. Given the existence of a useful torpedo- and level bomber in the Firebrand, this two-seater was designed as a dive-bomber (1600lb bomb; capable of carrying but not dive-bombing with 2000lb bomb or torpedo). Dive brakes would permit particularly steep torpedo-bombing dives. This requirement resulted in the O.5/43 Spearfish.

HMS IMPLACABLE (1942)

EXTERNAL PROFILE AND PLAN

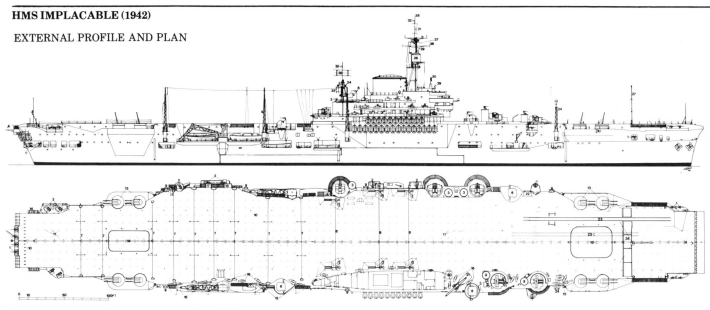

KEY (External profile and plan)

1 Single 20mm mountings
2 Twin 20mm mountings
3 Pompom directors (with aerials of radar Type 282)
4 4-barrel pompom mounting
5 8-barrel pompom mounting
6 HA/LA directors (with aerials of radar Type 285)
7 Arresting wires
8 Safety barriers
9 Wireless mast
10 Landing lights
11 Securing points
12 Aircraft elevator
13 Twin 4.5in HA/LA mountings
14 Depth charge racks
15 Aircraft outrigger
16 Mines
17 Talker's position
18 Aircraft control position
19 Forward control position
20 Bomb elevator
21 Mobile crane
22 Catapult control
23 Catapult
24 HF/DF mast
25 Transporting rails
26 Wind screen
27 Telescopic mast
28 Type 72DM aircraft homing beacon
29 Type 242 aerial
30 Type 277 radar aerial
31 Type 79B aerial
32 Type 243 aerial
33 Type 281B aerial
34 Type FV1 radar reflector
35 Type 91 TBS aerials
36 Type 87 TBS aerials
37 Fighter direction aerials (port and starboard on outriggers)
38 Type 86M TBS aerial

KEY (Internal profile and sections)

1 Aircraft elevator
2 Cable locker
3 Elevator machinery
4 Workshops
5 Sliding door
6 Hangar
7 Fire curtain
8 Torpedo body room
9 Torpedo parting space
10 Catapult gear compartment
11 Boiler room
12 Engine room
13 Auxiliary machinery
14 Bomb room
15 Aviation fuel
16 Pompom magazine
17 4.5in magazine
18 Asdic office
19 Asdic compartment
20 Practice bomb store
21 Torpedo warhead room
22 Fighter ready room
23 Flight control room
24 Briefing room
25 Operations room
26 Aircraft direction room
27 TBR ready-room
28 Aircraft handling party ready-room
29 Compass platform
30 Oil fuel
31 Fan room
32 Bomb elevators
33 Bomb transfer lobby
34 Small-arms magazine
35 Steering gear
36 Main plane store
37 Spare parts store

INTERNAL PROFILE AND SECTIONS

There remained the issue of the strike leader. During 1942 the Royal Navy considered building a long-range torpedo-bomber/scout somewhat like the type being designed at the same time in the United States. In the absence of a new generation of very powerful aero engines (such as the US 3000hp R-4360) it required twin engines, and was expected to come to as much as 28,000lb, even carrying one rather than two (as in the US case) torpedoes. It was ultimately rejected in favor of a two- or three-seat reconnaissance type, which might carry a bomb load 'as an afterthought', but which would function primarily as navigation and radar leader for the smaller aircraft. There was some hope that ultimately it would carry a torpedo as

well. In any case, limited by British carrier flight decks, it became the S.11/43, the Short Sturgeon.

In addition, the Royal Navy adopted a very long range twin-engine fighter, the Sea Hornet. Part of its justification, in wartime, was the expectation that it could carry large unguided rockets ('Uncle Tom', designed to strike underwater) which could be used in attacks on the Japanese Fleet. As one of the few survivors of the wartime development program, the Sea Hornet proved most useful postwar as a fast two-seat night fighter, serving in detachments aboard carriers until its replacement by the jet Sea Venom in 1954. The larger De Havilland Mosquito was also adapted to carrier operation as the Sea Mosquito

torpedo-fighter, but at the end of the war the program was cancelled, with few built; indeed, the Sea Mosquito was probably most significant for the Royal Navy in that carrier trials in 1944 demonstrated the viability of large twin-engine fighter-bombers at sea.

Although the US Navy eschewed any hope for an amalgamation of the fighter and attack classes, it was not nearly so oppressed by lack of aircraft stowage as was the Royal Navy. In 1944 the latter issued a Specification for a naval fighter with a secondary attack capability, which produced the Westland Wyvern, the eventual successor to the Firebrand. By the time it approached service, the hope of amalgamation which it represented was no longer a practical one, as with the appearance of jets the Wyvern could no longer function as an effective fighter. Even so, it suggests British concerns and ideas.

Of all of the specially designed types, only the single-seat attack aircraft, the Firebrand and the Wyvern, ever entered the service for which they had been intended. The Sturgeon was retained as a target-tug; the Spearfish was cancelled after only a few had been completed. Perhaps by 1945 British air groups were too fighter-heavy to accommodate such great variety. Postwar budgets were thin, and it was far better to spend on advanced projects than on already obsolescent piston types. Moreover, there was no immediate prospect of ships large enough to accommodate heavy strike aircraft, since the new *Eagle* would not be ready until 1951 and even the prewar and wartime armored deck fleet carriers were soon reduced to subsidiary service in favor of the smaller light carriers, which were less expensive to operate.

Wartime British naval fighter development consisted

On 25 March 1944 the Royal Navy successfully landed a De Havilland Mosquito aboard HMS *Indefatigable* to prove that a twin-engine high-performance aircraft could indeed operate from a fleet carrier. Although the Sturgeon strike reconnaissance aircraft program for which the landing had been a test was later cancelled, the Royal Navy was encouraged to order several twin-engine aircraft, including a naval version of the RAF's Hornet long-range fighter. The Sea Hornets shown formed the equipment of 801 Squadron aboard HMS *Implacable*, 1949–51; here the carrier is moored at Brest, 1 June 1950. The wing-fold joints in the aircraft nearest the camera are clearly visible. *Conway Picture Library*

The Westland Wyvern was the final expression of the single-seat attack concept in the Royal Navy. Like the Firebrand, it was conceived originally as a fighter, but from the first it had a secondary strike role employing rockets, bombs (1–2000lb or 3–1000lb) or a torpedo. However, with the advent of jets, the Wyvern was developed primarily as a strike aircraft, in which form it saw brief Royal Navy service. This Wyvern S4 served aboard HMS *Eagle* with 830 Squadron, the only Wyvern squadron to see action, in the Suez operation of 1956. *By courtesy of Richard L Ward*

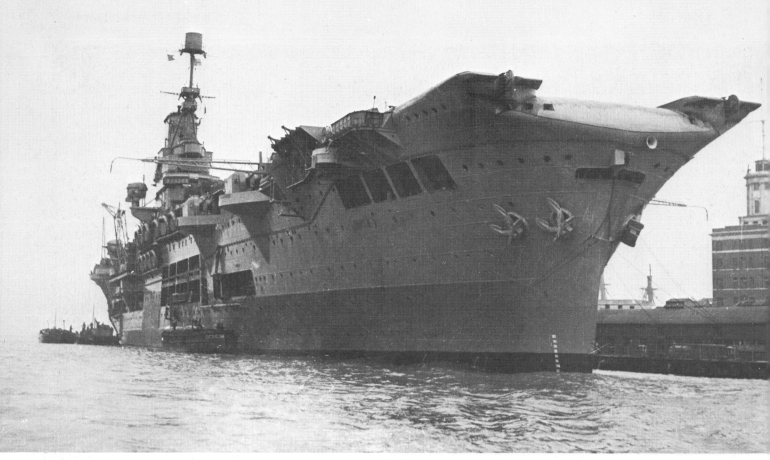

HMS *Ark Royal* was the first of the modern British carriers, introducing a full-length flight deck and main battery weapons in sponsons at or near flight deck level. Like her predecessors, she had a double hangar, evident in this 1940 view by her immense freeboard. Also visible here is her armor belt, built up amidships to cover machinery, as in a cruiser. The external cable was for degaussing, and she carried a Type 72 homing beacon – but no radar – at her single masthead. *Conway Picture Library*

The carriers which followed *Ark Royal* had armored flight decks. Part of the cost, on a displacement limited by treaty, was the elimination of one hangar and half the air group. HMS *Illustrious*, the prototype armored carrier, is shown as completed in 1940, with the big homing beacon and also the topmast for Type 79 air search radar; the second radar mast has apparently been painted out by the censor. In this form she launched the classic carrier raid on Taranto. *MoD(N)*

largely of the adaptation of new RAF types; unlike the strike aircraft, these types did appear in the postwar Navy in some numbers. Operating off the European coast, the Royal Navy felt, in 1943–44, that it faced much the same aircraft as did the Royal Air Force. There were, moreover, only a very few British aircraft manufacturers capable of designing high performance fighters, and they were fully occupied with RAF orders – a legacy of the prewar period of a very thin naval aircraft budget and hence few orders. The Navy was, therefore, willing to accept substantial sacrifices in such carrier characteristics as take-off distance. Extemporized land types such as the Sea Hurricane

and the early Seafires could not be provided with folding wings and so had to use deck parks, which complicated carrier operations. In wartime, the very heavy load on the British airframe industry, and the relatively small number of specialized fighter manufacturers, made it difficult for the Navy to obtain specialized aircraft, apart from the two-seat Fairey Firefly; it had, therefore, to adopt land-based types: the Seafire (which had high performance as an interceptor but suffered from short endurance and poor landing characteristics), and then the late-war Sea Hornet and Sea Fury. Indeed, even the principal postwar Royal Navy jet fighters were generally products of

development programs partially designed for land operation: the Supermarine Attacker, the Sea Hawk and the Sea Venom. Only the Sea Vixen and the Scimitar, among fighters, were designed to Naval requirements.

Prewar British carrier air groups emphasized the strike role. Thus the new carrier *Ark Royal* was designed in 1934 to operate 48 TSRs and 24 of the new FDB (Skua) types. This proportion was, however, cut to 48 TSRs and only 12 FDBs shortly afterwards and the new proportion, which de-emphasized fighters, was even further skewed in that direction in the new armored flight deck carrier *Illustrious*, designed in 1936 to operate 30 TSRs but only 6 FDBs. Her protection would come from her armor, not her combat air patrol. In addition, British carrier design emphasized defensive gun armament, which in the new armored carriers included eight twin dual-purpose guns, roughly twice the battery of the contemporary US *Yorktown*s, as well as numerous lighter weapons.

The confusion over fighter roles was, indeed, reflected in radical shifts in air group composition. For example, in February 1934 it was decided that the ratio of fighters to other aircraft should drop from 2:3 to 1:2, just as the other types were being amalgamated by the introduction of the TSR. The ratio continued to fall, so that in practice in 1939 it was nearer 1:5 in favor of non-fighter types. During the Munich crisis the C-in-C Home Fleet intended to eliminate all fighters from HMS *Furious* and to retain only two Gladiators in HMS *Glorious*, which had a much larger capacity, 'in view of the greater value of TSR aircraft than fighters in the present emergency'.

War experience showed that the standard proportion of fighters was inadequate. Even the low-performance Fulmar proved quite valuable in breaking up attacks, and its numbers increased. For example, in September 1940 the new armored flight deck carrier *Illustrious* operated only 18 TSRs, but 15 (rather than 6) Fulmars. The more capacious *Ark Royal* cut her TSR complement to 30, but operated 24 Fulmars. In the Mediterranean, where carriers faced extremely fierce air opposition, air groups became even more fighter-heavy. For example, in August 1942 the armored carrier *Victorious* operated 18 Fulmars, 6 Sea

The final development of the original *Illustrious* design was the *Implacable* class, represented here by HMS *Indefatigable*, late in World War II. A full lower hangar was provided, but at the cost of hangar depth, so reduced that Corsairs could not be carried. In view of the shortage of Grumman Hellcats, HMS *Implacable* had to ship 48 Seafires in addition to her Fireflies (12) and Avengers (21). Even so, her Air Engineering Department used the lower hangar as a workshop, and she required a large deck park. *MoD(N)*

Hurricane single-seat fighters, and only 14 TSRs (Albacores). This air group was beyond her hangar capacity, yet so many fighters were needed that the choice lay between a permanent deck park and the complete elimination of strike aircraft. With a deck park, carrier fighter complements could rise even further. For the invasion of Sicily the armored carrier *Formidable* operated 12 TSRs (Albacores) – and 33 single-seat fighters (28 US-supplied Martlets and 5 Seafires).

By 1944 many British carriers were operating US Corsairs and Hellcats, and these aircraft were sometimes used as fighter-bombers. Permanent deck parks were required; for example, in her operations off Okinawa in the Spring of 1945 HMS *Illustrious* had to maintain 14 Corsairs permanently on deck in order to operate a total of 36 Corsairs and 16 Avenger strike aircraft. By this time the Barracuda had largely passed from service, and the new strike aircraft of the 1943 program did not as yet exist. There were Fireflies in service, often acting as close escorts for strike aircraft, and Seafires, which had relatively short endurance, were being used as interceptors and for combat air patrol. The longer-range US-built fighters were used as strike escorts and for independent attacks on enemy airfields.

Postwar British carrier air groups remained fighter-heavy because the primary function of the Fleet Air Arm remained fleet air defense, which now included cover for the increasingly important light anti-submarine forces. A second vital function was ASW itself, given the probability that in any future war the main Soviet naval effort would be a new Battle of the Atlantic. Indeed, the British naval construction program of the late 1940s was largely oriented towards a new generation of fast ASW frigates. Last came air strikes against ground targets, the carrier

▲ The largest British carrier program of the Second World War produced the light fleet carriers, one of which, HMS *Vengeance*, is shown (3 May 1945). The design began in mid-1941 as a fighter carrier for fleet air defense, speed being limited to 25kts and protection entirely eschewed. Alternatives considered included the conversion of a *Hawkins* class cruiser or a liner; however, a new austere carrier was designed instead. Measures for quick production included the choice of propelling machinery (half a standard cruiser set) and the selection of Vickers-Armstrong to carry out the entire design. Every effort was made to keep building time down to 21 months, although ultimately 24 was accepted, and of ten ships built five (and two repair ships) were in commission by V-J Day, 15 August 1945. *MoD(N)*

The first of the US Navy's fast carriers, USS *Lexington*, steams through an aerial smokescreen on 26 February 1929, shortly after the conclusion of the Fleet Problem. Her deck park, already typical of US practice, is visible on her foredeck, as are four of her eight 8in/55 guns, insurance ▼ against surprise by cruisers.

mission largely devised during the war. Even so, by 1945 British naval thinking had turned to a capability for sustained strikes. HMS *Illustrious* was designed in 1936 to deliver 1½ torpedo attacks per TSR, as well as four bomb loads per aircraft. In 1946 the new *Ark Royal* and *Hermes* were to carry almost as many torpedoes per aircraft (more in the new 'Ark') as well as nine bomb loads per strike aircraft, for up to 36 and 26 strike aircraft respectively – out of total air groups of 75 and 50 aircraft respectively. In addition there would be large numbers of rockets for the fighters which, unlike the early wartime types, would all have some ground attack capability.

As for the performance of the airborne ASW mission, for the Royal Navy that was to be much affected by the loss of nearly all the specialized ASW carriers, which had been provided by the United States under Lend-Lease. The few built in Britain were urgently required as merchant hulls, to make up for the great losses of the Battle of the Atlantic. By way of contrast, in the US Navy there remained after 1945 a large force of escort carriers, both active and in reserve, which could be assigned ASW duties while the fast carriers were reserved for strikes against land targets; the anti-ship strike mission was largely abandoned, given the character of the most likely future enemy, the Soviet Union. It followed that specialized ASW aircraft could be developed for use from existing escort carriers, and, moreover, that they would not compete with strike aircraft for space aboard existing carriers. The Royal Navy faced similar demands, and indeed regarded ASW as its first priority. However, without a large number of second-line carriers it had to choose between operating strike carriers largely or partly as ASW ships, or else designing ASW aircraft for use aboard notional ASW carriers which would come into existence only in an emergency. Even given the use of the large carriers, the Royal Navy had to face prospective limitations in the number of ASW platforms (and even of ASW aircraft) which would have been intolerable during World War II.

US CARRIER AVIATION BETWEEN THE WARS

The US Navy, like the Royal Navy, experimented with shipboard aircraft even before 1914, and indeed was the first to carry out both take-offs from and landings onto a warship. However, the US approach was to develop the catapult, and the shipboard seaplane or floatplane, for scouting; such equipment was fitted to three armored cruisers in 1916–17 but removed when these ships were assigned to Atlantic convoy duty, as it interfered with their after turret guns. It appears that US interest in carriers was largely inspired by US contact with the Royal Navy, both through the medium of the Grand Fleet and through the presence in the United States of a British naval constructor, 'on loan' to the US Bureau of Construction and Repair, Stanley Goodall. Goodall, who later became Director of Naval Construction for the Royal Navy, helped prepare a US carrier design in the Summer of 1918. In describing British concepts, he emphasized the value of the carrier as a scout ('Air fighting has become a feature of naval operations, and the tactical movements of a fleet before an engagement opens will most probably be governed by information obtained from air scouts . . .') and appears not to have mentioned the Beatty concept of a mass strike on the German fleet with torpedo-bombers. However, US officers attached to the Grand Fleet were well aware of such types as the Sopwith Cuckoo torpedo-bomber, and the US Navy quickly began the development of their equivalent. For example, Characteristics for a US carrier, prepared in 1919–20, followed Goodall's proposals with the signal exception that they called for a large number of torpedo planes to be included in the air group.

One reason for ready acceptance of the carrier concept within the US Navy was probably the existence of an internal Navy 'think tank', the Naval War College, one of whose most important functions was the evaluation of weapons as yet only in the proposal stage. In the early 1920s wargames were still based on the concept that carrier aircraft would be no more than auxiliaries to the battleships, but they already appeared to be at least potentially far more important than cruisers or destroyers. Spotters might well extend the effective range of battleship shellfire to a decisive extent, and for them to be effective fighters would have to achieve air superiority over the battle area. Torpedo planes and level bombers might well be able to slow an enemy battle line sufficiently to force a decisive action: the US Navy of this period was uncomfortably aware that its battle line was slower than that of its two most likely rivals, Britain and Japan.

Thoughts also turned to the purely offensive use of the carrier. For example, as early as 1923 the Annual Fleet Problem (maneuver) included carriers (simulated by battleships with floatplanes) attacking the Panama Canal. It was concluded that an aggressive air attack would probably disable the vital locks. A growing awareness of the offensive capability of the carrier almost certainly shaped US carrier air groups, which were heavily loaded in favor of attack aircraft. It also shaped US carrier operating practice, which emphasized maximum numbers of aircraft per carrier and the fastest possible deck cycle.

To some extent the development of the US carrier air arm was a consequence of the existence of two very unusual carriers, *Lexington* and *Saratoga*. Although plans for ships of much their size and speed had been evolved even prior to the Washington Naval Conference, the Treaty which resulted from it guaranteed that the US Navy would have two very fast, very large ships, since two very fast battlecruisers were to be converted to carriers. It was a happy accident that these ships, so much larger than necessary to accommodate the small air groups then in prospect, were large enough to accept considerable technical growth over the entire interwar period.

There was considerable skepticism as to the value of such large ships. Indeed, the unsatisfactory *Ranger* was an attempt to achieve instead the smallest effective carrier, which under the Treaty could be built in the largest numbers and so support the largest possible seaborne naval air force. However, once in service the two large, fast carriers showed entirely unsuspected operational capabilities, while the smaller converted collier *Langley* demonstrated the severe limits imposed by a small flight deck. The qualities of the two large carriers were a major factor in the evolution of US carrier doctrine, as they participated in the critical naval exercises of the early 1930s. The enthusiasm they aroused was responsible for the decision to abandon the *Ranger* type in favor of a much larger carrier (*Yorktown*, CV5) even before the former had been laid down.

The two large carriers were so much faster than the US battle line that it was natural for them to operate independently, screened by heavy cruisers. Such tactics were tried as early as Fleet Problem IX of 1929, and by the early 1930s the concept of the independent carrier task force, built around a single carrier screened by heavy cruisers, was well established. It was also well understood that the first target in a battle would be the enemy's carriers; both the US and the Japanese naval air arms considered the carrier both immensely potent and yet extremely vulnerable to air attack. Both also considered the defensive fighter the best protection for a carrier. Even so, many

▲ The *Ranger* (CV4) was the US Navy's attempt to trade size for numbers, given the overall carrier tonnage limits written into the Washington Treaty. Her original plans contemplated a completely flush deck, and the enclosed conning position under her flight deck forward was a survival of that concept. Visible, too, are some of her numerous 0.50 caliber machine guns in flight-deck galleries, as well as two of her forward 5in/25s. This photograph was taken at Hunters Point Drydock, San Francisco, 2 March 1937.

The *Yorktown* (shown here as completed in 1937) was the prototype for US carrier development during World War II. Her light battery is not visible here, and her hangar shutters are closed. The projection from the forward hangar (barely discernible by the tip of the second boom) is the end of an athwartships catapult, a feature this class shared with the ▼ smaller *Wasp* and also with early units of the *Essex* class.

exercises suggested that a carrier might be considered as good as disabled, if not lost, once she was detected by aerial scouts.

AIR GROUP COMPOSITION

Like the Royal Navy, the US Navy began with a combination of fighters, bombers, and observation/spotting aircraft, representing a doctrine of combined operations with the battle line. The fighters would gain air superiority and so both protect the spotters and deny the air over the engagement to enemy spotters; the heavy torpedo-bombers would function both as long-range scouts and as a means of slowing the enemy's battle line. The balance between scouting and attack varied. For example, the standard US torpedo-bomber of the late 1920s began life as

the result of a March 1925 specification. Originally designated a scout (Curtiss SC), it was soon redesignated a torpedo-bomber (T2M), then modified for improved visibility as the T3M, T4M and TG. It was the 10,000lb bomber which the *Ranger* was designed to operate, and was quite a massive airplane for its time.

The effect of independent carrier operations was to make the spotter less and less useful aboard such a ship. Instead, spotters were provided for all battleships, while scout floatplanes were to be carried by the cruisers. Carriers attached to the battle fleet might provide it with air cover, but from 1929 onwards it was clear that at least one important phase of the future war would involve carrier task forces operating independently of the battleships. In an offense-oriented air group slow spotters took up space bet-

ter devoted to long-range attackers and scouts. As for fighters, they would serve both as interceptors and as escorts for the attackers. In neither case did the US Navy view to the two-seat fighter with any great enthusiasm. It is not clear in retrospect whether the performance penalty associated with the second seat was unacceptable, or whether the Navy assumed that a pilot alone would be quite capable of navigating home. The few two-seat fighter designs produced in the early 1930s were soon redesignated, first as scouts and then, in most cases, as scout (dive) bombers.

One major factor in US naval aircraft development was the influence of the Marines. Marine aircraft were all supplied by the Navy, and the Marines were involved in a series of small wars in the Caribbean through the 1920s and early 1930s. They were responsible both for US interest in dive-bombing and for the development of the first of the classic US dive-bombers, the F8C-2 Helldiver, which was originally intended as a replacement for the elderly DH4B. Both Marine considerations and the basic US war plan, which envisaged the seizure of Pacific islands en route to Japanese waters, made the US Navy more conscious than its contemporaries of the requirements of ground attack.

Perhaps the most characteristic feature of the prewar US naval air arm was its emphasis on dive-bombing, a means of bomb delivery so accurate that it practically ensured hits on even a maneuvering warship. Dive-bombing in the US Navy began with fighter squadrons,

The new carrier *Lexington* shows her air group: Martin T3M-2 torpedo-bombers of VT-1B (Torpedo Squadron One, Battle Fleet) and Curtiss F6C fighters of VF-5S (Fighting Five, Scouting Fleet), which would shortly be redesignated a fighter-bomber squadron, VB-1B. This shift reflected the success of dive-bombing trials in 1926, including a mass attack on the Pacific Fleet by the F6C-2s of VF-2 in October. VF-5S developed similar tactics and demonstrated their efficacy in the late summer and early fall of 1927. All US Navy fighters were adapted to carry light bombs; the F6C could carry five 30-pounders, four under the wings and one under the body. This fighter-bomber policy continued through the prewar period. The photograph shows the two arresting-gear systems in use in 1928, a series of fore-and-aft wires visible beneath the large torpedo-bombers, and a series of transverse wires, the first of which is visible beneath the foremost T3M. The fighter closest to the camera shows clearly the series of hooks along the spreader bar of its undercarriage, intended to catch the fore-and-aft wires and so to prevent a landing airplane from being blown over the side. These wires were soon abandoned in favor of the now-conventional series of athwartship wires engaged by a single trailing hook, however. Note that the airplanes are lashed down.

some of which were specially designated bomber-fighters; the prewar US Navy was unique in requiring its fighters to carry substantial bomb loads. At first the intended role of the dive-bomber was to disorganize enemy anti-aircraft fire so as to permit the true ship-killers, the torpedo- and horizontal bombers, to penetrate almost unopposed. However, the latter proved relatively ineffective in exercises, whereas dive-bomber loads increased sharply; the new carrier *Ranger* was completed as an all-dive-bomber ship, without torpedo stowage. At the same time a new carrier, which would become the *Yorktown* (CV5), was under design. The US Navy considered incorporating in her an armored flight deck, ie a defense against dive-bombing.

Martin T4M-1 torpedo bombers of VT-1B aboard USS *Lexington*, sometime between 1928 and 1932. In 1929 this unit was 28-strong, compared with 13 fighters and 15 fighter-bombers (VB-1B) plus 12 scouts or observation aircraft (VS-3B). However, the fighter and fighter-bomber squadrons were soon strengthened at its expense, so that a year later there were 20 F3Bs in VF-3B and 18 F4B-1s in VF-5B, formerly VB-1B, (ie formerly explicitly a bombing unit), compared to 19 torpedo-bombers. This was not entirely a diminution in offensive power, as the fighters and the observation planes were capable of dive-bombing with a 500lb bomb. The scouting squadrons were gradually strengthened in the early 1930s, so that in June 1935 *Lexington* operated eighteen scouts, as well as two fighter squadrons (with, respectively, 26 and 24 aircraft) and 19 bombers. The T4M was a radial-engined version of the T3M (with which *Lexington* commissioned), which was itself a derivative of a Navy-designed bomber produced by Curtiss and then by Martin as the SC. Martin sold its Cleveland factory to the Great Lakes Company in October 1928, and the latter continued production of the basic design as the TG, the final version being the re-engined TG-2. It served with VT-2 until 1937, its poor performance contributing to the general disenchantment with torpedo attack.

However, it was clear that on the available weights no sufficient deck could be provided, and the armored flight deck idea was not to be revived in the United States for another decade.

In 1925 the Chief of Naval Operations ordered dive-bombing to be included in the competitive exercises for the following year, and two fighter squadrons independently worked out anti-ship dive tactics; attack with gas, demolition, and fragmentation bombs of up to 100lb was envisaged, against destroyers and carriers. The 1926 tests with Chance Vought UO-1 Corsairs (the only available carriers for such weapons) led to the installation of bomb racks on current fighters, and a simulated bombing attack on the Fleet as it sortied from San Pedro in October 1926 proved extremely successful. Although the ships had warning of the attack, the almost vertical dives from 12,000ft achieved complete surprise. Live tests against moving targets the following year increased Navy interest in the new weapon, and the Bureau of Aeronautics began a dual program of development, for bombers capable of diving

with 1000lb bombs as well as two-seat fighters, such as the F8C-2, which could dive with a 500-pounder. The former would carry a load similar to that of a torpedo-bomber, although in addition it would be stressed for steep dives and pull-outs. The BuAer specification of 1928 demanded, for example, that the heavy dive-bomber be capable of pulling out with its bomb still in place. It led to the design of the Martin T5M, whose designation betrays its dual (torpedo/dive-bombing) function; it was later redesignated BM, in a new class of heavy bombers.

Even as the large BM was being developed, the Bureau of Aeronautics looked towards a lighter type which might also serve as a scout, to range 1000nm with an external tank, or 750 with a 500lb bomb, or 400 with a 1000lb bomb. A second seat was provided as essential to the scouting mission; the resulting airplane (1932) was the Great Lakes BG, which was both more compact than and considerably faster than its predecessor. The BuAer interest in scouts was a direct result of fleet exercise experience.

As a concomitant of independent carrier operations with long-range attack aircraft, the carriers required scouts whose performance would match that of the strike groups. For example, a four-day series of futile searches by both opposing carriers in Fleet Problem XI (1930) showed a need to enlarge onboard scout squadrons, and specialized scouts, derived from prototype two-seat fighters, soon appeared. Their tasks were not limited to seeking out enemy surface forces. Scouts were also to be assigned to 'aerial picket stations' from which they could report the approach of enemy aircraft, so that shipboard fighters might scramble. Such aerial scouting would be supplemented by lookouts on surface pickets around the carrier force; it was the best means of providing early warning of a raid in the absence of radar.

It was natural to combine the functions of scout and light, fast, two-seat fighter/dive-bomber, particularly as aero-engine development in the mid-1930s permitted con-

Observation aircraft such as this Vought O2U-2 of VS-3B (denoted by the Indian Head insignia under the second cockpit, and serving aboard *Lexington*) formed an important part of US carrier air groups until the mid-1930s, when they were replaced in scouting squadrons by high-performance two-seat fighters (Grumman SF-1s) or by scout (dive) bombers (Vought SBU-1s) themselves derived from experimental two-seat fighters. The O2U was the first Vought airplane to be called Corsair, and it served widely aboard battleships and cruisers as well as aboard the carriers; it also served with the Marines in Nicaragua. The O2U-1 had racks for ten 30lb bombs, but the O2U-2 illustrated could carry a 500lb bomb and was, in effect, a dive-bomber. Defensive armament comprised one fixed and one flexible machine gun. *USN by courtesy of Norman Polmar.*

The Grumman FF-1 was the only one of a generation of two-seat fighter prototypes to see production as a fighter; others were developed as the SBU and SBC dive-bombers. This FF-1, a restored civilian aircraft, shows to advantage the Grumman system of undercarriage retration, which was retained through the F4F Wildcat, and was extended to several other manufacturers. The aircraft is painted to represent a section-leader's plane in VF-5. The FF-1 served as a fighter with VF-5B and, in slightly modified form, as a scout with VS-3B aboard the *Lexington* (as the SF-1). A scout-bomber derivative of the SF-1, the XSBF-1, failed in competition with the SBC and SBU.

Grumman built the last of the US Navy's biplane fighters, the F2F-1 (illustrated) and the very similar F3F, which had a longer fuselage, longer wings, and a more powerful engine (R-1535-84 instead of the -72 in the earlier fighter; the F3F-2 and -3 had the larger-diameter single-row R-1820-22). All had bomb racks for two 116lb bombs, the lighter weapons having been abandoned by that time. The machine illustrated was flown by the squadron leader of VF-5 (USS *Yorktown*, denoted by a red tail), and shows the fully-colored cowling and the fuselage band of the section leader of the first section (both red). This squadron, 'The Striking Eagles', used as its insignia an eagle diving across a yellow star on a blue field. It was formed as VF-3S, redesignated VF-7B, and ultimately designated VF-5. The photograph was taken in August 1938. *USN by courtesy of Norman Polmar.*

siderable advances in carrying power using the same airframe. The line of development was twofold: fleet observation planes already in service were considered deficient in speed and radius of action, not to mention survivability in the face of enemy fighter opposition. Thus the two-seat fighters (F8Cs) were redesignated as observation types (O2C, O3C). Their successors, although initially designated as fighters (F10C, F12C) were soon redesignated scouts (S3C, S4C). Late in 1933 the Bureau of Aeronautics, 'considering that the striking power of scouting airplanes . . . on carriers must be increased', established a new class of scouts capable of dive-bombing with 500lb bombs. This actually involved modification of two-seat fighter/dive-bomber prototypes, originally designed to carry two 100lb bombs. For example, the S4C became the SBC Helldiver, the last US biplane dive-bomber. Its R-1510 engine was replaced by a more powerful R-1820, it received a controllable-pitch propeller, tail area was increased, and

The Great Lakes BG-1 was among the first heavy dive-bombers designed as such to carry a 1000lb bomb 400 miles, or a 500lb bomb 750 miles, or to scout (with an external tank) over a range of 1000 miles. This is the third aircraft of the fourth section of VB-3B, flying from the carrier *Ranger* in 1935 and from the *Lexington* in 1936–37. It was replaced by the first of the monoplane scout/dive-bombers, the Vought SB2U.

The Vought Vindicator was the first monoplane dive-bomber to enter US service. It was designed to a 1934 specification for a 5000lb airplane to carry a 500lb bomb, competing with the Brewster SBA monoplane and with the Curtiss SBC, Grumman SBF, and Vought SB3U biplanes. A parallel competition for a 6000lb airplane to carry a 1000lb bomb produced the Northrop BT, the direct ancestor of the SBD Dauntless. In June 1935, before their aircraft had been completed, both Vought and Curtiss modified their VSB entries to carry 1000lb bombs, and the VSB and VB categories merged. These three SB2U-1s of VB-3 ('High Hats') formed the fifth of six sections of the squadron; they show the combination of a fuselage band and cowling color used to indicate the different aircraft of a section. For the fifth section, these markings were willow green. Tail color indicated the carrier, white for *Saratoga* which operated VB-3 at this time. For this training flight over the Sierra Nevada mountains, all three were in scout configuration, with 50gal drop tanks.

displacement gear (a bomb crutch) was provided for its single bomb. The Vought SBU was similarly derived from a two-seat fighter design.

The Bureau held a new competition in the summer of 1934, looking for new generations of scout bombers (5000lb airplanes to carry 500lb) and heavy dive-bombers (6000lb to carry a 1000lb bomb). However, Northrop proposed a single aircraft which could meet both requirements. It became the BT, and then, in modified form, the Douglas Dauntless, the SBD, which cracked the Japanese fleet at Midway. In June 1935 the other two competitors, the SB2U and the SBC, were redesigned to take the heavier bomb, and for all practical purposes the heavy dive-bomber category was abolished.

The successful development of scout bombers somewhat

simplified US carrier air groups in that the same airplane replaced both the former bomber-fighters and the former scout-spotters. However, pilot training still differentiated scouts from dive-bombers, so that the presence of twice as many nominal attack aircraft on a flight deck did not necessarily imply twice the offensive power. For that matter, defensive scouting (the aerial pickets) was extremely important prior to the advent of radar for, given the efficacy of dive-bombing, the only effective defense of a carrier was active defense.

As important as the Navy considered dive-bombing, the torpedo/horizontal bomber did not quite die out. Although at one point there remained only a single torpedo squadron in the Fleet, the advent of a new modern torpedo-bomber, the TBD Devastator, considerably improved matters, and

The Douglas TBD Devastator restored high performance to US torpedo squadrons and in large measure its existence encouraged the Navy to continue to develop aerial torpedo attack. Unfortunately it had become obsolescent by 1942, and suffered terribly at Midway. These TBDs are from VT-6, on board *Enterprise* just prior to that battle. Only four of the airplanes in the photo returned.

The Douglas Dauntless was the classic US carrier attack airplane of World War II, responsible for the ultimate victory at Midway. Here, nearly at the end of their combat careers, SBDs of VB-5 prepare to take off from the carrier *Yorktown*, October 1943. Their perforated dive brakes are clearly visible, as is the bomb crutch of the first aircraft in line. *USN by courtesy of Norman Polmar*.

indeed the TBDs performed effectively as level heavy bombers in several carrier raids early in the war. It had to be admitted that a dive-bomber could not impart sufficient velocity to an armor-piercing bomb to drive it through heavy deck armor, and therefore that only a torpedo-bomber could hope to sink a heavily armored warship. However, the latter, attacking alone, was quite vulnerable both to anti-aircraft fire and to defending fighters. On the eve of war US attack tactics called for simultaneous dive and torpedo attacks, with the dive-bombers neutralizing defensive fire. Both types of attack aircraft were armed defensively, and indeed at first it appears that few if any fighter escorts were contemplated: the principal duty of the fighters was carrier self-defense.

US CARRIER AIR GROUPS 1941–45

Thus, in 1941, the standard US carrier air group had stabilized at four squadrons of eighteen aircraft each: one fighter, one scout, one dive-bomber, and one torpedo/horizontal bomber. The *Ranger* had two scout squadrons.

At the outbreak of war the standard US carrier fighter was the Grumman F4F Wildcat. Although superseded by the more powerful Hellcat aboard fleet carriers, it remained in production through the war for service aboard escort carriers. Most were built by the Eastern Aircraft Corporation, a subsidiary of General Motors; these are FM-2s, the license-built version of the Grumman XF4F-8 with its taller tail, lighter airframe, and more powerful engine (R-1820-56 in place of the R-1830-86 of the standard production F4F-4). Armament was reduced from six to four 0.50 caliber machine guns, and bomb shackles carried two 250lb bombs or the two 58gal drop tanks shown. Like earlier US fighters, the initial production Wildcat, the F4F-3, was designed to carry a pair of 116lb bombs, this increasing to 250lb only with the final model, the FM-2.

The Grumman F6F Hellcat, perhaps the most successful US Navy fighter of the Second World War, began as an interim project, a Wildcat derivative powered by a more powerful R-2600 or R-2800 engine. It emerged in 1943 as a far more potent machine, an entirely fresh design. These F6F-5s are being catapulted from USS *Randolph*, a procedure adopted because deck parks were so large that the first aircraft could not otherwise take off. By the end of the war fully 40 per cent of all carrier take-offs were by catapult. These Hellcats show the overall glossy sea blue color scheme authorized in March 1944, and the white geometric tail and wing markings applied very late in the war to identify individual carriers.

The Hellcat was built in numbers because the new carrier fighter pro-
grammed as a Wildcat successor, the Vought Corsair (F4U), was originally declared unsuited for carrier operations. It was given to the
Marines (for land-based use) and to the Fleet Air Arm, and entered US
carrier service only late in 1944. Ultimately the F4U became the standard US Navy carrier fighter, operating even from escort carriers. These
four aircraft show standard postwar markings, the red horizontal stripe
in the national insignia having been authorized in January 1947. The
three-digit numbers indicated the first fighter squadron of the carrier air
group, the second and third digits indicating position within the squadron. Tail identification letters indicated the air group; the color of the
strip above the code letter indicated the squadron. These aircraft are probably from USS *Midway,* about 1950. *USN by courtesy of Norman Polmar.*

Quite soon after the outbreak of war many fighter squadrons were enlarged, up to 27 aircraft being included. The
new *Essex*s were designed to operate a fifth (fighter)
squadron, for a total of 36 such aircraft. When they entered
service, they generally operated a single double-strength
fighter squadron and at the same time the bomber and
scout squadrons were merged as bombers, leaving two
double-strength and one single-strength (torpedo) squadron. By this time fighters were in great demand as strike
escorts as well as fleet defenses.

One important difference from Japanese tactics, which
also emphasized carrier attack aircraft, was that at the
outbreak of war US carriers were largely intended to operate either independently or in divisions of two. Advantages of the latter arrangement included the presence of a
spare flight deck in the event of damage to one carrier, and
the economy of sharing a single combat air patrol. However, given the paucity of US carriers during most of 1942,
they often operated entirely independently. Not until the
massive building program had begun to produce carriers
in numbers were three- and four-ship carrier task groups
formed, with their own supporting surface ships.

By that time (1943) it was already clear that fighters
would be needed in large numbers. The *Essex* air group
was not changed until late in the war, but the new *Independence* class light carriers were to operate two (reduced)
fighter squadrons and a reduced torpedo squadron of nine
aircraft, for a total of 36. As Japanese fighter and bomber
opposition increased, carrier fighter complements
increased in proportion. Fortunately the existing fighters
were effective fighter-bombers, so that the apparent loss of
offensive power was partly balanced; thus in the Spring of
1945 an *Essex* air group normally included a fighter
squadron, a fighter-bomber squadron, and somewhat
reduced (15-plane) squadrons of dive- and torpedo-
bombers. By that time the fighter squadrons often
included small detachments of photo-reconnaissance and
night fighters, forebears of the many specialized types
which would complicate carrier air groups postwar.

By this time there was also strong interest in specialization. At the close of hostilities the light carriers were scheduled to surrender all of their attack aircraft in favor of all-fighter air groups which would protect the heavy carriers while their aircraft struck land targets. At the same time a new fighter, the Grumman F8F Bearcat, was about to enter service; it would be a specialized interceptor rather than a general-purpose aircraft suitable for strike escort. An *Independence* would accommodate 48 Bearcats, as compared to 36 Hellcats or Corsairs.

There was also specialization on another level. Beginning in 1942 there were increasing numbers of escort carriers, which operated conventional torpedo planes (Avengers) but also low-performance fighters (Wildcats, which were being replaced by Hellcats in first-line carrier air groups). The low speed (hence low wind-over-deck) and relatively small flight deck of the escort carrier together limited air group performance. However, many escort carriers were required if air support for amphibious operations were to be effective; they faced land-based aircraft. The Bureau of Aeronautics tried, therefore, to develop a series of limited-performance fighter and attack aircraft suitable for escort carrier use. They included the radical Ryan FR Fireball, which combined a small piston engine with a jet for combat power, and also a new lightweight attack airplane, the Kaiser BTK. To some extent the lightweight Grumman F8F, intended as an interceptor, was also particularly suitable for escort carrier operation.

The US Navy fought World War II with the aircraft it had either in production or in the advanced design phase at the beginning of the war. Its standard bombers, the SB2C

Helldiver and the TBF/TBM Avenger, were the products, respectively, of 1938 and 1939 design competitions. The Helldiver, the first US dive-bomber capable of internal bomb carriage, could also be converted to take a torpedo; however, at first the conversion required several hours and so the desired changeover of carrier groups to a single attack airplane was impracticable at best. Moreover, the Helldiver suffered from numerous problems, so much so that in peacetime it would probably have been cancelled. Some followed from a requirement that two folded Helldivers fit a standard carrier elevator, for quicker travel between flight and hangar decks; this requirement reflected the US desire for the fastest possible strike effort, but also made for a short airplane with too little directional stability. Adaptation for mass production, and unexpected wartime demands, made for considerable overweight. Although the Helldiver was ordered into mass production in 1941, it did not enter combat until the Fall of

From Midway onwards, the Grumman Avenger (TBF, or, in its General Motors-built version, the TBM) was the standard US torpedo-bomber. In practice it functioned far more often as a glide bomber or as an anti-submarine attack airplane flying from escort carriers; postwar, Avengers remained in service for ASW and also for Airborne Early Warning. These two TBM-3Es were photographed in March 1950, flying from an escort carrier, denoted by the double letter on the tail. The 400-series numbers denote the squadron. The 'E' suffix in the designation indicated provision for an underwing APS-4 radar, just visible above 401's engine cowling. Barely visible under the left wings of both aircraft are the eight rocket rails installed as standard equipment, but the typical offset 0.50 caliber turret gun is readily discernible. There were also two fixed forward-firing 0.50s, and the bombardier had a ventral 0.30 caliber weapon, which was eliminated at the end of the war to save weight, the bombardier's position being taken over by a radar operator. APS-4 was a surface search radar, employed against submarines as well as surface ships.

The Curtiss 'Beast', or, officially, SB2C Helldiver, was the Avenger's stablemate in the fast carriers; it was too large to operate from escort carriers. Although overweight and generally unsatisfactory, it was to have superseded the Avenger at the end of the war due to its greater flexibility. These are probably SB2C-1s, the initial production version with a three-bladed propeller and without wing stubs for rockets. The underwing antenna visible on the nearer airplane is a yagi aerial for an internal ASB radar, corresponding to the British ASV series of surface search sets. Small underwing bomb shackles are also visible, as are the twin 0.30 caliber machine guns firing from the rear cockpit. After the first 200 aircraft, a pair of 20mm wing guns replaced the original 0.50s; the heavier weapon appears to be visible here. The diagonal tail stripe denoted USS *Yorktown* and Carrier Air Group 1; *Yorktown* aircraft also had green spinners. This photograph was probably taken early in 1944 as the Helldiver first saw action in November 1943.

1943 and was not considered combat-worthy until about a year later. On the other hand its stablemate, the Avenger, proved quite effective, both as a torpedo-bomber and as a glide-bomber.

As for fighters, at the beginning there was the F4F Wildcat, supplied to the Royal Navy as the Martlet. Although it had appeared quite advanced in the late 1930s, it was far outclassed by new European land-based fighters such as the Spitfire – and by the Zero. In 1938, with the advent of a new class of extremely powerful air-cooled engines, the Bureau of Aeronautics held a fighter competition which produced the Chance Vought F4U Corsair, eventually an extremely successful shore- and carrier-based fighter. However, development was not as rapid as expected. In order to obtain an interim high-performance fighter, the Bureau of Aeronautics asked Grumman to modify the existing Wildcat to take a far more powerful engine, in the Fall of 1940. This interim airplane became the Hellcat, the fighter of the fast carrier task forces until the introduction of the Corsair late in 1944.

The same fighter competition which produced the Corsair also produced a twin-engine fighter, the Grumman F5F Skyrocket. In principle a twin-engine fighter might out-perform a single-engine type by providing far more power but not much more drag. From a carrier point of view, it had the major disadvantage that it could not be folded nearly as compactly; at the least, the pair of propellers would impose limits on how closely such aircraft could be spotted. Even so, when the Bureau of Aeronautics ran a new competition for a single-seat fighter, it selected the twin-engined Grumman F7F. Design requirements at the

time included a very long range (1000nm) and the ability to carry two 1000lb bombs. In effect the F7F corresponded to the F6F Hellcat as the F5F had corresponded to the F4F Wildcat: in each case power but not drag was doubled. The big Tigercat was intended to be compatible with existing fleet carriers and was not, as it sometimes said, connected with the project for a much larger carrier which ultimately produced the *Midway*. In practice, however, it was never used extensively aboard carriers. Its dimensions approached the limits set by hangar deck clearance (eg, the airplane could not easily be jacked up for maintenance), and it exceeded the weight limit set by the deck-edge elevator. Finally, probably because of the constraints imposed on a twin-engine airplane intended to exceed single-engine performance, it was considered inadequately stressed for carrier operation.

The F7F was the last fighter of pure prewar design and conception. In conjunction with its efforts to achieve a much longer range carrier attack group, the Bureau of Aeronautics attempted to develop a very long-range escort fighter, which became the abortive Boeing F8B. Range and a considerable bomb load (the F8B could, for example, carry a torpedo) cost the kind of performance demanded for a carrier interceptor. The new program, then, was pursued alongside one for a new lightweight fighter, which became the last of the Grumman propeller types, the F8F Bearcat. In effect the F8F was the minimum airplane which could be built around an engine developed from that of the Hellcat. Sacrifices included combat radius (216 vs 340nm for the Hellcat); in postwar carrier air groups the Bearcat was often used alongside the longer-range Corsair, as a deck-launched interceptor. Although the F8F saw carrier service in considerable numbers, the much larger F8B fell victim to other demands on Boeing production facilities as well as to the death of the generation of attack aircraft it was intended to escort.

The force of wartime development was not felt until postwar, but it shaped postwar air groups, particularly in their attack component. First, the character of air warfare did not follow prewar expectations. Aerial pickets were gradually discarded, given the success of shipborne radar, although they returned in a much-modified form later as Airborne Early Warning (AEW) aircraft. It followed that scouting squadrons could be much reduced, and that the primary consideration in scouting would be range rather

USS SARATOGA (1945)
EXTERNAL ARRANGEMENT

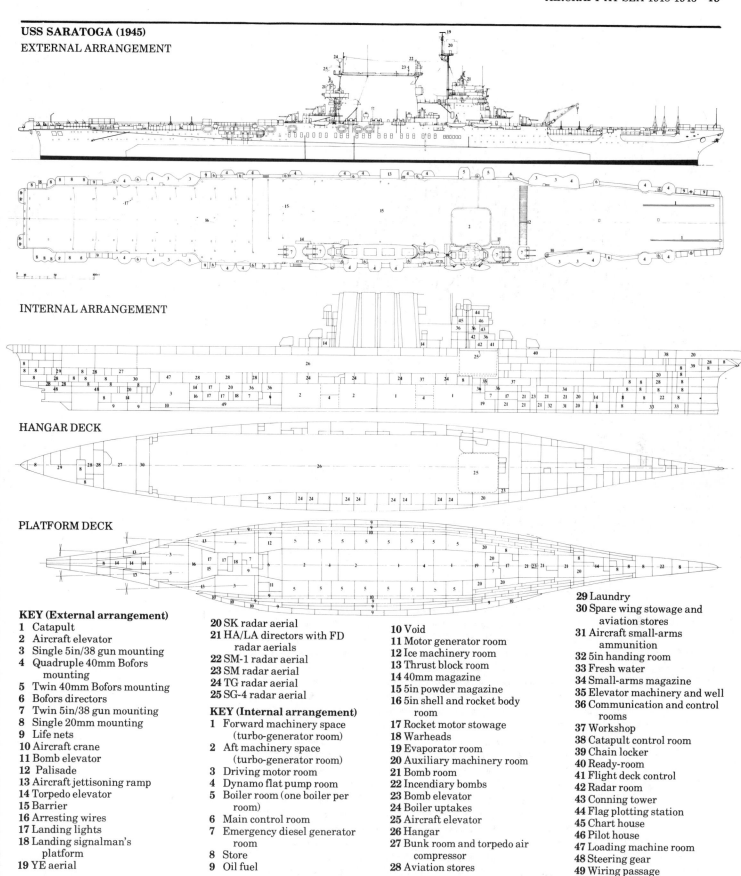

INTERNAL ARRANGEMENT

HANGAR DECK

PLATFORM DECK

KEY (External arrangement)
1 Catapult
2 Aircraft elevator
3 Single 5in/38 gun mounting
4 Quadruple 40mm Bofors mounting
5 Twin 40mm Bofors mounting
6 Bofors directors
7 Twin 5in/38 gun mounting
8 Single 20mm mounting
9 Life nets
10 Aircraft crane
11 Bomb elevator
12 Palisade
13 Aircraft jettisoning ramp
14 Torpedo elevator
15 Barrier
16 Arresting wires
17 Landing lights
18 Landing signalman's platform
19 YE aerial

20 SK radar aerial
21 HA/LA directors with FD radar aerials
22 SM-1 radar aerial
23 SM radar aerial
24 TG radar aerial
25 SG-4 radar aerial

KEY (Internal arrangement)
1 Forward machinery space (turbo-generator room)
2 Aft machinery space (turbo-generator room)
3 Driving motor room
4 Dynamo flat pump room
5 Boiler room (one boiler per room)
6 Main control room
7 Emergency diesel generator room
8 Store
9 Oil fuel

10 Void
11 Motor generator room
12 Ice machinery room
13 Thrust block room
14 40mm magazine
15 5in powder magazine
16 5in shell and rocket body room
17 Rocket motor stowage
18 Warheads
19 Evaporator room
20 Auxiliary machinery room
21 Bomb room
22 Incendiary bombs
23 Bomb elevator
24 Boiler uptakes
25 Aircraft elevator
26 Hangar
27 Bunk room and torpedo air compressor
28 Aviation stores

29 Laundry
30 Spare wing stowage and aviation stores
31 Aircraft small-arms ammunition
32 5in handing room
33 Fresh water
34 Small-arms magazine
35 Elevator machinery and well
36 Communication and control rooms
37 Workshop
38 Catapult control room
39 Chain locker
40 Ready-room
41 Flight deck control
42 Radar room
43 Conning tower
44 Flag plotting station
45 Chart house
46 Pilot house
47 Loading machine room
48 Steering gear
49 Wiring passage

than the kind of high performance built into a dive-bomber. At the same time it became evident that groups of attack planes would always be escorted by fighters, so that they would no longer require their own rear-firing weapons. In that case dive-bombers might be simplified; they would require only a single seat, they might carry their weapons externally, and they might even achieve fighter-like performance at low level. That would not convert them into fighters, since fittings such as dive brakes would still impose considerable performance penalties. In addition, there was no serious possibility of training pilots to perform as both fighters and dive-bombers. The first of the new dive-bombers was the Martin Mauler, closely followed by the Douglas Skyraider which would dominate US Navy attack aviation through the 1950s.

At first the new single-seat attack aircraft were designated simply bombers, rather than scout bombers, since they did not have the observer required for scouting. However, they could carry a torpedo, so torpedo-bombing was added as a secondary function, the new aircraft being

The Grumman Bearcat (F8F-1) was one element of the four-plane Bureau of Aeronautics midwar program to see production; it was the culmination of US piston-engine fighter development. However, it had very short range, and was soon relegated to reserve units. Orange bands around the fuselages of these Bearcats denote their reserve status, and the 'V' tail marking indicates the Glenview Naval Air Station. The enormous propeller, which accounted for the Bearcat's remarkable climb rate, is particularly evident. *By courtesy of Norman Polmar.*

designated in a new BT series. After the war, with the demise of the specialized torpedo-bombers, they became simply attack aircraft (A).

The new attack aircraft were part of an integrated program which would increase carrier strike range from the 350nm of the SB2C-5 to about 450nm. Beside the new dive-bomber, there were to be a new torpedo-bomber/scout and a new escort fighter (F8B). The torpedo-bomber was selected as the scout because it was not nearly as highly stressed as was the dive-bomber. In structural terms, then, the additional crew member and additional scouting equipment would impose a much smaller weight penalty as, indeed, would the additional fuel tankage required. In each case bomb loads were to rise considerably above prewar levels. Thus in place of the prewar standard of 1000lb for a dive-bomber there was to be one 2000lb bomb or one

torpedo. For the heavier torpedo/horizontal bomber, it would be either two torpedoes or 4000lb of bombs.

All of the new types would be able to operate from existing carriers, thanks to the development of a new generation of 3000hp engines, the R-3350 and R-4360, which would replace the wartime 2000hp generation, the R-2600 and R-2800. A prototype of the new monster torpedo-bomber, the single-engine Douglas TB2D, was actually built, although a twin-engine alternative, the Grumman TB2F, remained no more than a project. When it was cancelled, Grumman was asked to develop the existing F7F into a scout (TSF). Grumman's final torpedo-bomber project, the TB2F, was a jet boost engine; it was not part of the BuAer long-range program. However, the shortage of design personnel made it necessary for the TSF to be cancelled in its favor. The TB3F itself was modified postwar for ASW, its jet engine eliminated. Indeed, its evolution was in a sense symbolic of the shift in naval priorities from surface attack to ASW.

Thus in theory, about 1943, the Bureau of Aeronautics could look towards carrier air groups consisting of four distinct types of aircraft: carrier interceptors for self-defense (F8F), and carrier attackers (BTM and TB2D),

▲ The Bureau of Aeronautics sought to increase greatly the reach of carrier strike forces through the introduction of a new generation of very heavy attack aircraft and specialized long-range fighters. Neither of the two prototypes, the Boeing XF8B-1 (pictured here) and the Douglas XTB2D-1, entered production, although a third type, the single-seat attack airplane, appeared postwar as the Martin Mauler and the Douglas Skyraider. The F8B was unique among fighters in possessing an internal bomb bay, which could accommodate two 1600lb armor-piercing bombs; wing racks could take a pair of torpedoes. Six wing positions could take either 0.50 caliber or 20mm guns. *Boeing Aircraft Company by courtesy of Norman Polmar*

The proposed production version of the Douglas XTB2D-1, the TB2D Sky Pirate, was to have had a power-operated dorsal turret with two 0.50 caliber machine guns, a third gun in a ventral bath, and four more in the wings. Four Mk 13 torpedoes or 1000lb bombs could be carried on the pylons beneath the wing center section. Only two prototypes of the Douglas machine were built, in 1945; this photo shows 36933, the first of them. ▼*By courtesy of Norman Polmar*

plus their escorts (F8B), to replace the former single carrier fighter type (F6F/F4U) and the former pair of attack types (TBF and SBD or SB2C). The multiplication of types implied by this plan seems not to have caused any worries at the time, although more recent experience suggests that such multiplication is a grave problem in carrier operations, as carrier stowage for spare parts is limited at best.

Events upset the Bureau's program, leaving only its dive-bomber component for the postwar Navy. By late

1944 the need for anti-ship attack, particularly at long range, declined compared to the desperate requirement for fighters, both for carrier defense and for sweeps over enemy airfields as an indirect contribution to fleet air defense. Perhaps most significantly, the need for carrier-based scouts, as compared to carrier-based photographic-reconnaissance aircraft, declined very sharply as the carriers shifted from ship to land targets – the latter could be found easily enough, only their details requiring clarifica-

The US Navy's first two fleet carriers remained active until World War II, although *Lexington* was lost early in that conflict. Here the much-modified *Saratoga* runs post-refit trials off Puget Sound (May 1945) after repair of Kamikaze damage. The very prominent blister was an earlier modification intended to restore some buoyancy: even in 1941 the two big carriers were badly overweight. Evident, too, is the very heavy battery of quadruple 40mm guns installed in wartime.

A late wartime photograph of USS *Wasp* (CV18) shows the deck park typical of US carrier practice, a mixture of the four principal late-war types: Helldivers, Avengers, Corsairs, and Hellcats. Also evident is part of the extremely heavy anti-aircraft battery common by 1945; some carriers had as many as seventeen or eighteen quadruple 40mm guns, 'short hull' *Essex*s having one rather than two mounts in their bows. Some unusual expedients were tried to increase firepower: the covered object in the gallery deck right forward (and forward of a series of twin 20mm cannon) is a power-operated quadruple 0.50 caliber Army-type machine gun, six of which were mounted experimentally in this ship and also aboard *Lexington*. They replaced 20mm mounts on the basis of six quad 0.50 for ten twin or fourteen single 20mm.

The *Essex*s were the culmination of prewar US carrier development. Here *Philippine Sea* returns home after a Korean deployment, showing much her original configuration but an air group composed of Panthers, Corsairs, Tigercats, and Skyraiders on deck, fore to aft. The big radar surmounting her tripod mast is the SX combined search and height-finding set, developed at the end of World War II; it is supplemented by an SU for surface search (in a small radome) and an SK-2 alongside the funnel. Mixed propeller/jet fighter groups such as this one were common aboard carriers which had not been rebuilt for jet operations, and aboard which the operation of jet fighters could be marginal.

tion. Moreover, by the end of the war large airborne radars (AEW), designed principally for detecting low-flying aircraft, were in prospect. They could also detect surface ships at ranges as great as 200nm, and so to some extent they replaced the medium-range scout.

By this time the US Navy was beginning to turn to its central postwar theme, the exploitation of the command of the sea it had won during World War II. Operationally, that meant that the carrier and her attendant ships were to be used to project naval power ashore, to attack land targets. Such a task force would be concerned with enemy warships only insofar as they might hinder its operations; the destruction of the enemy's navy would not be an important end in itself. Carrier air groups would remain fighter-heavy because a task force operating in enemy waters would be subject to the only effective form of attack – air attack. Furthermore, the carrier's offensive weapon, her attack aircraft, might well require escorts. In fact the principal new postwar factors would be jet aircraft and a new offensive weapon, the atomic bomb, which converted the carrier from a tactical into a strategic instrument.

JAPANESE CARRIER DOCTRINE

Like its US opponent, the Japanese Navy began its experiments with carrier aviation strongly influenced by its British counterpart. Floatplanes were used in the attack on Tsingtao in 1914, and the first carrier, *Hosho*, was ordered in 1918; accounts differ as to whether it was built on a hull originally designed as a tanker or whether it was designed as a carrier from the keel up. In any case the greatest impetus for naval aviation development appears to have come from the arrival of a British mission in 1921. Details of current British carrier design as well as the prototypes of modern British aircraft, such as the Gloster Sparrowhawk, were provided, and for its first few years the Japanese Navy was equipped almost completely with foreign types built under license.

One major difference between the Japanese Navy and its Western counterparts was its extensive use of long-range land-based bombers. Throughout the interwar period the primary strategic problem of the Japanese Navy was the defeat of a numerically superior US fleet which would, nonetheless, have to pass through island chains mandated to Japan at the close of World War I. Although carrier strength was limited by the Washington Treaty, there was no limit whatever on the land-based air force which might be based in the Mandates. Unlike Western air arms, the Japanese Army Air Force appears not to

have opposed the naval development of heavy bombers, and indeed throughout World War II the primary very long range Japanese bombers would be Navy types. Perhaps the chief reason for this tolerance was the Army's concentration on the problems of war on the Asian mainland, which appeared to require shorter ranges. Thus in practice, when the Sino–Japanese War began in 1937, it was the Navy which made long-range attacks and which discovered the need for long-range escort fighters.

British influence on the early course of Japanese naval air development showed in carrier design: like the reconstructed British 'light battlecruisers', the *Akagi* and *Kaga* each had an auxiliary flight deck for fighters. Operating doctrine echoed that of the Royal Navy, in that aircraft were struck below as they landed, so that the operating capacity of the carrier was equated with her hangar capacity. Thus, like the Royal Navy, the Japanese Imperial Navy found itself operating significantly fewer aircraft per ton of carrier than did its chief potential adversary, the US Navy. For example, the ex-capital ships were credited with only 60 aircraft each, compared to perhaps 80 or 90 for the *Lexington*.

British influence was strongly felt in carrier aircraft design. Mitsubishi relied on Herbert Smith, formerly of Sopwith, to design the first generation of Japanese carrier aircraft, produced to a 1921 Navy requirement: the 1MF (Type 10) fighter, the 2MR (Type 10) carrier reconnaissance biplane derived from it, and the 1MT (Type 10) triplane single-seat torpedo-bomber; the last proved unsatisfactory and was replaced by a two-seat biplane, also designed by Smith, the 2MT, which the Japanese designated Type 12 and also B1M1. There was also a three-seat version, the B1M3, and both remained in service as late as 1938. As in other navies, fighter replacement was most urgent, resulting in a 1926 design contest. It was won by Nakajima, with a British design, the Gloster Gambet, which had originally been designed as a private venture with the Fleet Air Arm in mind. It became the A1N1/2, and served into the early 1930s. The rate of aircraft development shows in the need for a new torpedo-

Like the US and Royal Navies, the Imperial Japanese Navy converted two capital ships to carriers. This is the former battleship *Kaga*, running trials (and as yet without her twin 8in turrets forward), showing her three flight decks forward and her long funnels for smoke disposal aft. Alone of the major carrier-building navies the Japanese operated fleet carriers with flush decks, apparently encountering none of the smoke disposal problems which made the design of the postwar *United States* and the original (flush-deck) *Forrestal* so difficult. *By courtesy of Norman Polmar*

bomber design as early as 1928; this contest, too, was won by a British (Blackburn) design, a three-seater which entered production as the B2M. Meanwhile Nakajima, like Boeing in the United States, produced a series of highly maeuverable biplane fighters powered by air-cooled engines, the A2N and A4N, which remained in service up to 1937.

It seems noteworthy in retrospect that none of these aircraft corresponded to the fleet gunfire spotter of British practice – indeed, there was no specialized carrier reconnaissance type, although both Mitsubishi and the Navy's own aircraft factory (Yokosuka) produced prototypes in the late 1920s. Rather, the long-range torpedo-bomber was adapted as a scout, and most fleet reconnaissance duties were concentrated in the floatplanes of the heavy cruisers. Ultimately it was Japanese doctrine to employ the carrier-based scouts as pathfinders for strike forces, a role demonstrated at Midway. No specialized carrier-based scout would be developed until late in World War II.

As in the US Navy, it appears that the advent of very fast, powerful carriers in itself had a strong influence on the development of their tactical doctrine. The Japanese Navy became interested in the ability of the carrier to strike at very long range, and through the 1930s emphasized range in its aircraft specifications. At the same time it retained a strong belief in the primacy of the capital ship. By 1933 this pair of convictions had translated itself into a battle doctrine in which the carriers would mount a surprise attack on US carriers prior to the surface battle, so as to assure air superiority over the battle area. Thus, although the carriers would support the battle fleet, they would do so indirectly, and would operate either independently or with the scouting forces.

Keenly aware of their numerical inferiority, the Japanese tended to split up their fleet so that a superior US force could not destroy all of it at once. Japanese tacticians

favored 'encircling' attacks – reminiscent, to modern ears, of Soviet anti-carrier doctrine – in which these units would be able to concentrate their fire on the enemy fleet without becoming a mass target. Japanese carrier tacticians went further and saw the carrier as both supremely potent and totally vulnerable to enemy air attack, so that an engagement would have to begin with the most massive possible attack on the enemy carriers. However, the Japanese later observed that scouting forces had not been built up to match this requirement; scouting was largely relegated to the type of low-performance aircraft which cruisers could launch. It was true, on the other hand, that the Japanese Navy made an unusual effort to provide cruisers with air facilities.

By the end of the 1920s Japan had developed an adequate pool of aeronautical engineers to assure a considerable degree of self-sufficiency. The Navy began to modernize. Thus, although the B2M had just entered production, a new bomber design contest was held in 1932, resulting, again, in a biplane, the B3Y. Another contest in 1934 had a similar result, the B4Y, which contrasts with the contemporary US BT and TBD. However, in 1935 the Navy again asked for new designs, this time all-metal low-wing monoplanes. The B5N (Kate) which resulted was the standard carrier torpedo- and level bomber through most of World War II.

At the same time, publicity accorded US naval dive-bombers (Helldivers) led the Japanese Navy to experiment with the type; prototypes (which proved unsuccessful) were built at Yokosuka in 1931–32, followed by an open design competition in 1933. As in the case of the torpedo-bombers, a biplane was selected (the Aichi D1A1), but a competition for a more modern type soon followed: in 1936 the D3A ('Val') was selected. Both B5N and D3A were the basis of the Japanese offensive force in 1941–42. They were parallel to, and somewhat later than, the US TBD and SBD.

The Navy had somewhat mixed feelings about a high-performance fighter to parallel the new attack aircraft. Pilots of the mid-1930s were far more impressed by maneuverability than by speed, a phenomenon which resulted in a spate of very fast land-based bombers which might, in theory, outrun defending fighters. In Britain this was the time of the Bristol Blenheim and the Gloster Gladiator. In each country, too, there was a feeling that a fast interceptor, perhaps not very maneuverable, would be needed to counter the fast bomber. The Japanese Navy of this period was apparently particularly impressed by the advent of such fast US commercial aircraft as the Northrop Gamma, which was imported in 1933. It cannot have escaped Japanese notice that Northrop might well adapt the Gamma technology to naval attack use. The result was a decision to hedge, to go for higher speed but to attempt to retain considerable maneuverability. A 1935 specification produced the Mitsubishi A5M ('Claude'), a fixed-

In this overhead view *Kaga* shows fighters lined up on her lower flight deck, with larger aircraft on the main flight deck, and radio masts folded outboard. *By courtesy of Norman Polmar*

The Japanese equivalent of the British *Ark Royal* and the US *Yorktown* was the *Zuikaku* which, unencumbered by treaty, was larger than either. Note the island, much smaller than in US or British practice, and the uptakes abaft it, which the Japanese Navy found quite sufficient for 152,000shp. *By courtesy of Norman Polmar*

undercarriage fighter roughly equivalent in performance to the US Wildcat produced to a contemporary requirement.

One important difference between the Japanese and Western interwar naval experiences was that Japanese carriers attacked land targets repeatedly during the war in China. Thus for example aircraft from the large carrier *Kaga* bombed Shanghai during the 'Shanghai Disturbance' of January 1932, and carrier bombers supported the 1937 landings at Shanghai. At that time, too, carrier-based fighters provided the only possible support for long-range Japanese naval bombers flying out of Formosa. Experience in China propelled the Japanese Navy into demands for both very long range and performance quite comparable with that of land based fighters: the combination produced the outstanding A6M Zero ('Zeke') fighter in 1940. At that time aircraft engines were not yet powerful enough to provide a Western fighter, much more heavily built and armored against machine-gun fire, with a comparable performance: the Zero-Sen dominated the Pacific at the outbreak of the Pacific War.

Unlike the US Navy, the Japanese Navy appears not to have contemplated the wholesale replacement of its horizontal and torpedo-bombers by dive-bombers. Indeed, it considered the heavy horizontal bombing capability of these aircraft as important as their ability to deliver torpedoes; this may reflect Japanese interest in strikes on enemy land installations. Certainly their prewar experiments showed a continued role for the aerial torpedo. For example, just before the outbreak of war they expected to exceed 80 per cent torpedo hits in daytime against a fast battleship, and over 70 per cent at night. Dive-bombing would secure 40 per cent hits, and level bombing from 10,000ft 10 per cent hits. The torpedo- and level bombing performances were both bettered at Pearl Harbor, albeit against static targets (90 and 27 per cent respectively). In that battle, of ninety torpedo-bombers in the first wave, fifty operated as level bombers, using converted 16in armor-piercing shells (which the dive-bombers could not lift in any case); all 54 torpedo-bombers in the second wave functioned as level bombers. These figures may reflect some lack of confidence in the operation of torpedoes in the shallows of Pearl Harbor, and the feeling that only an armor-piercing bomb could sink a battleship.

Each wave was accompanied by a large fighter force, 43 in the first and 35 in the second (together with, respectively, 51 and 78 dive-bombers). This massive use of fighter escorts was the consequence of combat experience in China, where modern Chinese fighters had opposed Japanese bombers. The need for escort was, then, far more apparent than it was in Western air arms more heavily imbued with the doctrine that 'the bomber always gets through'.

RE-EQUIPMENT – AND THE LESSONS OF WAR
Like its US and British counterparts, the Japanese Navy contemplated a new generation of naval aircraft in the late 1930s, to take advantage of rapidly advancing engine technology. A new trio of carrier aircraft was designed to a set of 1937 specifications. The fighter specification called for a combination of very high speed, maneuverability comparable to that of previous types, and great range. It was, moreover, to be very heavily armed for its time, with two cannon and two machine guns. The result was the outstanding, but very lightly built, A6M Zero-Sen, the standard Japanese fighter throughout the Pacific War. The light construction of the Zero was a consequence of the combination of carrier requirements (such as a short take-off and limited size and total weight) and combat requirements (speed, maneuverability and range) which had to be fulfilled with an engine considerably less powerful than those available in the West: the Sakae 12 of production A6M2s was rated at 925hp, whereas the contemporary Grumman Wildcat had an R-1820 rated at 1200hp and the new generation of US fighters in the test stage in 1940, when the Zero entered production, were powered by engines in the 2000hp class, such as the R-2800.

A new dive-bomber was to equal the new fighter in speed, excel it in range, yet carry the standard Japanese 250kg bomb. Procurement of the German He 118 was contemplated, but in the end a high-speed research project developed by Yokosuka was adapted as the D4Y Suisei ('Judy'). In the event, this ambitious program was not executed on time, due to the severe limitations imposed by the Japanese industrial base. Only the Zero entered service prior to the outbreak of war in the Pacific; the 'Judy' was available only in small numbers at Midway, and the

The Zero-Sen was above all the symbol of the Japanese naval air arm, victorious from Pearl Harbor until Midway, and still in production to be expended in Kamikaze attack at the very end of the war. The Zero, or Mitsubishi A6M, was very lightly built, but it was also extremely heavily armed for its time, with a pair of 20mm cannon and two 7.7mm machine guns. This captured example shows the minimal degree of wing-folding applied. Unlike Western carrier aircraft, the Zero folded only to permit it to fit the standard Japanese 11m carrier elevator; there was no attempt to achieve particularly compact stowage. Indeed, A6M3s had their wing span reduced to 11m (slightly over 36ft) and the folding tips eliminated entirely. *USN by courtesy of Norman Polmar*

The standard Japanese dive-bomber of the early stages of the Pacific War was the Aichi D3A1 ('Val'). Its offensive load, a single 250kg (551lb) bomb, seems small in relation to a large airframe, and compares with standard weapons twice as heavy carried by contemporary American scout bombers. *USN by courtesy of Norman Polmar*

'Jill' did not enter service until late in 1943, ie roughly when the US SB2C, designed to a 1938 requirement, appeared.

Japan decided rather earlier than the United States to attempt to unite the dive- and torpedo-bomber functions, and in 1941 a specification for a fast attack airplane capable of lifting either a 1000kg torpedo or an 800kg bomb was issued. It resulted in the final wartime carrier attack type, the B7A Ryusei ('Grace') which, in the event, did not enter production until 1944. The B7A was associated with a new carrier fighter project, the A7M Reppu ('Sam') of 1942, which also suffered from the effects of industrial disruption late in World War II.

The Japanese Navy began to practice large combined attacks in 1939, but found that much time was lost while aircraft from distant carriers assembled. Previously the carriers had been kept widely separated, but now proponents of massed operations began to argue that the combined fighter force of several carriers would provide enhanced protection. Thus on 10 April 1941 six carriers and their air groups were combined into the First Air Fleet. Although it was intended specifically to destroy enemy carriers by mass surprise attacks, this force fought largely against shore installations during its six months of combat. In fact, the full concentration of the carriers was planned only for attacks against shore targets, whereas there would be some minimal dispersal for action against carriers. However, at Midway the First Air Fleet was disposed for an attack against a shore installation. The concentration of the carriers did indeed assure their destruction, but only once their protective fighters had been borought down almost to sea level to counter a US torpedo attack. The Japanese concluded that a compromise between concentration and dispersal was called for. After Midway they operated in three-carrier divisions.

As in the case of Britain, Japan was unable to build fleet carriers in the requisite numbers in wartime. A light fleet carrier, based on the prewar *Hiryu* and powered by standard cruiser turbines, was put into production; this is the prototype, *Unryu*, newly completed. Only two others out of a total of fifteen planned were completed; three more were launched but then stopped. *Unryu*, *Amagi*, and *Katsuragi*, the three units completed, formed a task group at Leyte but operated few aircraft, as by then the Japanese Navy had suffered the loss of most of its pilots in the Battle of the Philippine Sea. *By courtesy of Norman Polmar*

In theory the separate divisions would bring back the old virtue of protection by dispersal. Thus for the Battle of Santa Cruz the Japanese fleet operated three carriers together (the large *Shokaku* and *Zuikaku*, and the smaller *Zuiho*), and, separately, the medium carrier *Junyo*. The US strike pilots found and damaged the larger force, but *Junyo* was undamaged, and her pilots struck the US carrier *Hornet*. By 1944 the divisional philosophy had been elaborated to the point where divisions, not carriers, had integral air groups: at the Philippine Sea the Japanese Navy operated three carrier divisions, with three divisional air groups.

Reconnaissance was the greatest Japanese weakness. Even before Midway, which was generally recognized as a reconnaissance disaster, the Naval Staff issued a specification for a new specialized carrier scout, which became the C6N1 Saiun ('Myrt'). It proved superior to the US scouts, which were standard attack aircraft assigned reconnaissance duties, but it was too late for combat. At both Midway and the Philippine Sea two years later, the standard Japanese carrier scout was the D4Y ('Judy') dive-bomber.

Japanese carrier air groups reflected the Japanese emphasis on attack. For example, as reconstructed in the mid-1930s the large *Akagi* and *Kaga* were assigned, respectively, 19 and 24 dive- and 35 and 36 torpedo-bombers. Each had 12 fighters. These figures compared with the *Kaga* air group of 24 A1N fighters and 36 B1M torpedo-bombers at Shanghai in 1932. On the other hand the *Shokaku*, designed to a 1936 Staff Requirement, was to operate 27 dive- and 27 torpedo-bombers, as well as 18 fighters, and by 1942 the other large carriers were also operating increased fighter squadrons of 18 aircraft each. All also carried spare aircraft, not counted in their air groups, held in reserve against damage.

In each case aircraft operating capacity was equated with hangar capacity. Thus when the Japanese Navy, aware of the vulnerability of its carriers, moved to an armored flight deck design in the *Taiho*, it had to accept a considerable reduction. As one means of making up for this loss, she was to operate a new dual-purpose dive/torpedo bomber, the B7A Ryusei ('Grace'). Numbers had, however, to be foregone: the *Taiho* was designed to operate 24 fighters, 24 attack aircraft, and 4 specialized scouts. A later version of the design, the abortive Hull 5021 (1943), returned to the previous offensive emphasis, with 27 attack aircraft but only 18 fighters – and 6 scouts.

The Japanese Navy also developed a series of light carriers, beginning with the *Soryu* and *Hiryu* of the 1931–32 Supplementary Program: they were developed in wartime as the *Unryu* class. A typical planned air group might be 18 dive- and 18 torpedo-bombers, plus 9 fighters. Before the outbreak of war, construction of such carriers was limited by treaty; however, the Japanese Navy knew that in the event the treaties were terminated it would be unable to compete with the productive capacity of its most probable enemy, the United States. It therefore undertook a program of 'shadow' carrier construction, ie of the con-

struction of ships particularly suited to conversion to carriers. This produced the fleet carriers *Hiyo* and *Junyo*, originally laid down as liners but subsidized to incorporate naval features from the start; they were designed to accommodate 18 dive- and 18 torpedo-bombers, as well as 12 fighters, with a total of 10 more aircraft in reserve (2 dive- and 5 torpedo-bombers, and 3 fighters). Late in the war, however, *Hiyo* operated 18 dive- and 6 torpedo-bombers, as well as 27 fighters.

The balance of the 'shadow' program produced fast light carriers, perhaps comparable to the US light fleet carriers: two former submarine support ships, *Zuiho* and *Shoho*, which received destroyer machinery to increase their speed to 29kts; their somewhat larger half-sister *Ryuho*; and the ex-seaplane tenders *Chitose* and *Chiyoda*. In addition, as in the US and Royal Navies, merchant ships were converted into escort carriers primarily intended for ASW.

Again, as in the Allied navies, the effect of war experience was to force up the minimum size acceptable in a fleet carrier. For example, interviewed just after the war, a captain on the Japanese Naval Staff observed that 'experience had shown *Hiryu* type to be too small for operations with the battle fleet, and that *Shokaku*, although large enough to operate the heavier and more powerful types of aircraft, proved to be inadequately protected for this service. *Taiho* design was regarded as satisfactory for this kind of work. Carriers of *Unryu* class, produced by progressive improvement of *Soryu* design, were regarded as suitable for strikes against convoys protected by cruisers and escort carriers. Here the lighter types of plane would suffice, and this type had the advantages of simplicity and rapidity of construction. The smaller carriers were intended for escort duties.'

By May 1944 the Japanese Navy had introduced fighter-bombers in the form of modified Zero-Sens, to supplement the striking capacity of its smaller carriers. The Fleet was then organized into three divisions, each of which had roughly homogeneous carrier air wings. Naval Air Group 601 flew off the big carriers *Taiho*, *Shokaku* and *Zuikaku*, each of which operated 27 Zero fighters, 27 D4Y ('Judy') dive-bombers, 18 B6N ('Jill') torpedo-bombers, and 3 D4Y scouts. Air Group 652 flew from the medium carriers *Junyo* and *Hiyo* and the very small carrier *Ryujo*. Each carried 18 Zero fighters and 9 Zero fighter-bombers as well as 6 B6N torpedo-bombers. The two larger ships each carried 18 dive-bombers as well, but the poverty of the Japanese aircraft industry showed in the fact that *Junyo* had only 9 of the modern D4Ys and 9 of the old (fixed-undercarriage) D3As ('Val'); *Hiyo* had only the latter. Finally, Naval Air Group 653 flew from three carriers converted from naval auxiliaries: *Chitose*, *Chiyoda* and *Zuiho*. Each operated only 6 Zero fighters, but also 15 Zero fighter-bombers. Once more, poverty was evident. There were no dive-bombers, but of nine torpedo-bombers per ship, only three were of the new B6N type, and the other six were of the B5N ('Kate') type used at Pearl Harbor. This was the last carrier operation in which the Japanese Navy could provide full air groups to its ships; after the decimation of the 'Marianas Turkey Shoot' there was not enough time to train replacement pilots for the battles around Leyte, and many of those available were assigned to land bases on Formosa. The fighter-bombers were presumably an attempt to slip past US CAP forces. It does seem notable that even in 1944 Japanese fighter forces were not up to the US level of 1941. It is not clear what conclusions were drawn from the battle nor what carrier air group structure the Imperial Navy would have adopted had it been able to re-form in 1945.

Only Italy and Japan tried to refit liners as fleet carriers. This is the Italian *Aquila* (ex-*Roma*) under reconstruction, 1941. She was essentially complete when work stopped just short of sea trials at the Armistice, September 1943. *Italian Navy*

FRENCH POLICY 1918–45

The only other Navy to operate a carrier before World War II was that of France. Sketches for the conversion of the torpedo depot ship *Forbin* to a primitive carrier preceded the outbreak of war in 1914, and indeed an airplane was flown from the ship that May. These experiments were followed, after the end of the war, with a further series on an improvised flight deck aboard the unfinished battleship *Béarn*, and in 1922 her completion as a carrier was authorized. The Royal Navy provided considerable assistance, the final design incorporating features of such ships as the *Eagle* and *Hermes*. There was, however, no secondary flight deck as in several British conversions. Nor did the French Navy adopt the Royal Navy's view that arresting gear was unnecessary; instead it developed its own transverse system, which was also adopted by the Japanese Navy.

Béarn was completed in 1927, the slowest and the least capacious of the capital ships converted to carriers under the Washington Treaty, with a nominal air group of 40 aircraft. Nor did she have any immediate successors, given the low state of French finances during the interwar period. Thus the long-range naval aviation program of 1922, under which the ship had been completed, could not be realized; it had envisaged the construction of two 30,000-ton carrier-cruisers, one of which would replace the slow *Béarn*. The French aircraft industry of this period produced a series of advanced prototypes, but received few large orders, with the result that aircraft actually in service were frequently obsolescent. The small size of the carrier air arm cannot have helped matters. For example, in 1930 the French Navy decided to adopt a dive-bomber, and a fighter design was modified as the Gordou-Leseurre 430. Two prototypes carried a 50kg bomb, and were succeeded by an order for five GL 432s, which could lift a 150 or 225kg weapon – and which were not even ordered until 1935, when the US Bureau of Aeronautics was trying to decide whether its fast scout could accommodate the thousand-pounder (454kg). Similarly, fighter development led to advanced prototypes in the early 1930s, when only France operated monoplanes; but these same parasol monoplanes were standard fare as late as 1939.

The prospects for more carriers were not encouraging. Design studies of 1930–32 showed a tonnage of 15,000 to 18,000 and high speed (which accorded with contemporary French cruiser design) as well as cruiser protection and an all-anti-aircraft battery, but aircraft capacity was limited to 20–30 aircraft. Only in 1936 did serious planning for a new carrier begin, and at first that was on the basis of the

Before World War II the French Navy completed only one carrier, the converted battleship *Béarn*. In June 1940 she was in the French West Indies, having loaded a cargo of US aircraft for France. She remained there, blockaded by the US Navy, until 1943 when she was released for conversion to an aircraft transport for the Free French forces. She is shown here on 18 November 1943, devoid of anti-aircraft armament but not yet converted. Her unusual hinged elevator doors are visible.

conversion of the two earliest French 'treaty cruisers', retaining, in some versions, one of the 8in turrets. Aircraft capacity would be limited to 12 or 14. An alternative design for a new carrier showed up to 70 or 80 aircraft in two superimposed hangars, light cruiser protection, and a speed of 30kts, on a displacement of 23,000 tons. This ship, too, ran afoul of budgetary constraints.

At this time it was estimated that the cost of a carrier would equal that of a battleship, or three heavy cruisers, or of all French naval land-based aviation. Moreover, the carrier would not be useful except beyond the radius of action of land-based aircraft, ie outside the Channel and the Mediterranean, in the North Atlantic more than 400 miles from shore, and in distant areas. It was also noted that North Atlantic weather did not seem conducive to air operations. Additionally, it might be argued that the presence of a carrier would be an embarrassment to a fleet; it would require two destroyers as escorts, would take an hour to launch an air strike, and nearly half as long again to recover one. Thus if the aircraft had an endurance of three hours, the carrier would have to follow a fixed course for six hours, constituting an ideal target. Nor was the carrier airplane by any means the ideal scout, with its single observer. Thus the carrier would have to be considered only as an offensive weapon – and it was by no means clear that its aircraft would prove effective in that role. The French Navy feared that the rapid development of land-based aircraft would outpace that of those suitable to a carrier. However, the most telling argument was fiscal: it was by no means clear that the Navy could recruit or retain sufficient personnel to man 70 aircraft.

These arguments are of interest because they are the classic prewar ones mounted against the carrier; it seems noteworthy that the French Navy alone of those operating carriers during this period took them seriously. Nonetheless, two 18,000-ton carriers, *Painlevé* and *Joffre*, were authorized in 1937, to operate a combination of single-engine fighters and twin-engine scout/bombers. Had the latter entered service, then, they would have been quite unique among the world's navies. Alternative two-seat (attack) and three-seat (scout) versions of the twin-engine aircraft were envisaged; in 1939 an alternative single-engine type, the Latécoère 299, was ordered as an alternative in view of its impressive performance.

The fall of France quashed these plans, and French carrier design efforts were reduced to a series of studies intended to keep design teams employed. They included a variety of carriers with heavy armor protection and even with heavy gun batteries, both of which leaned in precisely the opposite direction from that in which other carrier navies were proceeding. One study, the only one pursued postwar, was far closer to contemporary foreign practice, calling for a displacement of 14,000 tons and a speed of 25kts, with a pure anti-aircraft battery and an air group of 18 twin-engine aircraft: heavy fighters and bombers to be built under the 1943 program. The latter called for a radius of action of 3000km (1600nm), which soon led to a unit weight of 10 to 11 tons. Two such aircraft were actually built postwar, the N1500 Noreclair and the NC 1070. They were beyond the capability of contemporary catapults, although both would have had to be launched by this method. The 1946 'rearmament' program envisaged construction of 105 such aircraft. The 'heavy fighter' was to be the 582, capable of 465mph at 30,000ft and a radius of action of about 1500nm. After the war it was replaced by the SO 800 Narval, of which 70 were to be built under the 1946 program. All were intended to operate from the new carrier authorized by the French Parliament in August 1947, which was to be somewhat larger than the wartime project. In fact, however, both carrier and carrier aircraft proved beyond the resources of a France still recovering from the effects of war and the German occupation, and no new French carrier would appear for a decade. Thus a series of new aircraft designed under the 1946 program were built only in prototype form, and all of the new naval aircraft programs were abandoned by 1953.

3. The Postwar Revolution

For the US Navy and the Royal Navy, the single greatest strategic fact of 1945 was the replacement of a sea power, Japan, by a land power, the Soviet Union, as the most probable enemy in a future conflict. Such a war, as envisaged in the late 1940s, would open with Soviet or satellite troops moving across land frontiers, perhaps deep within the Eurasian land mass or at any rate far from existing Western bases. Moreover, while the Soviet Union maintained, at least on paper, a very large standing army, the Western allies were unwilling to support comparable forces. They preferred to rely on a combination of superior technology, reflected largely in air and naval forces (not to mention the atomic bomb) — and on the inherent flexibility of sea power, which would permit them to move those forces they did possess to threatened areas far from home, almost as easily as the enemy could move his land forces. For their part, the Soviets would probably contest such movements with submarines and with land-based aircraft, much as the Germans had; in 1945 they had, after all, captured much of the new German technology for both types of warfare.

THE QUESTION OF ROLE

The role of the carrier in this new world was subject to some debate. Air forces, for example, argued that navies would exist primarily to keep sea lanes open, while strategic bombers made the primary attacks at very long range with nuclear weapons. Indeed, the destruction imposed on the Soviet Union by those bombs would be so great that even the armies would fulfill very much a secondary role. For its part, the US Navy considered land attack, even deep within enemy territory, the primary future role of the carrier. In many areas carriers would be the only available air bases. Their inherent flexibility would make them a very economical means of applying air power at great distances. Moreover, some within the Navy argued that a new generation of carrier aircraft might be the ideal delivery vehicle even for strategic nuclear attack.

Even the ASW mission might best be served by long-range naval bombers. In 1945 the outlook for conventional anti-submarine forces was quite pessimistic, given the development of the Type 21 U-boat and the prospective development of the Walter submarine. Some new strategy was called for. For example, submarines proceeding to and from their bases would remain vulnerable to mines — which might be laid either by Allied submarines or by long-range carrier aircraft. It was also possible to imagine attacks on submarines in port, although wartime experience suggested that such boats would probably be held in pens protected from all but the heaviest bombs. Thus although air attack on Soviet ports seemed the most efficient anti-submarine tactic, it also required a new generation of naval aircraft, to combine the requisite range with capacity for bombs of up to 12,000lb, compared with the 2000lb of wartime types.

The existing carrier forces were not well adapted to strategic air warfare. For example, they could not carry very heavy bombs (which alone could attack heavy concrete submarine pens or, for that matter, some industrial targets) and so the total bomb loads of very large carrier formations were relatively disappointing. When Task Force 58 raided Tokyo in February 1945 it delivered about 450 tons of bombs; a typical B-29 raid delivered about ten times as much, albeit at a far greater cost in aircrew. There had been no great incentive to develop heavy naval bombers as long as the primary targets of carrier aircraft had been ships. That is, a ship could be sunk with a single hit by a one-ton torpedo or even, for that matter, by a 1000lb bomb dropped by a dive-bomber. A factory would survive a large number of similar hits because its vital points were spread over a large area. Thus the same carrier aircraft proved far more successful in attacks on Japanese shipping in July 1945. This experience undoubtedly influenced Admiral Mitscher, commander of the fast carriers, in his decision to press for a new type of carrier bomber which could deliver a 12,000lb bomb. Perhaps fortuitously, the same load might be equated to the new atomic bomb. In 1945 there was little hope that it could ever be reduced much below 10,000lb. So large a bomber would of course best be operated by a new carrier, and in December 1945 the US Navy's Bureau of Aeronautics began a combined program of bomber and carrier development which led, eventually, to the *Forrestal* and thus to modern US carriers.

The Bureau looked toward three phases. In the first, piston engines would be used to drive a 30,000lb bomber over a combat radius of about 300nm carrying a 8000lb bomb. A speed of 362mph at sea level was expected. In the next phase, turboprops would power a 45,000lb bomber, which would achieve a combat radius of 1000nm and might make 500mph at 35,000ft. Finally, the Bureau hoped to develop a 100,000lb bomber with a combat radius of 2000nm, which could strike any Soviet target from a carrier task force well out to sea; note that this figure compares closely with the performance of the Polaris missile. Although the first two types might operate from existing or modernized carriers, the third would require a wholly new ship. In fact the Bureau needed a sketch design around which the Bureau of Ships could design a carrier, which was laid down in 1949 as the unfortunate *United States* (CVA58). The 300nm bomber became the North American AJ Savage; the second, the turboprop A2J. Each aircraft of the program was to be able to carry a 12,000lb bomb at a sacrifice in range and performance, so that the entire program could be read, particularly by a hostile critic, as a means of giving the Navy an atomic capability.

Certainly that is how the US Air Force saw matters. In 1946, as the Navy program began to gain momentum, it had its own intercontinental bomber, the B-36, and defense funds were extremely tight. The Air Force saw itself as the arm of the future, and hoped that nuclear-armed bombers might dominate any future war. Although

The postwar revolution in carrier aircraft was matched, in the US and Royal Navies, by a revolution in carrier design. USS *Oriskany*, an *Essex* class carrier, was suspended after the end of World War II and completed as the prototype for a series of SCB-27A conversions. Here she is shown leaving San Francisco, 2 December 1955, still in much her original configuration. The principal visible aviation features are the clearer flight deck, with deck guns removed, and the prominent escalator outboard of the island, which connected ready rooms with the flight deck. It and the new ready room location were intended to avoid the vulnerability of the former gallery deck location, just beneath the wooden flight deck. Not at all evident is the installation of two high-capacity H-8 catapults, replacing the former H-4s and providing jet capability. Of the suit of carrier landing aids, only the SPN-8 precision radar, in a small radome at the after side of the island, is in evidence. The island also carries SPS-8 for height-finding (fighter control) and two air search radars, a long-wavelength SC-5 and a centimetre-wavelength SPS-6, the latter barely visible half way up the radar mast. More visible are a surface search set (forward) and a YE homing beacon (aft – TACAN had not yet been introduced), with ECM radomes above. In 1955 topweight had not yet edged out defensive armament: *Oriskany* was designed to mount fourteen twin 3in/50, as well as eight open 5in/38. Only a few of the former had been landed by this time, and mounts are visible below the bridge and right aft. *USN by courtesy of Norman Polmar*

The next steps were an angled deck and an enclosed (hurricane) bow, as in USS *Intrepid*, shown here as newly modified, still mounting some 3in/50 guns. She has the electronic suit current in the late 1950s: reading from the lowest radar level up are an SPS-8 height-finder for fighter control; an SPS-12 air search set forward with SPN-6 marshalling radar (for Carrier-Controlled Approach) looking aft; and above both an SPS-10 surface search set. TACAN surmounts the mast. The small oblong antennas are IFFs slaved, respectively, to the SPS-8 and the SPN-6. Finally, SPN-8 is barely visible abaft the island. The two arrays slung from the forward end of the flight deck are ship-to-air radio antennas, and a mirror landing aid is just visible on a sponson, with its lights further aft. *The Floating Drydock*

it could not directly stop Navy aircraft development, it could attack the Navy program by attacking the very expensive carrier which the advanced Phase Three airplane required. The *United States* was cancelled a few weeks after it was laid down, and BuAer was ordered to scale down the advanced airplane to the point of compatability with existing decks. On the other hand, the program for carrier modernisation, which included a new catapult and new arresting gear, was not stopped, and there was reason to hope that the advanced catapults designed for the new super-carrier might eventually be placed aboard existing ships.

THE US NAVY NUCLEAR BOMBER
The carrier cancellation affected the weight of any new bomber. Even on 100,000lb, it appeared that the Bureau would be unable to meet its range requirements. For example, a December 1947 study showed that with two

turboprops and a jet for boost, the bomber might easily exceed the 500mph speed requirement – but radius would be only 960nm, including a 500nm combat run in and out of the target. Radius was critical for the strategic attack mission, and indeed partially justified the size (and cost) of the new carrier. However, speed was also vital, as the bomber would probably have to approach its targets unescorted. Thus in 1948 the Bureau began to consider an all-jet alternative, with a speed of at least 525kts (over 600mph) at 40,000ft. Although it still wanted a combat radius of 2000nm, it was now willing to accept as little as 1700nm, if the speed requirement could be met.

Douglas managed to win the competition, even after the cancellation of the big carrier cut the maximum allowable weight to 70,000lb. It did not quite meet the specification: it had a combat radius of 1000nm and a speed of 511kts at 35,000ft; on the other hand it did remain within the new limit, it was suitable for existing carriers (and so preserved the Navy's strategic role), and it could lift 12,800lb of bombs. Moreover, with the development of inflight refueling the A3D Skywarrior could fly over 1700nm for a high-altitude attack with a 6650lb bomb.

The A3D was the principal heavy carrier bomber of the 1950s and early 1960s, succeeding the North American AJ in service from March 1956 onwards. Its existence as an ongoing project probably ensured the construction of the new *Forrestal*, in that the Navy could retain its strong interest in the future of strategic attack even in the face of the cancellation of the *United States*. The existing AJ did not have the potential to overcome jet fighters, not did it

In the US Navy, the true product of the jet and nuclear age is the super-carrier. This is the first of them, the newly-completed *Forrestal*, in 1955. The forward sponsons had to be removed for improved seakeeping, and much more electronic equipment added, but it is remarkable that this ship has served for a quarter-century without major reconstruction. Her compact island shows two masts, the after one of which carried the usual complement of ECM antennas. Both had to fold down to permit passage under the Brooklyn Bridge to the New York Navy Yard. Of the antennas visible, the small one mounted directly on the island abeam the funnel is a radiosonde (weather balloon) receiver; the remainder correspond to those aboard the *Intrepid* at about the same time.

have the range to strike the most important Soviet targets. As for the A2J, it proved less than impressive, and was cancelled in favor of the A3D in June 1953.

The big new carriers were designed, then, to operate the A3D, whose size in turn was largely determined by the 10,000lb of the atomic bomb. However, as the A3D moved towards production, the bomb designers showed that they could produce weapons suitable for aircraft much closer to fighter-bomber size, such as the Mk 5 (3300lb, about 120kT), the Mk 7 (1680lb) and the Mk 8 (3250lb, about 20kT, but capable of ground penetration, eg for attacks on submarine pens). With these weapons in prospect, the Chief of Naval Operations ordered virtually all existing

The North American AJ-1 Savage symbolized the transformation of the US carrier force from short-range tactical operations to strategic attack. Here two of these heavy bombers await catapult launch from the modernized carrier *Lake Champlain*, 14 August 1953. The Savage on the left clearly shows the dorsal air intake for its tail jet engine, and jet blast deflectors are erected behind both bombers. The 'N' in their tail codes indicates assignment to the Pacific Fleet. *By courtesy of Larry Sowinski*

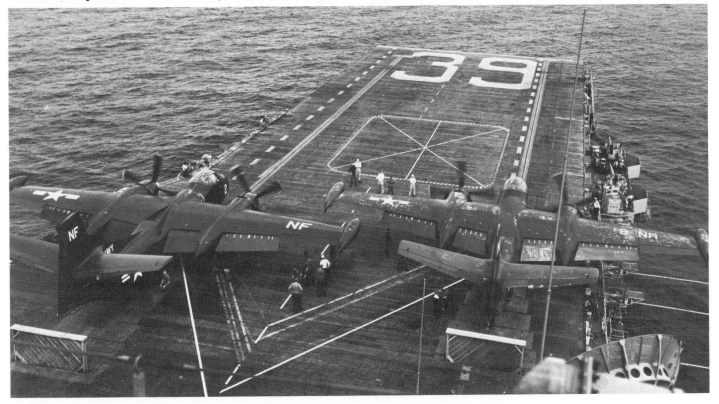

The successor to the Savage, and the 70,000lb bomber which figured prominently in the design of the *Forrestal* class super-carrier, was the Douglas A3D Skywarrior, seen here in formation with another famous Douglas product, the A4D Skyhawk. In 1962 these aircraft were redesignated A-3 and A-4 respectively, by which time the A-3 was serving largely as an ECM platform. This EKA-3B was assigned to Tactical Electronic Warfare Squadron VAQ-33 when this photograph was taken during the RIMPAC exercise, 24 April 1978. The two small propellers powered auxiliary generators, as existing aircraft generating capacity was insufficient for the array of jamming gear aboard. At least thirty A-3Bs were converted to the EKA-3B combination tanker/countermeasures configuration during the Vietnam War, providing both fuel and jamming cover to strike groups.

KEY (USS FORRESTAL)
1 Aviation workshop
2 Hangar Bay 3
3 Hangar Bay 2
4 Hangar Bay 1
5 Aviation stores
6 Incendiary bomb room
7 Steering gear
8 Pump room
9 Emergency generator room
10 20mm ammunition (aircraft)
11 Bomb and rocket fuze magazine
12 Bomb fin stowage
13 Bomb magazine
14 Modular ammunition magazine
15 HEAF service tank
16 Avgas
17 2.75in rocket magazine
18 Sidewinder G/C units
19 Squadron ready-room
20 Uptake space
21 Central control station
22 Main machinery room
23 Auxiliary machinery room
24 Carrier approach and air operations rooms
25 Shop
26 Strike check-out area
28 Display decision room
29 Hangar fire-doors
30 AN/SPN 35-A radome
31 AN/SPS-43 aerial
32 AN/UPA-43 aerial
33 AN/SPN-6 aerial
34 AN/SPS-10 aerial
35 AN/SPS-58 aerial
36 AN/SPS-48A aerial
37 AN/WSC-3 aerial
38 SPN-42 aerial
39 SASS elevator
40 Bomb elevator
41 Catapult machinery room
42 Universal tie down magazine
43 Sparrow G/C stowage
44 Sparrow wing and fin stowage
45 Flare magazine
46 Sparrow ready magazine
47 Rocket-head magazine
48 Fuel oil
49 Chain locker
50 Secondary conning station
51 Flight deck
52 Gallery deck
53 02 level
54 01 level
55 Main deck
56 2nd deck
57 3rd deck
59 1st platform
60 2nd platform
61 Hold

KEY (USS ORISKANY)
1 Aircraft elevator
2 Arresting wires
3 Barrier stanchion
4 Deck lights
5 LSO platform
6 Monitor sensor platform AN/SPN-41
7 Shock panels
8 Bomb elevator
9 Bomb jettisoning ramp
10 AN/SPN-41 aerial
11 Optical landing gear
12 ECM room
13 Safe parking line (alternate white and red 6ft sections)
14 Air crew escalator
15 6500lb bomb elevator
16 Hinged blast deflector
17 Deck cooling panels
18 Catapult type C11
19 Expansion joint
20 Sliding hatch cover
21 Catapult officer's control station
22 Launch line-up line (white)
23 AN/SPS-37A radar aerial

fighters and attack aircraft to be configured for bomb delivery (November 1951). Even earlier (1950) the Bureau of Aeronautics had issued a requirement for a tactical nuclear day bomber with some secondary non-nuclear capability for interdiction, a speed of 500mph, and a combat radius of at least 460nm with a 1000lb bomb – which in itself gives some indication of the shrinkage of nuclear weapons. Douglas managed to halve the Bureau's expected empty weight of 30,000lb in its A4D Skyhawk, ordered in June 1952. In fact Skyhawk deliveries could not begin until well after the introduction of the new lightweight bombs.

Existing fighters, then, were modified to carry the new lightweight nuclear weapons, and designated fighter-bombers. The primary types were the Banshee, the Cougar, and the Fury (a derivative of the North American Sabre), although in July 1955 the Chief of Naval Operations also called for adaptation of the McDonnell Demon fleet interceptor and even the unusual (and short-range) F7U Cutlass. For the future, the new Phantom fleet air defense fighter would have a secondary high-speed nuclear delivery role. At the same time the existing Douglas Skyraider (AD) attack bomber had a nuclear role, penetrating to its target by virtue of its very low-altitude flight profile. Of all the nuclear attack aircraft of the 1950s, it alone was part of the pre-nuclear carrier air groups.

The new strategic situation of the late 1940s and the 1950s changed the conditions under which carriers would have to operate in wartime. The US Navy of the interwar period was essentially a Pacific navy: now it became an Arctic navy. For example, hangar spaces had to be enclosed more effectively and heated, and indeed heating had to be provided for flight deck operations. Deck wetness meant icing. Ordinary shipbuilding steel might crack in the extreme cold. Much rougher weather had to be expected, yet the carrier and her escorts would have to maintain very high speed in it; speed was, after all, the principal insurance against submarine attack. More than carrier hull design was involved: the demand for sustained high rough-water speed was perhaps the greatest factor forcing up the size of the task force escorts, which in time became frigates (DL) and then missile cruisers.

The strategic shift alone would have sufficed to bring about a revolution in carrier operations and, therefore, in design. Thus, for example, the US Navy began a new carrier design, to operate a new generation of heavy attack

aircraft, which became the first phase of the Bureau of Aeronautics plan of the following December. Two other contributions to carrier offensive operations forced further, larger, changes in carrier design: the atomic bomb and the jet engine. Although nuclear weapons were not placed aboard carriers until 1949, their advent transformed the carriers into a strategic attack vehicle, the pre-missile equivalent, almost, of a Polaris submarine. In the mid-1950s carriers were to be maintained on alert, particularly in the Mediterranean and the Pacific, with nuclear-armed aircraft always on catapults ready for launch. In turn, carrier design was driven by the requirement to accommodate very long range A3Ds and their successors, themselves shaped by the 10,000lb weight of early nuclear bombs. New carrier construction, which benefited from the general increase in defense funds due to the Korean War, was in part justified on grounds of the relative invulnerability of the mobile sea-based airfield.

Carrier and aircraft evolution through the 1950s was strongly affected by considerable inertias in both aircraft and ship design. Thus the A3D, which did not enter service until 1956, imposed a kind of lower limit on the design of the new carrier *Forrestal*, which itself entered service the year before. However, the *Forrestal* was designed in the Fall of 1950. At that time the only existing modern carrier design was the *United States*, which had been based on the notional BuAer 100,000lb attack bomber. Inevitably the new carrier reflected many features of the earlier one, not only in basic design but also in such details as its catapults, arresting gear and elevators. Moreover, once an effective carrier design existed, there was a strong tendency to continue to improve it, rather than seek some new design based, perhaps, on a new, smaller carrier bomber which might be practical given the new smaller bombs. The A3D itself had been sized by the large bomb, but its large bomb

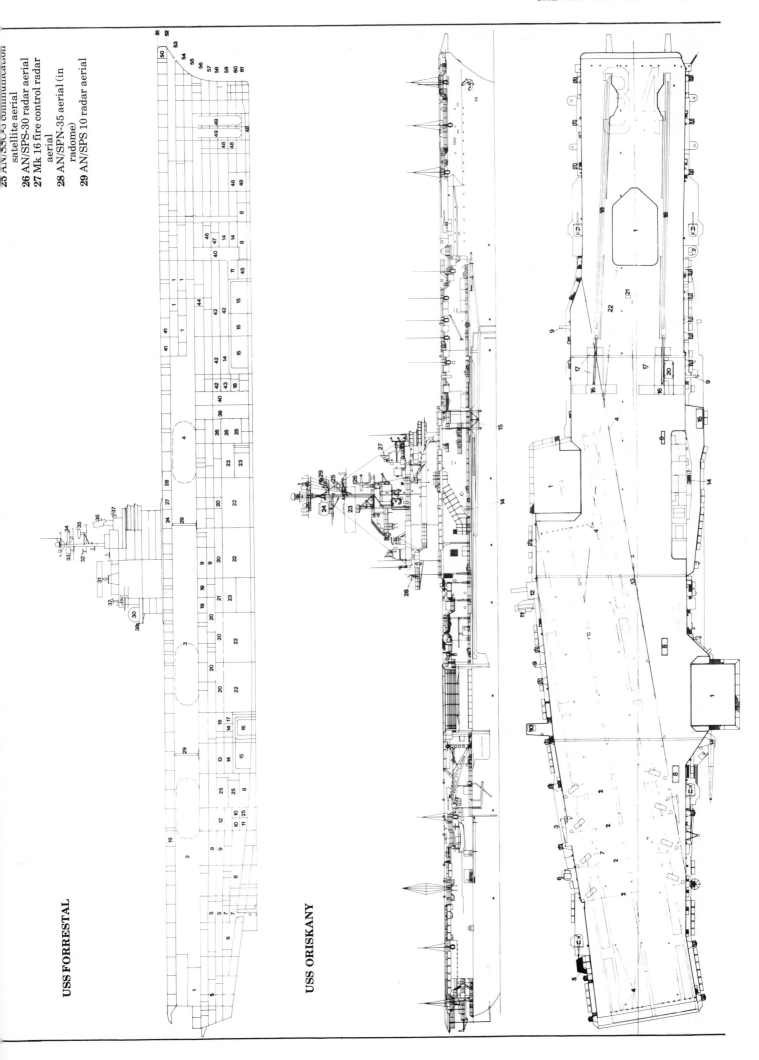

USS FORRESTAL

USS ORISKANY

25 AN/SSC-3 communication
satellite aerial
26 AN/SPS-30 radar aerial
27 Mk 16 fire control radar
aerial
28 AN/SPN-35 aerial (in
radome)
29 AN/SPS 10 radar aerial

The graceful A-5 Vigilante was the ultimate US Navy heavy attack bomber, designed to achieve immunity from enemy defenses by virtue of its very high speed at high altitude. Almost as soon as it entered service, however, the strategic attack role shifted to missiles, and Vigilantes were converted to a reconnaissance configuration. This RA-5C of Reconnaissance Heavy Attack Squadron RVAH-9 was photographed over the Mediterranean, 26 October 1967; USS *Saratoga* steams below. The 'AC' tail code indicates Atlantic Fleet, the nose number denotes the squadron and aircraft number within the squadron (2), and the tail number is the Bureau of Aeronautics serial number or 'Bureau number'. The ventral fairing carried side-looking radar as well as a variety of cameras, and each of four underwing pylons could carry a 400 US gallon fuel tank or 2500lb of weapons.

bay could carry several smaller ones, and it could trade off bomb weight for greater range. Not only was there no great incentive to cut the size of the heavy carrier bomber, but the existence of large carriers set a new high limit on their size. With improvements in bomb design and in aircraft, it became possible to trade off bomb load for a higher level of performance which might improve the bomber's chances in an increasingly hostile environment.

US carrier development of the mid-1950s had another twist as well. As early as 1955 it was generally assumed that nuclear power would soon be applied to carriers, and indeed that all subsequent carriers would be nuclear. Thus, just when a new conventional carrier design might have been in order, it seemed far wiser to build repeat *Forrestal*s than to build one or two of a completely new class, which would involve a great design and lead-ship cost. Other factors forced up the size of the nuclear *Enterprise*, and attempts to design smaller nuclear carriers were unsuccessful. However, the only post-*Enterprise* conventional carriers, *America* and *John F Kennedy*, were seen as interim projects pending a fall in the cost of nuclear power: again, wholly fresh designs were rejected on cost grounds. Once nuclear carrier construction was resumed with the *Nimitz*, the advantages of a large carrier, quite aside from the operation of heavy attack aircraft, were obvious, and a *Forrestal*-size hull was again selected. Thus the logic of much smaller carriers and much less capable aircraft, forcefully pushed in a changing strategic environment in the late 1950s, never did affect actual carrier construction.

In the mid-1950s, when the ultimate US naval strategic bomber, the North American Vigilante (A3J, later A-5) was designed, it seemed that the need for high performance coupled with very long range would continue to drive up the size of carrier bombers and, by extension, of carriers themselves. Moreover, it was argued that the number of defensive fighters a carrier needed was fixed quite independently of the size of the ship. Similarly, the 'overhead' represented by electronics was fixed, independent of the size of the air group. If the carrier were to project power in the most economical way, then the amount of such overhead chargeable to each attack aircraft had to be minimized, which implied that the carrier with the most numerous air group – the largest carrier – would be the most economical in terms of offensive power. This argument is quite general. It survived the demise of the heavy carrier bombers. Indeed, it remains valid even if the entire carrier air group is converted to V/STOL aircraft which make almost no demands of their own on the flight deck and which can fly from very small decks indeed.

Thus a US carrier fleet designed originally to perform much the same mission as the current generation of strategic attack submarined proved quite adaptable to Korean-style conventional warfare, since the large size originally adopted to support heavy strategic bombers also made for economical support of large numbers of conventional attack aircraft. Large size also carried with it a large capacity for conventional ammunition, so that a carrier delivering sustained air attacks, as off Vietnam, did not have to replenish her stocks on a daily basis. In addition, the current generation of carrier fighters, such as the F-14, approaches the larger attack bombers in size and therefore in demands placed on catapults, arresting gear, and flight deck layout. F-14 performance is required for a combination of fleet air defense (Phoenix-CAP) and the escort of attack aircraft (dog-fighting); without such performance the carrier would have to support many additional fighters, which in turn would crowd out attack aircraft. It is ironic that self-defense now costs as much as did the offensive in the early 1950s, but it seems fortunate that the US Navy did not proceed to a program of small carriers upon deciding to give up the carrier strategic attack mission in the late 1950s.

The impact of the jet was both earlier and, if anything, more pervasive than that of the atomic bomb, inspiring the greatest carrier design innovations of the 1950s, the steam catapult, the angled deck, and mirror landing. With their short endurance, jets required a new kind of deck operating cycle and, ultimately, a new kind of flight deck. They also changed the character of carrier vulnerability. A World War II carrier was at risk largely because of her large load of gasoline, which could form an explosive vapor. Jet aircraft, on the other hand, burned non-vaporizing fuels much closer in consistency to bunker oil; indeed, current US carriers can burn jet fuel in their boilers, and can trade off bunker space for air group endurance. On the other hand, jets drink fuel in far greater quantities than did their piston-engined predecessors, and fuel must be available continuously on the flight deck. Thus flight deck fires have a much greater potential for spreading down into the ship. Jets also came to have very great load-carrying capacity as well as a great sortie rate (high speed even if short endurance) and so drove up the requirements for carrier ordnance loads – which are now the greatest single consumers of internal hull volume. With so much explosive so concentrated, a carrier is perhaps most vulnerable to a single catastrophic hit in her magazines.

FLEET AIR DEFENSE
There was one other new technological factor in 1945: the guided missile. As an anti-ship weapon, it made the heavy land-based bomber a serious adversary. The latter might approach in any weather, acquire a carrier by radar, and fire from long range. Night attack, which in World War II had been a relatively minor annoyance, would become standard. The same might be said of high-altitude attack. To some extent wartime and prewar naval interceptors had been able to meet land-based attackers by accepting high-altitude penalties in return for medium- and low-altitude performance: torpedo attacks had to be made from low level, dive-bombers generally began their dives at no more than about 7500ft, and even Kamikazes could not begin their dives at very high altitude for fear that their targets would evade them. Now all was changed. For that matter, the great radius of destruction of a nuclear weapon made it, too, an effective candidate for high-altitude delivery. Moreover, the guided missile practically assured an attacker of one hit per successful penetration of fleet air defenses. The carrier interceptors and the surface ships would have to stop attackers at much greater distances, and a much larger proportion of the time.

The US reaction to this threat was twofold. First, a shipboard anti-aircraft missile program, 'Bumblebee', was begun in 1944 to counter the German weapons. Shipboard guns could not engage the missile-carrying bombers at sufficient range or, for that matter, with sufficient probability of a kill. Missile development soon became more urgent. A Kamikaze had to be destroyed in flight, whereas conventional anti-aircraft fire, missing its target, might nonetheless spoil the pilot's aim. 'Bumblebee' alone promised the requisite kill probability. Postwar, it was assumed that the Soviets would (as they in fact did) continue German work on bomber-launched anti-ship missiles; the 'Bumblebee' program ultimately produced the US Terrier, Talos and Tartar, most of which were mounted aboard carrier escorts, although some did appear aboard the carriers themselves.

The existence of such weapons complicated fleet air defense, imposing further control responsibilities upon the fleet commander's staff. US practice in World War II was to control fighters from the carrier's Combat Information Center (CIC), whose responsibilities in the 1950s would expand to include control of all fleet long-range anti-aircraft weapons. For example, it was necessary to establish free fire zones for missiles from which the carrier interceptors would be excluded. Missiles were available only in relatively restricted numbers, and the fleet would have to allocate them carefully to overcome saturation raids. In at least one case, a carrier was provided with stowage for escort surface-to-air missiles, to permit replenishment at sea between raids.

FIGHTER DEVELOPMENT
Fighter development was a complementary approach to fleet air defense. First, the carrier had to be able to operate

Although the US Navy looked primarily towards the heavy bomber, its most effective attack aircraft in the first postwar decade was the Douglas Skyraider. Here a Skyraider of VA-702 takes off from the converted carrier *Kearsarge* for a Korean War strike. The 'Spad' remained in service well after its planned demise, sharing carrier flight decks with a new generation of jet-propelled light bombers and distinguishing itself in the Vietnam War. *USN by courtesy of Larry Sowinski*

her aircraft under as large a proportion of weather conditions as possible. That meant, first, a greater emphasis on seakeeping in carrier design, a natural one in any case given the need to launch attack aircraft in the Arctic. Night and foul-weather operation required blind-landing aids: CCA (Carrier-Controlled Approach). All-weather fighter operation made it desirable that every carrier fighter be a night fighter, particularly given the limited accommodation aboard ship. Thus the new generation of night fighters would require a very high performance, which in turn implied particularly lightweight radars and highly automated weapon systems. As in the case of the surface weapons, the night fighter would have to achieve a far better kill ratio than its predecessors, which meant missiles of its own – and the consequent increase in airplane size to accommodate them without too great a loss of performance.

All of this development took time. In 1945 the US Navy had under contract a variety of day jet fighters, the McDonnell FH-1 Phantom designed under a 1943 contract and three designed under a 1944 competition (the F2H Banshee, Chance Vought F6U and North American FJ). All were merely faster equivalents of existing day fighters. Many problems were foreseen: for example, early jet engines produced relatively little thrust in proportion to aircraft weight, so that the aircraft accelerated slowly and required either long deck runs or catapults. Sluggish acceleration was also seen as a problem on landing, as wave-offs would be difficult. The streamlined jets had high stall speeds which in themselves imposed strains on arresting gear and catapults. Thus the 1944 competition rules permitted catapult-only take-offs: stall speed (fully-laden) could be increased to 90kts, compared to about 80 for a Hellcat. Other requirements included a deck space equal to or less than that occupied by the F4U Corsair, and a very high rate of climb. Range was also important. For example, the successful F2H began as a Phantom converted to take two more powerful (J-34 instead of J-30) engines. It proved necessary to enlarge the fuselage to provide enough fuel for a 300nm radius, and a thinner wing was required if the airplane was to realize the speed potential inherent in its more powerful engines. Later, in the F2H-2, the wings were strengthened to take tip tanks for a maximum radius of about 650nm.

As it entered service in 1949, the Banshee required a total of 16,160lb of fuel, or 877 US gallons, to achieve a

The FH-1 (later FD-1) Phantom was the US Navy's first operational jet fighter, and also the first airplane of the McDonnell Aircraft Company to enter production. This example, under test ('NATC', for Naval Air Test Center, on tail), shows the 295 US gallon drop tank which increased combat radius to 320nm. *USN by courtesy of Norman Polmar*

The twin-engine Banshee was considered the most satisfactory of the early US naval jet fighters, with a very long range achievable by shutting down one engine in flight, and a considerable fuel capacity. These F2H-3s flying over the Mediterranean in January 1954 illustrate the transition from 'midnight blue' to a short-lived natural metal color scheme.

combat radius of 480nm, flying at an average of 426kts, mostly at high altitude. By way of comparison, an F6F-5 Hellcat, with 2400lb (400 US gallons) of gasoline, was credited with a combat radius of about 340nm at 173kts. A carrier with a gasoline capacity of about 200,000 gallons could, then, support 500 Hellcat flights, or, say, 7 air strikes by a fighter-heavy late-war air group. However, the same tankage would support only 228 Banshee flights, each of which would be far shorter than the Hellcat flight. In effect, then, the jet could strike at a far greater distance than could its predecessor, but it could not match the loiter time of a piston airplane. The combat radius of the Banshee represented a flight *time* of only 135 minutes, compared to nearly four hours for the Hellcat – which, moreover, could increase its endurance (in CAP or over a target area) far more easily by throttling back its engine. Jet engines were far less efficient in cruising performance, although the Banshee had a great advantage over most jets in that it could cut out one engine for extended endurance.

These endurance figures only suggest the effects of jet aircraft on carrier operations. For example, both jets and propeller aircraft had to be maintained continuously on

Combat Air Patrol. In World War II a CAP endurance of about two hours was considered almost the minimum consistent with normal flight deck operations. That included a generous allowance for combat at the end of the patrol, and it required six CAP sections launched per day, four aircraft per section, to cover the carrier during daylight. Jet endurance might well cut CAP endurance to as little as an hour, and with the development of a night fighter version of the Banshee flights might be needed on a 24-hour basis, say a total of 92 Banshee sorties each day, rather than 24 Hellcat flights. Thus with jet aircraft the rate of fuel consumption for CAP alone might rise by a factor of almost nine.

From a carrier's point of view, there was little hope of reducing the hourly or daily rate of jet fuel consumption; nor was there any hope of improving jet landing or take-off characteristics. If land-based aircraft were to be met on equal terms, then improved aircraft performance would have to be absorbed by the carrier herself, in improved catapults and arresting gear, and in vastly increased fuel capacity. Thus, for example, the *Essex* of 1940 was designed for about 209,000 gallons of aviation gasoline, and the *Midway* of 1942 (completed 1945) for 330,000. In 1950, however, the new *Forrestal* was designed to accommodate 750,000. This was to be mixed on a one-for-one basis with heavy fuel oil carried in unprotected wing tanks, so that the ship actually carried (in effect) 1.5 million gallons of aircraft fuel. Since the mid-1950s, US jet aircraft have been fueled by JP-5, which can be treated essentially like ship fuel oil, and capacities have risen beyond 2 million gallons. Even so, such ships require frequent replenishment to sustain air operations, given the fuel capacities of modern aircraft. For example, where the Banshee, in its enlarged version (F2H-3 with drop tanks), might carry 1442 gallons, the F-4B Phantom II of the Vietnam War typically carried 3326. Moreover, from the 1950s on, jet endurance was often increased by in-flight refueling, so that figures for the fuel capacity of an airplane do not reflect total fuel consumption by the carrier air group.

In 1945, with a new jet day fighter in hand, the Bureau of Aeronautics foresaw three lines of development: a new night fighter, a new general-purpose fighter or fighter-bomber, and a new aircraft of extreme performance, which might test the potential of the new power sources. The night fighter came first. Although the Navy had shown that a single-seat fighter could perform effectively as a night fighter (witness such types as F6F-5N, F8F-2N, and the F4U-5N which actually served as the principal early

Although considered inferior to the Banshee, the Grumman Panther was only about half as expensive, and was therefore procured in greater numbers. This new F9F-5 still bears factory markings, with the last three digits of the 'Bureau number' painted on the nose, as in World War II. *Grumman History Center*

The Cougar was essentially a swept-wing development of the Panther. It, too, was a day fighter and it could not accommodate the kind of radar necessary to operate all-weather long-range Sparrows; thus the introduction of missiles into Fleet fighter squadrons meant Sidewinders for the Cougars. This F9F-8 shows, in addition, the air-to-air refueling probe in the nose. Below it, just visible between the two inner 20mm cannon, is the triangular frame of a barricade deflector, designed to prevent the shipboard crash barrier from slipping over the fighter's nose. The large bulge beneath the Cougar's nose housed a UHF homing adapter antenna, AN/ARA-25, for the new TACAN (Tactical Air Navigation) carrier beacon/navigation system just being introduced. The F9F-8 also incorporated increased wing area for better low speed performance and, incidentally, increased fuel tankage; the fuselage was also lengthened for the same purpose, giving a net increase of 140 US gallons over the 919 of the earlier F9F-6.

postwar night fighter), all piston-engine types suffered in performance due to the drag of their large wing-mounted radomes. A jet such as the Banshee, with a large nose volume, could be able to support a larger radar, for greater intercept range, with no great loss in performance: a night fighter Banshee was in fact planned, and proved quite successful. Even so, there were advantages associated with a second crew member, and in 1945 the Bureau issued a requirement for a specialized two-seater to operate at 40,000ft at 500mph, and over a combat radius of 500 miles, with four 20mm cannon. A demand that the radar operator sit beside the pilot complicated matters, as it implied increased drag. There were to be two engines. Douglas won in April 1946 with the F3D Skyknight which, however, proved too large for carrier operations. Grumman was asked to switch to a day fighter, which became the F9F-2 Panther and served alongside the Banshee.

With both the day and night slots filled, the Bureau turned to the high-performance experiment project. In 1946 it asked for an aircraft of unusual design powered by the new afterburning engine; Chance Vought won the contest with its tailless F7U Cutlass, which actually passed into Fleet service. In fact the high-performance fighter was a new type, a deck-launched interceptor (DLI). Given the limited fuel capacity not merely of the airplane but also of the carrier, there was interest in a fighter of such high performance that it could be held on deck in readiness against an incoming raid. The DLI concept became more attractive as the performance of likely attackers improved. CAP was better in principle, but it would after all be difficult if the bomber could outrun the interceptor. For example, at a January 1947 symposium a representative of the Bureau described the future bomber threat as a missile-armed 550mph aircraft flying at 40,000ft; at this time the F2H-1 Banshee was credited with no more than 555mph at 14,000ft. In theory the DLI would receive radar warning at 100nm, and would have to destroy the bomber within 9 minutes in order to protect the carrier from attack at a range of about 17.5nm. Thus a fighter launched 5 minutes after warning would have to climb to 40,000ft in 3.5 minutes. This specification was the first for a true naval interceptor; it was the basis for the Douglas F4D Skyray.

These aircraft set the direction of US Navy fighter development through the 1950s. By 1948 the Navy was looking for a new general-purpose fighter (CAP, all-weather escort of attack aircraft) which would incorporate the new swept wing. It bought a swept-wing version of the Panther (which became the F9F-6 Cougar) but continued to look for some solution to the inherent limits of the carrier deck. The Bureau wanted, ideally, an endurance of about four hours and a radius of action of about 470nm.

Grumman proposed to compromise between low-speed (landing and take-off) and high speed performance by means of a swing-wing, in the unsuccessful F10F Jaguar, which figured prominently in notional US carrier air groups of the time. For a time it appeared that the swing-wing would come close to permitting take-offs without the catapult, in 960ft with 25kts wind-over-deck.

Meanwhile there was a new design contest for a DLI, which was now to operate at 50,000ft at Mach 0.95; its mission profile allowed for a six-minute climb after half a minute of warm-up and a one-minute catapult take-off, and a forty-minute loiter at altitude followed by five minutes of combat. Purely carrier requirements included a stall speed of 105kts and a maximum span, folded, of 25ft 4in, to fit carrier elevators. The McDonnell F3H Demon won; its closest rival was an F4D derivative rejected because the F4D itself was already under contract. Ironically, another competitor was a derivative of the North American Sabre – which would be ordered in 1951 as a stop-gap answer to the Soviet MiG-15s in North Korean hands.

By this time even the clear-air interceptors required some considerable sophistication, which from the carrier point of view meant more electronics maintenance shops and more spares and more technicians. For example, given high bomber and fighter speeds, the fighter would have to succeed on the first pass; there would be little chance for re-attack. The necessary sophistication could go either aboard the airplane or in its weapon, and the Navy developed three systems: an unguided 2.75in rocket (FFAR) fired in salvo; a self-guiding homing weapon, Sidewinder; and a long-range missile, Sparrow, which was guided by a large radar in the fighter's nose. Sparrow had the great advantage of very long range, which would permit one fighter to destroy several oncoming bombers, and it became the standard weapon of specialized Fleet Air Defense fighters, beginning with the Skyknight.

From the carrier point of view, Sparrow meant other things: check-out facilities, low-density stowage, maintenance shops, even weapon assembly facilities, since the missile was generally stowed without its fins, to achieve some semblance of efficient use of magazine volume. Aircraft capable of carrying it were relatively large, and the missile itself was most useful in the CAP role – which

The early postwar period was one of experimentation, and the US Navy Bureau of Aeronautics was willing to order very exotic aircraft into production. The F7U (F7U-3 shown) was the winner of a design competition for a fighter to use afterburning engines. The unusually long nose strut provided an angle of attack of 20° for catapult launches. The non-standard finish, 'Cutlass' name painted on the nose, and the apparent absence of gun armament (above the air intake lips) all seem to indicate a test aircraft; production Cutlasses also had a somewhat shorter canopy. This airplane is poised on the catapult, with the canopy open to permit the pilot to escape should he lose power and go into the water.

With the advent of long-range radar-guided air-to-air weapons, the carrier fighter force split into all-weather 'fleet air defense' and daylight air superiority components. Ironically, the F3H Demon, designed for the latter role, was the first important example of the former. This test airplane, photographed in October 1956, shows the Sparrow long-range missiles of the all-weather air defense mission, but not the four 20mm cannon, under the air intakes, that were characteristic of all service Demons. Missile-armed aircraft were designated F3H-2M. *McDonnell Douglas*

The FJ Fury, an adaptation of the North American F-86 Sabre, was a standard day fighter and nuclear fighter-bomber of the mid to late 1950s. This formation of four FJ-3Ms flew from USS *Lexington* (20 June 1957). They were powered by a new J65 engine, and so were not precisely equivalent to any contemporary Sabre. Armament included four 20mm cannon, and the 'M' suffix indicated provision for Sidewinders, one of which is just visible beneath the wing of aircraft '101'. *By courtesy of Larry Sowinski*

meant long loiter endurance, and therefore large fuel capacity.

In 1951, as Sparrow approached operational use, the F10F was fading as a serious general-purpose fighter prospect. The F4D was promising, but it could not carry either Sparrow or its radar. The F3H was experiencing severe engine trouble, but it remained promising, and the Bureau of Aeronautics made the painful decision to re-design it as an all-weather general purpose fighter, in effect the successor to the all-weather version of the Banshee and the predecessor of the Phantom II and the F-14 Tomcat. Changes included a new engine (J71 in place of the earlier J40), a new wing for high-altitude man-euverability, and far more fuel. Thus combat radius, fully fueled, rose from 315 to 365nm, but the sparkling climb performance of the original DLI version could not be maintained. Ultimately the Demon was fitted to carry four Sparrows. An alternative missile fighter, a modified Cutlass, was far less successful, as its combat radius fell to 160nm, for a 1.15-hour mission.

As the F3H entered fleet service in the mid-1950s, a series of earlier general-purpose fighters and nuclear attack fighter bombers, such as the Cougar and the North American Fury, was being replaced by the new specialized light attack bomber, the Douglas Skyhawk.

THE SUPERSONIC REQUIREMENT

It might have seemed that the big general-purpose fighters would solve the problem of maintaining both DLI and long-range types on the same limited carrier flight deck, but that was not quite so. Existing engines could not provide a long-range missile-CAP fighter with performance to match the new supersonic land-based aircraft; BuAer asked eight manufacturers to design a new supersonic day fighter, to exceed Mach 1 and yet land at about 100kts (September 1952). Specification OS-130 called for a structural design speed of 630kts, barely supersonic at altitude, and a 300nm combat radius 'to maintain air superiority in daylight fair weather during the period of task force air strikes when the enemy will mount large numbers of aircraft'. Chance Vought's V-183 became the F8U Crusader, modified for higher speed (800kts) to take advantage of forthcoming engine developments. A special feature was a variable-incidence wing to improve low-speed performance. As an air-superiority fighter, the Crusader was limited to cannon and FFAR or Sidewinder; it was, therefore, incapable of either all-weather CAP or fighter-bombing. However, when the big Phantom replaced the F3H in the CAP role, it was only marginally operable by existing *Essex* class carriers, and a limited all-weather version of the Crusader was the only available air defense for these ships.

The success of the Crusader eluded the career of the other early US Navy supersonic fighter, the Grumman Tiger (F11F), which began as a derivative of the subsonic Cougar incorporating a new J65 engine with an afterburner. A lengthy study of improvements for increased performance led to an entirely new design, one of the first to incorporate 'area rule'. The Tiger's design origin shows in its original designation of F9F-9, which was only later changed to F11F to show the great difference between it and the subsonic Cougar. Ultimately it was the minimum airframe which could accommodate the J65, and consequently it suffered from insufficient fuel tankage and therefore from insufficient range. Thus although it was accepted for carrier service in March 1957 (at the same

The Skyray (Douglas F4D) was the first carrier-borne supersonic fighter, and also the only Navy fighter to serve as part of the US North American Air Defense System. This example, photographed in 1959, shows a Navpac, consisting of a VHF navigation system (ARN-14) and a marker beacon, attached to the centerline hardpoint, which is mounted on the panel swung down for maintenance. Each of the four stores pylons shown could accommodate a Sidewinder or a seven- or nineteen-FFAR rocket package; alternatively, the Skyray was armed with four 20mm in its wings. The tanks shown are probably of the 300gal type; with them, the Navpac and four FFAR packages, the fighter had a ferry range of 1000nm. The nose radome accommodated an all-weather intercept radar (APQ-50).

time that the first Crusaders were accepted), it was retired to advanced training status late in 1959.

That left open the question of a successor to the Demon, with its long-range missile. In 1954, with the Sparrow not yet in fleet service, the Bureau of Aeronautics studied a supersonic missile-CAP fighter with a secondary nuclear attack mission. By this time prospective nuclear weapons were so small that the usual quartet of Sparrows was both heavier and larger. Thus differences in size and weight between a tactical nuclear bomber and a Sparrow-CAP fighter tended to disappear; the difference in weights would be reflected only in a greater range for nuclear attack. The study did not address the value of supersonic speed in the CAP fighter, but other studies of fleet air defense suggested that, even given the long reach of Sparrow (about ten miles), a CAP fighter facing widely spaced fast attackers would need high speed to intercept very many of them in time. In fact the better the task force radar, the farther out the CAP, and hence the greater the distance the CAP fighter might have to cover in order to intercept its target.

Now McDonnell, which had been a loser in the OS-130 competition, proposed a big twin-jet attack fighter, tentatively designated AH. The Bureau study had assumed an internal bomb- or missile-bay, whereas the McDonnell project carried all weapons externally, but the basic conclusions of the 1954 study remained valid, and the Bureau decided to convert the AH into the next CAP fighter (July 1955), providing it with a long-range radar and a specialist

The short-lived F11F Tiger was the last of the Panther/Cougar series, quickly abandoned in favor of the supersonic Crusader. This test example, photographed over Patuxent River, shows the standard quartet of 20mm cannon (under the intake duct), but not the four pylons of production aircraft. *USN by courtesy of Norman Polmar*

The Vought Crusader, F8U and later simply F-8, gave the fleet a carrier fighter at least equal in performance to any land-based type. Although F-8s are no longer operational in US service, examples sold to the French Navy in 1964 remain operational, and the RA-5C Vigilante is being replaced by remanufactured RF-8Gs. As this is written, there are proposals to refit and recommission an *Essex* class carrier. Since such ships cannot safely operate Phantoms, F-8s will have to be withdrawn from storage for them. This F-8E of VF-211, landing aboard USS *Bon Homme Richard* in the Tonkin Gulf (May 1967) displays the characteristic Crusader variable-incidence wing, which made carrier landing performance and supersonic speed compatible. She is the eighth aircraft of the first fighter squadron aboard the carrier; the letters 'NP' on her tail indicate a Pacific Fleet Carrier Air Wing.

The F-4 Phantom progressed from a heavy subsonic ground-attack project (AH-1) to a supersonic fleet air defense fighter with a secondary nuclear attack role to a multipurpose fighter-bomber. This is aircraft six of VF-103, based aboard USS *Saratoga*, taking off from Rota, Spain, in Ssptember 1970. The F-4J (illustrated) introduced a pulse-Doppler fire control radar (AWG-10) with look-down capability as well as a one-way data link for automatic carrier landing and drooped ailerons and a slotted stabilator for better low-speed performance. The infrared seeker of the original Navy F-4B was eliminated. The example shown is unusual in that it carries no Sparrows. *USN by courtesy of Norman Polmar*

radar operator in a second seat behind the pilot. The eleven weapon stations of the AH were reduced to a single hard point for a nuclear bomb, and four Sparrows could be carried semi-buried in the fuselage, where they actually reduced overall drag. The result was the Phantom, or F4H (redesignated F-4 in 1962), the standard US Navy fighter well into the 1970s.

Just as the Phantom was being planned, the US Navy was reappraising its carrier strategy. Alongside the heavy attack aircraft, it had developed a series of fleet missiles, Regulus I and II, the first of which became operational in 1954. The next year a special Long Range Objectives (LRO) group was formed within the Office of the Chief of Naval Operations to propose a shipbuilding program for the next decade. Among its conclusions were that enemy defensive weapons would make heavy naval strategic bombers less and less effective. On the other hand, the fleet would retain in its long-range missiles a valuable strategic attack weapon; the carriers might therefore shift to tactical operations and to the support of ground troops. Moreover, the new study suggested that as the Soviet Union built up its own strategic arsenal, full-scale war between the two super-powers would become less and less likely. Wars would probably be local affairs on the periphery of the Communist world, and the United States would find itself intervening on a limited scale.

The LRO group also looked at available new technology. Its goal was a long-range naval program which could be carried out within available levels of funding. However, at the same time the Navy found itself caught up in a series of extremely expensive anti-aircraft missile programs. Cost reductions were very attractive, and it appeared that by giving up the carrier strategic bombers the Navy could cut sharply the size and therefore the cost of future carriers. For short-range (tactical) nuclear attack the LRO group proposed a low-flying airplane which would survive by stealth rather than by high speed at high altitude, as the Vigilante (not yet in service or even in existence) would. Relatively low flight speed would make for low stall speed and therefore would place small requirements on catapults and arresting gear. Survival by stealth, moreover, would eliminate the need for an air superiority fighter such as the Crusader.

As for fleet air defense, it was possible to trade off fighter performance against radar and missile performance. The longer the air defense missile range, the less the fighter would have to maneuver to hit multiple attackers. In 1955 there were already proposals for a very long range missile, which might be carried by a low-performance fighter with a very large (and, therefore, high-drag) nose radar. In some versions the fighter was combined with an airborne early warning radar, so that it became, in effect, a flying missile ship. In others, it carried only a long-range fire control set. In either case, it would make far lower demands on a carrier than would the current or future (Phantom) generation of fighters.

There was some irony here. The LRO looked towards 1965–70, and indeed decisions on new aircraft and new weapons taken in 1956 would not produce prototypes until the early 1960s. Meanwhile the aircraft which would actually enter fleet service in the early 1960s, the Phantom and the Vigilante, were scarcely beyond the mock-up stage, and indeed the new generation of large carriers, which the LRO wanted to replace, was barely entering service, carrying an earlier generation of aircraft. Of the two closely related programs, ships and aircraft, the LRO tended to have far more effect on the latter, perhaps because of the inherent inertia of the shipbuilding program. In any case, both its 'stealthy' attack airplane and the low-performance missile fighter became serious programs, the former actually entering service in large numbers as the Grumman A-6. The LRO's concern with low ship-impact shows in the prototype's swivelling jet pipes, for STOL performance on flight decks.

The LRO could call for small carriers partly because it expected nuclear weapons to be used even in the limited wars it predicted. In that case carrier magazine volume was no great limit on carrier support of ground forces: the typical sortie involved only a single nuclear weapon, weighing perhaps a ton or less. Nor did the LRO envisage the kind of sustained attack operations common in the limited war, Vietnam, where carriers would launch attack aircraft until they had emptied their magazines, then retire, replenish, and return to the strike line. In a Vietnam-style war carrier efficiency might be measured by the fraction of time wasted in replenishment: the larger the magazine capacity (in relation to the air group), the more efficient the carrier. Thus it was fortunate that, although the LRO's reasoning concerning the future of carrier-based strategic attack was correct, it was unable to shift the US Navy towards small carriers.

ATTACK AIRCRAFT IN THE 1960s

The concerns of the time show in the specification which produced the A-6, which was written in 1956. There would be two missions: interdiction/close support (two 1000lb bombs, 300nm combat radius, one hour on station, launch from the H-8 of an early *Essex* conversion) and long range (one 2000lb-class nuclear weapon, combat radius 1000nm, launch from a steam catapult). Alternatively, the attack aircraft would be able to carry Corvus, a stand-off weapon the Navy hoped would defeat the thick surface-to-air missile defenses to be expected in the 1960s; it would have a nuclear warhead. In practice, bomb loads were far heavier. The A-6A has a rated maximum bomb capacity of 18,000lb, all of which it sometimes lifted in Vietnam. The LRO's requirement for 'stealth' was met by good low-flying characteristics in the airplane, and by a 'non-radiating' navigational system which would provide no warning to enemy listeners.

The low-performance missile fighter, tentatively designated Missileer (F6D), was not as fortunate. There was always some Navy sentiment favoring a less specialized airplane with higher performance, and indeed some writers have claimed that subsonic performance was actually imposed on the design to reduce its cost, over and above the cost of the advanced weapon system. However, the chief actor in the Missileer drama was Secretary of Defense Robert S McNamara, who entered office in 1961 determined to cut costs by forcing the Services to cooperate far more widely. For example, he was responsible for the mass redesignation of naval aircraft in 1962 to coordinate Navy and Air Force programs. He was also responsible for the amalgamation of the new fleet air defense fighter with a new Air Force program for a tactical nuclear fighter-bomber. Factors in favor of the combined project included the requirement of both aircraft for very long range, which in the CAP case meant a lengthy loiter over the fleet; in addition, as in the Bureau of Aeronautics study of 1954, it could be argued that the weight and volume of six heavy air-to-air missiles approximated that of one or two nuclear weapons. On the other hand, the Air Force required supersonic performance at sea level, which drove up the size of its airplane, the F-111; for its part, the Navy was perfectly willing to accept only subsonic performance at sea level, but tried to impose limits on aircraft size to ensure carrier compatibility. Even if it accepted the large USAF airframe, the Navy would also have to accept a smaller missile system radar, since the original Missileer set had a very large diameter radar dish which would have created too much drag in a supersonic fighter. The combination was unworkable, but it was the Navy's misfortune that Secretary McNamara saw its resistance to the F-111 as an attempt to evade his program of interservice cooperation. He held to the project until he left office in 1968.

Meanwhile events were not following the Navy's expectations as to carrier operations. Off Vietnam the carriers could not hit and run: they had to remain continuously on station, launching strike after strike against well-alerted targets defended by guns, missiles and enemy fighters. Fleet air defense fighters found themselves suppressing defenses and providing CAP over target areas, where enemy and friendly aircraft mixed quite freely. Whereas the air defense studies of the 1950s – which had led to the gun-less, Sparrow-armed Fleet Air Defense fighter – had tacitly assumed that incoming aircraft at long range would all be attackers, now it was necessary for fighters almost to come alongside suspected enemies before firing at them, for fear of destroying friendly aircraft. The long-range Sparrow was ill-suited to dog-fighting, and the heavy Phantom was not nearly as maneuverable as the air-superiority Crusader.

Vietnam did not, however, eliminate the need for the fleet air defense fighter of the 1950s. Rather, it was now clearer that the carrier task force would have to be able to fight two very different wars. One would be the classical air strike against Soviet territory defended by long-range bombers and missile-bearing ships and submarines. All of the studies showed that the best counter was a long-endurance CAP fighter with a long-range radar and a missile to match. The Missileer weapon system, designed to engage several targets simultaneously, would allow some economy in the number of fighters, given Soviet tactics designed to saturate carrier task force defenses.

The other war was limited, conventional, and drawn-out. In it the carrier might still be subject to attack, but at a much less intense level. On the other hand, her own attack aircraft would require continuous fighter escort and CAPs would have to be maintained over the target area, and perhaps over enemy airfields as well. This function would require a dog-fighter with a short-range armament, since it would be necessary to close with an enemy before attacking him. The Vietnam War also required much larger attack aircraft bomb loads and, by extension, enlarged magazine capacities.

Both functions would have to be performed within the same limited carrier air group. In 1967 Grumman, which had been a contractor for the Navy version of the F-111, proposed a new fighter, which would be able to carry the same weapon system, would use the same long-loiter engine, and would also incorporate a cannon for close-in combat. It would be far lighter than the F-111, and would combine the fleet air defense mission with air superiority and strike escort. Now it appeared that carrier air groups might be drastically simplified once again.

Vietnam experience also affected the attack aircraft. In 1961 the Bureau of Naval Weapons, successor to the Bureau of Aeronautics, was seeking a successor to the A-4 Skyhawk. One of Secretary McNamara's innovations was an increasing emphasis on conventional, as opposed to nuclear, warfare, so that any new attack airplane required a far larger bomb load. It could be subsonic, although by mid-1962 the new attack bomber was a swing-wing type about half the size of an F-111 and supersonic at high altitude (although subsonic at sea level). Secretary McNamara ordered it postponed and then re-oriented towards lower cost; the new attacker would be a modification of an existing airframe, subsonic, with a greater radius and greater load than the Skyhawk. It would employ a non-afterburning version of the TF-30 engine

The A-4 was succeeded in service by the LTV Corsair II (A-7), specifically designed for load-carrying, as symbolized by this view of an A-7A of VA-122. The outboard pylons carry Shrike anti-radar missiles; inboard of them are tandem triple ejector racks for low-drag 250 or 500lb bombs; and inboard of them are Walleye guided bombs. A Sidewinder air-to-air missile, carried for self-defense, is visible on a fuselage-side pylon, as is the muzzle of the starboard 20mm gun, just abaft the lip of the air intake, inside the warning 'triangle'. Several of the bombs appear to be fitted with Snakeye retarding fins for low-altitude delivery.

While the A-4 and A-7 were designed for day attack, the Grumman A-6 Intruder was intended to take advantage of bad-weather or night conditions. From the first, its design called for a radar operator alongside the pilot, and the prototype incorporated swiveling jet pipes to achieve STOL performance. The example shown, an A-6E, was used to develop a new attack sensor, TRAM (Target Reconciliation and Attack Multisensor), a combination laser rangefinder and FLIR which could be slaved to the large nose radar. *USN by courtesy of Norman Polmar*

Perhaps the most famous of all postwar US naval attack aircraft is 'Heinemann's Hotrod,' the compact A-4 Skyhawk. Here an A-4E displays its characteristic tall undercarriage as it prepares to land at Cubi Point in the Philippines, November 1974. Although it was adapted to carry a considerable range of underwing stores (four emptied Zuni launchers are carried by this example), the Skyhawk was designed to deliver a single nuclear weapon from the centerline pylon. This model, originally designated A4D-5, was optimized for ground support and conventional bombing rather than the original nuclear attack mission. Note the two 20mm cannon in the wing roots and the humped avionics compartment (atop fuselage) of the later A-4F.

developed for the F-111, which would make for some saving on engine maintenance and spare parts stowage. LTV won this June 1963 competition with its A-7 Corsair II, based on the Crusader. Special emphasis was placed on maintenance and quick turnaround, both important issues in sustained air strikes.

However, it had one defect; the Corsair represented a distinct aircraft type at a time when the fleet air defense fighter (such as the F-4) could also bomb, albeit at a far greater unit cost. Total carrier operating cost included the problem of providing separate spares, separate maintenance shops and separate technicians – none of them inexpensive. A carrier is above all limited in such internal spaces as those which accommodate the shops, spares and personnel. The more separate types she supports, the fewer of each can be maintained ready for flight, no matter how many appear in her nominal air group. The Defense Department staff had briefly considered a combination of the fleet air defense fighter and the new attack bomber in 1961, and the idea was revived in 1974. By that time the rising cost of the F-14 made it appear unlikely that it could be substituted for all existing F-4s; however, the Navy did intend to maintain a stable carrier force, and that required large numbers of fighters for attack escort as well as for fleet CAP. The latter role certainly required the F-14's advanced multi-target weapon system, but the former might be filled by a smaller dog-fighter armed primarily with short-range weapons.

The solution adopted was VFAX, a single airframe to be produced in both fighter and attack versions: it became the McDonnell Douglas/Northrop F-18, based on Northrop's unsuccessful contender for the Air Force lightweight fighter competition, the F-17. The A-18 version carries rather less ordnance that does the A-7, but it was argued that lesser weights might be acceptable if they consisted of 'smart' bombs with individually greater efficacy. Moreover, its commonality with the F-18 should sharply reduce maintenance loads on a carrier. Increased numbers of aircraft implied markedly reduced production costs, in a period of rapid inflation and low defense budgets. Ideally,

▲ By the mid-1970s the only surviving US carriers of World War II construction were the three *Midway*s, which (at least in theory) could be rebuilt to handle all modern aircraft, although in practice such capability would be limited by their 17ft 6in clear hangar depth. *Franklin D Roosevelt*, the least satisfactory of the trio, was never fully rebuilt after her initial SCB-110 reconstruction (1953–56), and she was stricken in 1977; she is shown here in her final configuration, in 1973. Note that although she operated modern attack and fighter aircraft she could not support the E-3 Hawkeye and therefore had to make do with the older and much less capable E-1B Tracer. A modernisation comparable with that completed on the *Midway* was planned for the FY70 program but cancelled in favor of an austere overhaul ($46 million vs $88 million), given cost overruns on the *Midway* refit. The retention of even older *Essex*s in reserve while 'FDR' was scrapped is sometimes explained on the ground that the hangar depth limited such ships to helicopter operations (given the disappearance of the E-1Bs) and that the smaller carriers would be far less expensive to operate. *The Floating Drydock*

Midway was extensively rebuilt at the San Francisco Naval Shipyard between February 1966 and January 1970. She is shown here operating in the Indian Ocean, late in 1979. Improvements included new C-13 catapults and new elevators capable of lifting 100,000lb, compared to 74,000lb in her sister-ships. Her gun battery, originally eighteen 5in/54, was first reduced to three mounts and then removed altogether, Sea Sparrow point defense weapons being fitted instead. The extent to which the original small island has been extended by sponsons suggests the degree of reconstruction; the lattice tower built up abaft the island supports CCA radars. ▼

The new carrier *Independence*, last of the original *Forrestal*s, lies at anchor in this April 1959 photograph. Her air group ranged on deck includes the Demon all-weather fighter as well as a few of the new Crusader supersonic air-superiority fighters. Also visible aft are two Skywarriors, still showing the 20mm tail cannon that would soon be replaced by an ECM fairing, and a Skyhawk; three more Skyhawks are to starboard, between the elevators. One of the carrier's Piasecki (Vertol) HUP air–sea rescue helicopters sits alongside a deck park of Skyraiders amidships.

In improved *Forrestal* class carriers, the island and one of the starboard elevators were interchanged to increase capacity feeding the two bow catapults. Here USS *Kitty Hawk* fuels the destroyers *McKean* and *Harry E Hubbard*, September 1962. She had Terrier missiles rather than 5in guns for self-defense; two SPG-55 guidance radars are visible on her island, and the Terrier launchers were mounted on her quarters. An SPS-39 frequency-scanned radar, characteristic of the Terrier and Tartar systems, replaced the SPS-30 pencil-beam fighter-control set of earlier ships. Also visible are the two waist (sponson) catapults and the four arresting-gear wires across the landing runway.

of course, the entire carrier air wing should be homogeneous. However, at least at present, the F-18 cannot replace the F-14 in fleet CAP, and its A-18 version cannot provide the all-weather capability of the A-6; indeed, in 1980 there is no specialized A-6 successor in place. As existing aircraft wear out, their unique abilities may be either lost or approximated by advanced avionics (either internal or podded) applicable to the A-18 and made practicable through miniaturization.

AIR GROUP COMPOSITION

All of this evolution in carriers and their aircraft is reflected in the evolution of US carrier air groups. At the end of World War II they were very fighter-heavy, consisting of double-size squadrons of fighters and fighter-

bombers, plus one smaller squadron of attack aircraft. The latter were replaced postwar by the new single-seat type, generally Douglas Skyraiders. The fighter squadrons were reduced back to prewar or smaller size, and a four-squadron organization was adopted. As jet fighters entered service in the late 1940s they replaced the piston interceptors. However, they could not carry substantial external bomb loads, as existing bombs created far too much drag: land-based fighters could afford the reduction in range (or the penalty in take-off distance to carry more fuel) but carrier-based types could not. Thus a typical air group of 1950, aboard the *Essex* class carrier *Valley Forge*, consisted of two jet fighter (interceptor/strike escort) squadrons (30 F9F-2B), two piston fighter-bomber squadrons (28 F4U-4B Corsairs), and one of piston attack bombers (14 AD-4 Skyraiders). Then there were the special-purpose aircraft, which were beginning to crowd out the others: 3 night fighters (F4U-5N), 2 photo fighters (F4U-5P), 2 night attackers (AD-3N), 4 countermeasures attackers (3 AD-4Q, 1 AD-3Q), and 3 AEW aircraft (AD-5W), useful both for air search and for sea search against small targets such as submarine snorkels.

Essex class carriers converted for jet operations could accommodate more jet fighters. In 1953, for example, *Lake Champlain* operated two squadrons of long-endurance Banshees, one of Panthers (F9F) and one of Skyraiders, as well as the usual complement of special types. At this time the Banshee existed in both fighter-bomber and night-fighter versions, and quite soon the standard carrier air group organization showed one squadron of day fighters, one of all-weather (fleet air defense) fighters (such as the F4D and the F3H Demon), one of light (fighter) bombers (such as the Grumman Cougar or the North American FJ-4B Fury), and one of medium attack bombers (Skyraiders). Squadrons generally numbered 14 aircraft, and in the late 1950s an *Essex* might operate 56 such aircraft, plus 12 special types – 3 photo, 5 ECM and 4 AEW, the last permitting one to remain airborne continuously. By then the fighter-bombers were being replaced by A4D Skyhawks. In addition, many carriers accommodated a detachment of three heavy attack bombers, North American AJ Savages or Douglas A3Ds. To some extent the AJs doubled as aerial tankers, foreshadowing the creation of yet another special type which would further crowd the flight decks.

By this time the emphasis was definitely on attack. The new *Forrestal*s could accommodate a full heavy attack squadron (eg 12 A3D) and a second squadron of light attackers (24 A4D), for a balance of 48 attack bombers (12 medium attack aircraft, AD), against 28 fighters and, at one time, as few as 10 special aircraft and two search-and-rescue helicopters. The *Enterprise* was even larger, sized not by aircraft but by a combination of propulsion and protection. She accommodated a second squadron of Skyraiders, and even more heavy attackers.

The Skyraiders were ultimately replaced by Grumman A-6s on a one-for-one basis. About 1960 it was expected that the mid-1960s carrier air group would consist of reinforced squadrons (16 aircraft) of air superiority (Crusader) and fleet air defense (Phantom) fighters, as well as three twelve-plane attack squadrons: A-4, A-6, and the new A3J (A-5) Vigilante. The greater maintenance requirements of the A-6 and A-5 were reflected in the elimination of one of the two A-4 squadrons. At this time it was also expected that by 1966 each of the two fighter squadrons would surrender four aircraft, so that a new eight-aircraft Missileer squadron might be formed.

Matters did not quite turn out this way, as the A-5s were used primarily for reconnaissance, not heavy attack, and all of the Crusaders were phased out in favor of an all-Phantom fighter force. On the other hand, special tankers

converted from attack aircraft (first Savages, then A-3s and A-6s) began to figure more prominently in carrier air groups. In the course of the Vietnam War all of the Crusaders were phased out, so that the typical large-carrier air group consisted of two squadrons of Phantoms, one of A-6s (including KA-6D tankers), two of A-7s (replacing the former pair of A-4 squadrons), and a few RA-5C heavy reconnaissance aircraft with a secondary strategic strike capacity. For example, the *John F Kennedy* operated (April 1972) 24 Phantoms, 24 Corsairs, 11 A-6s, 4 A-6s tankers, and 4 RA-5Cs, as well as 4 E-2A AEW aircraft and 3 EKA-3B tanker/ECM variants of the A-3. At that time it was hoped that both carrier fighter squadrons might be replaced by F-14A Tomcats. However, current plans call for replacement of only one fighter squadron by F-14s, the other by F-18; both A-7 squadrons will be replaced by A-18s, to give a total of 36 aircraft all of essentially the same design. The A-6s will remain.

There has been one further twist. Throughout the postwar period the US Navy operated specialized ASW carriers; during the 1960s and early 1970s these were *Essex*s, and they generally provided carrier task forces with ASW protection. As these ships aged, proposals were made for replacements, but nothing could be done; funding was barely enough to maintain the attack carriers. However,

A carrier flight deck gives a good indication of the relative size of naval aircraft. Here USS *Ranger*, in Japanese waters (April 1963), shows A-3 Skywarriors aft, with the then-new F-4 Phantoms nearby, and a single Grumman E-1B airborne early warning aircraft, its search radar in the 'flying saucer' radome. On the sponson to port are A-4 Skyhawk light attack aircraft and F-8 Crusader air superiority fighters, with a mixture of types, including a pair of A-1 Skyraiders, on the centerline. This mix reflects the standard air group of the time. The Phantom was soon to replace the remaining F-8s, the RA-5 the A-3, and the A-6 Intruder the venerable A-1. Phantoms had just replaced *Ranger*'s all-weather Demons. The 'NG' tail code refers to Air Group 9.

The carrier *John F Kennedy* shows clearly the deck arrangement of a modern US carrier in this December 1968 view. Catapult start points show jet blast marks: two in the bows, two in the waist, each pair fed by an elevator. The extension of the port sponson aft, parallel to the centerline, was intended to improve air flow abaft the carrier; the extension to accommodate the forward end of the landing path is also visible. At this time the *Kennedy* had sponsons for Sea Sparrow but the system had not yet been installed. Arresting wires can be discerned by the small circular white areas marking their ends across the landing path, and the Fresnel lens landing aid is visible on a small sponson on the port side, just abaft the extension of the landing path.

The Grumman Tomcat (F-14) is able to perform both long-endurance fleet air defense and air superiority missions, thanks to its variable-sweep wing, shown here in the low-speed (extended) position. Like the Phantom, it can carry long-range air-to-air missiles semi-externally. The aircraft on the left is carrying four Sparrows; the F-14 is designed, however, to employ the much larger, longer-range Phoenix. It also has a pair of Sidewinders on its port outboard pylon, which would otherwise take a Phoenix. On the other side, one of two under-fuselage hardpoints carries a drop tank, and the outboard pylon carries a Shrike anti-radar missile. The only armament element not visible is the 20mm cannon on the starboard side of the nose. The small 'blob' visible under the nose of each aircraft is an ALQ-100 (deceptive ECM) antenna. In practice, the F-14 weapon system has performed magnificently, but limitations inherent in the TF-30 engine, inherited (like the Phoenix/AWG-9) from the F-111B program, restrict its air superiority (dogfighting) effectiveness. The F-14 program originally envisaged development of an entirely new engine, and most aircraft were either to have been built with it or retrofitted. Shortages of funds have made that unlikely, and it appears that for the 1990s the Fleet will again have two distinct fighter types.

The US Navy's air superiority fighter of the next decade will probably be the F-18 Hornet, derived from Northrop's YF-17 entry in the (Air Force) lightweight fighter competition. This example displays the new low-visibility color scheme which will be standard on Navy F-18s; it also shows the standard missile armament of two Sparrows and two Sidewinders, supplemented by a 20mm Vulcan cannon carried internally. One advantage of the F-18 is its ground attack capability: present plans call for it to replace both the F-4 *and* the A-7 Corsair II, to reduce the number of different aircraft types on the large carriers. Much smaller than the F-14, the F-18 may also prove suitable for some of the smaller carriers now in the discussion stage. Not apparent in this photograph are the nine external store stations (hardpoints) built into the aircraft: besides the four missile stations shown, a Sparrow or ordnance can be carried on an outboard station under each wing, and a 610 US gallon tank under an inboard station. The port fuselage Sparrow station can carry an FLIR (Forward-Looking Infrared) pod, the starboard station an LST (Laser Spot Tracker) in the attack role. The centerline station can carry either a 300 US gallon tank or ordnance. With a triple ejection rack on the centerline and multiple ejection racks under the wings, the F-18A should carry as many as nineteen Mk 82 500lb bombs. *McDonnell Douglas*

with the increasing capability of Soviet submarines, carrier task forces needed more, not less, protection. As a compromise, the US Navy investigated the operation of ASW aircraft and helicopters by the attack carriers. The new concept was designated CV rather than CVA; it required new ASW command and control facilities aboard the carrier, as well as new maintenance facilities – and further special types. Moreover, ASW air group operation proceeded on a 24-hour schedule, whereas the strike carriers usually operated on a 12-hour strike schedule, perhaps handing off operations between a pair of carriers. The first test was carried out aboard the *Kitty Hawk* in 1972. She landed her RA-5s and KA-3s and took aboard a mix of S-2 fixed-wing ASW search planes and SH-3D helicopters with dipping sonars; KA-6D tankers replaced the larger KA-3s. To some extent the F/A-18 substitution should simplify matters by reducing the number of disparate types.

In 1980 the nominal carrier air wing consists of two fighter squadrons (24 F-4 or F-14), two day attack squadrons (24 A-7), 1 medium attack squadron (10 A-6, 4 KA-6), 1 ECM squadron (4 EA-6B), 1 ASW squadron (4 E-2), 1 fixed-wing ASW squadron (10 S-3), 1 helicopter ASW squadron (6 SH-3), and 1 reconnaissance detachment (3 RF-8G or 3 RF-4; formerly it might have been 3 or 4 RA-5C). There is no longer any attempt at strategic attack, and indeed with the loss of the RA-5C the Fleet has lost a very powerful integrated intelligence system. The number of entirely distinct types has now risen to six or seven, where in the early 1950s variants of the attack bomber (AD) performed many of the special functions. Even if the F/A-18 enters service in large numbers, the number of distinct types will not fall by much, and this number is in itself perhaps the single greatest problem of carrier operations, given limited shipboard maintenance space. Indeed,

the future may hold even more distinct types, given the success of the 1977 evaluation of the Harrier (AV-8A) V/STOL fighter aboard the *Franklin D Roosevelt*.

BRITISH CARRIER POLICY 1945–56

In 1945 Britain faced a very different postwar world than did the United States. British naval strategy emphasized control of the sea in the face of land-based bombers, submarines and, perhaps, surface raiders. In peacetime Britain still intended to police a large overseas Empire, and to maintain a substantial naval presence to guard her vital interests 'east of Suez.' Before World War II, the police and trade protection missions had been largely the province of a substantial cruiser fleet, protected from enemy capital ships by a battle fleet. Now Britain could no longer afford to operate many cruisers, but war experience suggested that the new carriers were a viable substitute. Moreover, a single carrier could cover a far larger area of sea than could a cruiser. In this context strike operations were far less important than were fighter cover and ASW.

The end of Lend-Lease left the Royal Navy with relatively few of its wartime strike aircraft: now there were only the unsatisfactory Barracuda and the new Firebrand, only small numbers of which could be afforded. Numerous escort carriers had helped to make up for the small size of the prewar carrier-building program and the need to concentrate on ASW escort production in wartime: now they were almost all gone. In their place the Royal Navy had six large fleet carriers and eight light fleet carriers. Another two of the smaller units had been completed as aircraft maintenance ships, and there were six more building to a slightly modified design (*Majestic* class). Perceiving that all war and prewar carriers would probably be obsolescent in the near future, the Navy maintained two new, larger, fleet carriers (*Eagle* and *Ark Royal*) and four new light

RN MALTA CLASS (1945)
INTERNAL ARRANGEMENT

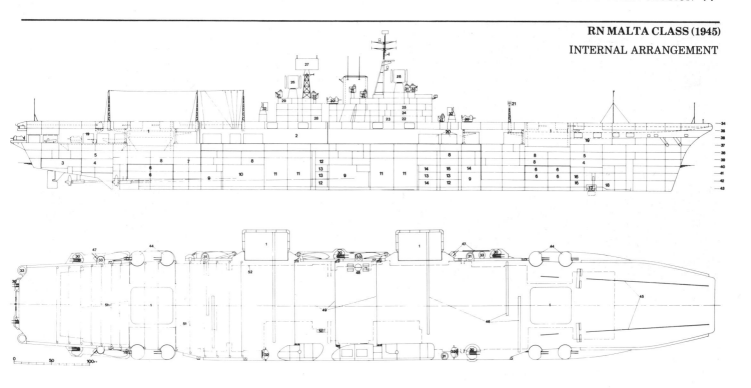

KEY

1 Aircraft elevator
2 Hangar
3 Steering gear
4 Aviation store
5 Torpedo stowage
6 4.5in magazine
7 Air intelligence and air chart room
8 Generator compartment
9 Aviation fuel stowage
10 Engine room
11 Boiler room
12 Small-arms magazine
13 Bomb room
14 Bofors magazine
15 Rocket motor magazine
16 Torpedo warhead room
17 Emergency bow rudder
18 Asdic compartment
19 Hangar extension
20 Roller shutter openings in hangar sides
21 HF/DF aerial
22 Briefing room
23 Aircraft control room
24 Operations room
25 ADR
26 Radar aerial WCH
27 Radar aerial Type 960P
28 Aircraft handling party ready-room
29 Flying control room
30 6-barrel 40mm Bofors mounting
31 MRS director
32 LRD director
33 CRS director
34 Flight deck
35 Gallery deck
36 Forecastle deck
37 Hangar deck
38 Main deck
39 Middle deck
40 Lower deck
41 Upper platform deck
42 Lower platform deck
43 Hold
44 4.5in twin HA/LA mountings
45 Aircraft catapults (162ft)
46 Side tracking gear
47 Single 40mm Bofors mounting
48 Aircraft signaling panels
49 Safety barriers
50 Bomb elevator
51 Arresting wires
52 Outline of hangar

Although the Light Fleets were considered no more than a wartime expedient they were relatively inexpensive to operate and formed the British postwar carrier force. Here HMS *Theseus* steams off Portsmouth, 18 May 1950, with the standard British naval fighter of the day, the Hawker Sea Fury, in evidence in numbers on her flight deck. Like contemporary fleet carriers, she shows both types of long-range air search radars (and an IFF, visible above the Type 281 on her foremast). Two Light Fleets, *Perseus* and *Pioneer*, were completed as aircraft maintenance ships, retaining their hangars as workshops. They were, in effect, successors to the prewar *Unicorn*, and formed part of the fleet train which the Royal Navy developed for Pacific warfare.

British postwar carrier reconstruction plans included all six of the large fleet carriers, although in fact only *Victorious* was begun. Planning for *Implacable*, shown here on 12 May 1948, included the consolidation of her two hangars into one deep enough to accommodate modern aircraft, the provision of a deck-edge elevator, and much improved electronics, including the new Type 984 radar. The immediate postwar reality was much different, and three years after the end of hostilities the Royal Navy operated only prototypes of the new generation of aircraft; operational squadrons retained obsolescent types, such as the Barracudas poised near the bow. Note the two different air search sets, 279 (long wave) and 281 (shorter wave), which combined to give better coverage, their fade zones differing according to their frequencies. A Type 277 height-finder/surface search set perches on the bridge, and the big 'dustbin' of an aircraft homing beacon (Type 72) surmounts the tripod foremast. *Conway Picture Library*

In 1945 the Royal Navy, with a wide variety of carriers still under construction, looked toward their modification as a means of meeting the demands of the new generation of aircraft. HMS *Eagle* (shown here in 1951) and *Ark Royal*, the largest ships remaining under construction after the cancellation of the *Malta* class, were only superficially altered, as their designs already fully reflected war experience. Their BH5 hydraulic catapults could launch a 30,000lb airplane at 75kts, compared to 14,000 at 70 for the wartime BH III; elevators could lift 35,000lb, and separate barriers were provided for propeller fighters, for the twin-engine Sea Hornet, and for jets. The heavy gun battery continued wartime practice, with a Mk 37 radar director (US type with British Type 275 radar) for each group of two twin 4.5in guns. These were supported by eight sextuple, two twin and twelve single Bofors, the multiple mounts being director-controlled (one Close Range Barrage Fire director for each sextuple, one simple tachymetric director for each twin mount). Air search radars were the new types developed at the end of the war: Type 960 for long range search, 982 for fighter control (precision two-dimensional search), and the 983 'nodding' height-finder; a YE aircraft homing beacon surmounted the foremast. The deck recognition letter, 'J', was duplicated on the tails of *Eagle*'s aircraft. *MoD(N) by courtesy of Roger Chesneau*

carriers (*Albion*, *Bulwark*, *Centaur* and *Hermes*) under construction. Only the fleet carriers and the two new classes would be able to handle the new heavy strike aircraft developed in wartime. On the other hand, the fleet carriers were expensive to operate, and the sacrifices entailed in an armored hangar meant that the first three of them could not take many more aircraft than could a light fleet carrier of about half the size.

Faced with a combination of very limited funds and an ongoing revolution in aircraft design and weaponary, the Royal Navy, like the other British services, chose to reduce existing operating forces to finance research and development. In 1947, for example, it maintained two fleet carriers – but five of the less expensive light fleets – in full commission. Three more ships were maintained in commission for harbor training, trials and aircraft ferrying, and they represented a mobilization reserve. The fully immobilized ships, the two *Majestic* class laid up incomplete, and the ships under construction were a war reserve, corresponding to the far larger US 'mothball fleet'.

In aircraft as in ships, the choice lay between continued production of existing types and research leading to aircraft which might well not enter service for a decade. Late-war efforts to develop jet aircraft, including some for naval service, were continued, albeit at a relatively slow pace. Thus the Wyvern turboprop strike fighter, successor to the Firebrand, flew (with a piston engine) in 1946 but did not enter service until 1954. The Royal Navy flew a jet fighter, an adapted RAF Vampire, from a carrier deck in December 1945, but neither the Vampire nor the other contemporary RAF jet fighter, the Meteor, entered British carrier air groups. Rather, a new design, which became the Attacker, became operational in 1951. The general policy was to develop a series of interim prototypes, but to avoid production on the theory that change was so rapid that such aircraft would soon be obsolete in any case. At this time the British Labour Government decided to base its defense effort on the expectation that there would be no major war before 1957, ie that no completely new generation of aircraft for either the Royal Navy or the RAF would be required until then.

There was one major exception: ASW. British postwar naval air policy emphasized fighters – to cover convoys and

HMS *Ark Royal* was completed to a modified design, incorporating the ▶
new angled deck (in an 'interim' 5½° version), a US-style deck-edge
elevator, and steam catapults. The principal cost of this improvement
was borne by the ship's gun battery. Thus the port forward group of 4.5in
guns, temporarily plated over for the angled deck, was permanently
landed in 1956. As compared to *Eagle, Ark Royal* had only half as many
sextuple and single Bofors, the sextuple mounting before her bridge
having been removed. Here she is shown as completed, in 1955. *MoD(N)*
by courtesy of Roger Chesneau

▲ In 1945 the Royal Navy also had four large light fleet carriers under
construction, the *Hermes* class; with the two *Ark Royals* they were to
comprise a tactically homogeneous carrier group. The first three were
completed in 1953–54. *Bulwark* shows the 'interim' (5¾°) angled deck, the
installation of which required the removal of three of the original eight
twin Bofors; there were also two sextuple (fore and aft of the island) and
four single mounts. In contrast to *Eagle*, there was only a single height-
finder (atop the bridge), with a pair of 982 and 960 atop the mast, and a
294 for surface search below it. The homing beacon was mounted atop a
stub mast on the side of the funnel. This photograph was taken almost
immediately upon the carrier's completion, on 31 January 1955. *MoD(N)*

As in the US Navy, there remained in the Royal Navy a large reserve of
carriers suitable for modernisation. HMS *Victorious* was the first and, as
it turned out, the only wartime fleet carrier to be taken in hand. She
emerged in 1958 with a full (9°) angled deck, a pair of steam catapults,
strengthened deck and arresting gear, the new Type 984 combined search
and interception radar, and a new battery of 3in/70 and Bofors guns.
▼ Here, about 1960, she shows the new Scimitars on deck. *MoD(N)*

Hermes was completed to a modified design, equivalent, perhaps, to HMS *Victorious* as modernized. She had a 6½° angled deck (said to be the maximum consistent with her size), steam catapults, deck edge elevator, mirror landing aid, and the new Type 984 radar. Here she is shown late in her carrier career, in April 1969, with a Sea Vixen FAW2 forward and a Gannet AS1 aft. Her single mast carries the British version of the TACAN aircraft homing beacon, and the 'lantern' abaft her superstructure carries Type 963 CCA (Carrier-Controlled Approach) radar. During her long refit (1964–66) an 'Alaskan highway' was built out to starboard of her island, adding 15½ft to her extreme beam, and all five twin Bofors were landed, replaced by two quadruple Seacat point defense missile launchers on her quarters. *Conway Picture Library*

fleets at sea and to destroy enemy aircraft opposing amphibious operations – and anti-submarine warfare. The fighters already existed, but airborne ASW was as yet a very undeveloped art. The existing Firefly fighter was adapted for ASW as the AS5, with a small search radar, and stowage for sonobuoys or for depth charges or mines: it could not combine in a single airframe the search and attack roles. Meanwhile work continued on a derivative of the wartime Spearfish, a large aircraft to be powered by a pair of turboprops driving counter-rotating propellers, so that one engine might be shut down to increase endurance. This, the Fairey Gannet, was originally built to a standard strike and reconnaissance bomber Specification (GR. 17/45); in 1949 its development was re-oriented towards ASW, and it ultimately combined the search and attack roles.

As in the United States, the Korean War proved a considerable stimulant. The Royal Navy had only wartime propeller-driven fighters at its outbreak, and soon saw the desperate need for high-performance jets. Thus two fighter projects, for what would become the Scimitar strike fighter and the Sea Vixen all-weather interceptor, in suspension at the beginning of the war, were revived, and the performance required increased. The Scimitar, originally a day interceptor, was given an interdiction and ground support capability, and made a super-priority project. Meanwhile the postwar program to complete the two new classes of wartime carriers proceeded, and in October 1950 the fleet carrier *Victorious* was taken in hand for reconstruction to operate the new generation of naval aircraft.

She was, however, the only one of the six existing fleet carriers to be so modified to a program originally set out in 1948. Moreover, although some design work for a new carrier was done, no new carrier project reached the construction stage.

EARLY JETS AND THE NUCLEAR ROLE

The first decade of British postwar naval fighter development reflected the initial postwar policy of building interim prototypes while financing longer-term development. Thus the Attacker and the somewhat more advanced Sea Hawk were built under 1945 and 1946 Specifications respectively, although both were wartime designs. Both were also the subject of pre-Korean War orders, in November 1949. However, the Korean War rearmament program brought many more orders, particularly for the Sea Hawk, and production had to be transferred to another manufacturer, Armstrong Whitworth. The other major line of British naval fighter development, the night fighter, was represented by the Sea Venom, a private venture. The land-based Venom night fighter first flew in August 1950, at a time when the RAF had already bought a private venture night fighter version of the earlier Vampire. Royal Navy evaluation of the Venom night fighter prototype was successful, and a naval version was ordered as the Sea Venom. It replaced the propeller-driven Sea Hornet, and served as an interim night fighter until the entirely new night fighter first ordered in 1946, the Sea Vixen, could enter service. The entire Sea Venom program was thus almost certainly a product of the Korean emergency and the increase in funding it inspired.

The Sea Vixen, on the other hand, was part of the long-range development program which looked towards a new generation of naval equipment about 1957. It, like the Sea Hawk, was designed to meet a 1946 Specification, and indeed was a design contemporary of the RAF Javelin. The Sea Vixen incorporated a swept wing and powered controls, and was selected by the Royal Navy in favor of a less advanced modernization of the existing Sea Venom design. In operational service, from 1958 onwards, it was one of the first all-missile fighters, with a battery of four

▲ HMS *Eagle* was scheduled for reconstruction following *Hermes*, and she, too, received much the same treatment as had HMS *Victorious*: a full (8½°) angled deck, an 'Alaskan highway' outboard of the island for stowage of flight deck vehicles, two steam catapults (one forward, one on the angled deck proper, so that both could launch simultaneously), and the new Type 984 and 965 (air search) radars. The entire Bofors battery and both forward pairs of 4.5in guns were suppressed, six quadruple Seacats being added. The bridgework was considerably enlarged, and a 25ft extension out to port was provided for Flying Control ('Flyco'), permitting control officers to watch aircraft approaching along the angled glide path. The mirror landing aid is visible on the edge of the flight deck to port, and the carrier approach radar (Type 963) is just visible in its lantern at the after edge of the island. Deck markings for the now-standard outfit of ASW helicopters are prominent in this 29 October 1964 view, taken soon after *Eagle* recommissioned. *Conway Picture Library*

Firestreak guided missiles and 28 2in unguided air-to-air rockets in retractable trays. Like the day fighters, it was equipped for alternative strike operations, and could carry four 500lb or two 1000lb bombs or clusters of six 3in rockets or packs of 124 2in rockets. Although it was very nearly cancelled just before the Korean War, the acceleration due to that war made up for lost time, and the Sea Vixen entered service in 1957.

The Sea Vixen's stablemate, the Supermarine Scimitar, was the consequence of a far more convoluted development. In 1945 the Admiralty became interested in a scheme for an undercarriageless fighter. The advent of jet engines had eliminated the need for clearance between aircraft and deck, and the Royal Navy developed an inflated flexible rubber deck on which an airplane could land. In theory the weight saved by the elimination of the undercarriage translated into increased performance, and the flexible deck was successfully tested, first on land in December 1947 and then at sea aboard HMS *Warrior* the following March. The airplane was a Sea Vampire, but Supermarine developed a wholly new heavy jet aircraft to

The Royal Navy evaluated jet aircraft using several types which never went into front-line service, such as this Sea Vampire, aboard the light carrier *Theseus*, 29 June 1950. Other Sea Vampires share the foredeck park with 1832 Squadron (RNVR) Seafires. The Sea Vampire was the first jet aircraft ever to operate from a carrier deck: on 3 December 1945 one piloted by then Lt Cdr E M Brown landed aboard HMS *Ocean*, a *Colossus* class light carrier. It was the converted Vampire I third prototype; the first Sea Vampire F20 flew in October 1948 and a total of 18 were built. The experimental F21 was employed in 'rubber deck' trials aboard HMS *Warrior* in 1949. *Conway Picture Library*

The postwar Royal Navy developed two types of interim jet fighter, the Supermarine Attacker and the Hawker Sea Hawk, while the more advanced Sea Vixen and Scimitar were evolved. These Attackers are shown parked forward aboard HMS *Eagle* (tail code 'J'), with three remnants of an earlier era: two Avenger AS4s, a US type supplied under Mutual Aid (and replaced, ultimately, by the Gannet) and a Firefly, which can be recognized by its wing radome. The Attacker wedded the laminar-flow wing developed for the abortive Spiteful/Seafang to a new fuselage, and was one of the few jet fighters to employ a tailwheel undercarriage. The very limited extent to which the Attacker wing could fold, compared to that of a propeller aircraft, also seems noteworthy. *Cdr A Tayler by courtesy of John Rawlings/Richard L Ward*

In 1950 the Royal Navy was developing the De Havilland Sea Vixen as its new all-weather interceptor when the Korean War began. The Venom, converted into an all-weather fighter as a private venture, became the Royal Navy's interim all-weather fleet interceptor, under Specification N.107, making its first carrier landing aboard HMS *Illustrious* on 9 July 1951. Sea Venoms line the foreground of this deck view of HMS *Victorious* off Portsmouth, September 1959. The first of the new generation of high-performance, swept-wing Scimitars, which became the Royal Navy's principal day fighter and nuclear light bomber of the 1960s, is in the background with wings folded, and a Sea Venom has just landed. The liner *Queen Elizabeth* is visible on the horizon. The device off to port of the flight deck is a mirror landing aid, its bank of lights visible at the deck edge near the Sea Venom aft. *Conway Picture Library*

Like the Attacker, the Sea Hawk was developed from a land-based fighter. However, it proved far more successful than its stablemate, and in 1981 remains in service with the Indian Navy, having seen action in the war with Pakistan in 1971. The last Royal Navy Sea Hawk squadron disbanded in 1960, converting to Scimitar day strike fighters. *By courtesy of Richard L Ward*

a 1947 Specification, the Type 508, with straight wings and a 'butterfly' tail, and powered by twin engines. Pending development of the flexible deck, it had a conventional landing gear and indeed served as the basis for an entirely conventional day fighter and strike aircraft, the Scimitar. The latter was derived from the Type 508 with swept wing and tail surfaces. As in the case of the Sea Venom, it would appear that the Scimitar was ordered into production because it was the only carrier-suitable high performance fighter already largely developed.

The Sea Vixen and Scimitar were somewhat more advanced than such US types as the Cougar and the Fury, but, unlike the latter, they had no attack bomber counterpart. All British postwar day fighters were designated figher-bombers or even fighter ground attackers, and had hardpoints for bombs and rockets, much as the postwar

Sea Fury FB11 had. There was also the Wyvern, a design contemporary of the US Skyraider. It did not occupy an analogous position in British service, however. Where the Skyraider was an essential element of the Navy-Marine close-support team, the Wyvern began as an extension of the wartime mission of torpedo attack, and died out with that mission, leaving no successor. There was no British equivalent of the US Skyhawk (A-4), because at the time of the Korean War the Royal Navy had no light nuclear attack mission. (Ironically, nuclear weapons shrank so rapidly that the Scimitar itself became a satisfactory tactical nuclear bomber.) This is not to say that the Royal Navy was entirely ignorant of the possibilities of carrier-delivered nuclear weapons, even at a much earlier date. For example, about 1948 an internal Admiralty paper investigated the problem of launching a long range strike with a 10,000lb bomb load, ie a nuclear weapon. Alternatives included a 100,000lb airplane to be flown from modernized or new type carriers, long-range missiles guided either by the carrier or by her aircraft, and a heavily overloaded aircraft within the 30,000lb limit then current, using some type of assisted take-off, either JATO or catapult, and counting on substantial wind-over-deck. Although a US commentator noted that 'it is understood that this paper has been receiving favorable attention in the Admiralty and that the Admiralty is preparing a favorable case for a new policy', in fact nothing could be done as yet. No British equivalent of the North American Savage appeared, and indeed the wartime project for a twin-engine strike bomber, the Sturgeon, emerged instead as a specialized target-towing airplane.

By 1951 the British nuclear weapons program was approaching the production of a prototype; indeed the first nuclear test occurred in October 1952. Although the Admiralty was interested in the possibilities of such a weapon (particularly as it knew the United States had succeeded in reducing its size and weight to the point at which a fighter-bomber could carry one), it was also aware of the political power of the RAF. Thus there was no official British naval interest in strategic nuclear attack. On the other hand, small nuclear weapons did appear to present an ideal solution to a new tactical problem: commerce raiding by the large new force of Soviet *Sverdlov* class cruisers. The postwar British naval construction program emphasized anti-submarine escorts, incapable of taking on any substantial surface ship. There would be far too few carriers to mount the sort of coordinated mass attacks which had proven effective in World War II: instead it would have to be very nearly one ship per attack. Thus in 1951 the Admiralty gained both an official requirement for a tactical nuclear weapon, for anti-ship use (which would not enter service, however, until 1959), and a Specification for its delivery system, which became the Buccaneer.

Given the prospect of weapon and airplane, naval

The Scimitar's stable-mate was the De Havilland Sea Vixen all-weather fighter, the final expression of the twin boom Vampire/Venom formula. Unlike the US Navy, the Royal Navy combined a powerful air intercept (search) radar with fire-and-forget (infrared) long range air-to-air missiles. This Sea Vixen FAW2 carries Red Tops, and shows extended tail booms carrying extra fuel (23 January 1963). The small scoop under the radome is an infrared seeker used in conjunction with the missiles. There was no internal gun armament, but two retractable pods each carried fourteen unguided rockets. *Conway Picture Library*

attitudes began to shift in favor of attacks on land targets, although this was not officially admitted for some time, presumably to avoid unneccessary conflict with the RAF; a generation of British naval leaders well aware of prewar defeats at Air Force hands cannot have been eager for a blood-letting similar to that which had recently been experienced by their US colleagues. On the other hand, a US Navy which had recently been given a substantial strategic nuclear attack mission was eager for support from its chief ally. The Atlantic Command of NATO, SACLANT, controlled a carrier strike force called the Strike Fleet, in peacetime the US Second Fleet. In wartime it was to deploy into the North Atlantic to strike targets in Northern Russia and to support amphibious landings in Scandinavia. Concerned over its own position in the US nuclear strike effort, the US Navy pressed the Admiralty to commit its carriers to the Strike Fleet. Although the Admiralty for its part did not wish to emphasize such a mission, it also did not wish to antagonize its ally. The Fleet began to participate in Strike Fleet exercises in 1952, and its nuclear strike mission was formally announced in the 1955 White Paper.

Even so, the Admiralty did not press for US-style heavy naval attack bombers; rather it thought in terms of strikes a few hundred miles from the parent carrier, against specific tactical targets where accuracy would be important. At the same time it continued to develop ASW aircraft, such as the Gannet, which would operate from the same flight decks: in effect the Admiralty adopted what the US Navy would call the CV concept. Thus nuclear strike became a valuable capability, but it could not achieve the driving force it did in US planning. Perhaps as importantly, the Navy retained sufficient unique missions to protect itself against the RAF in an era of limited defense budgets.

After Korea the overall British defense budget shrank, as crews expanded and the cost to maintain the more sophisticated carriers rose. The size of the fleet had to be reduced: where in 1952 the Royal Navy maintained six active carriers (*Eagle*, *Indomitable*, and four light fleet carriers) as well as five more (three fleet) for training and trials, two years later only three remained active (*Eagle* and two light fleets). All three commissioned wartime fleet carriers were employed in training and trials, and two of them were to be replaced in non-flying training by less expensive light fleet units. As the new ships (of modernised wartime design) entered service, all of the wartime ships were paid off: in 1955 there were only *Eagle* and *Ark Royal* of the new fleet type, and *Centaur* and *Albion* of the new light fleet type type, operational. *Bulwark*, another new carrier, was maintained for flying training, and three wartime light fleets were employed for non-flying work. Of five older carriers in reserve, one was being reconstructed (*Victorious*), and two more were about to be scrapped; *Formidable* had already been broken up. She had been scheduled for reconstruction, but a survey had shown her too badly distorted by wartime underwater damage. This four-carrier force was about the limit which could be afforded. Thus in 1957 *Bulwark* was fully commissioned to allow for the modernisation of the carrier *Centaur*. One of the wartime light fleets, *Warrior*, was partially modernised to permit her to participate in the 1957 nuclear test series, but soon afterwards she was transferred to Argentina. Meanwhile *Victorious* and the new *Hermes* remained under reconstruction.

RE-ASSESSMENT AND RETRENCHMENT

Now yet another technological revolution, the advent of the H-bomb, prompted a new re-evaluation of British defense policy. It was so destructive that previous concepts of extended wars, including tactical nuclear strikes, amphibious operations and ASW, seemed unrealistic. Some of the results of this review were announced in the 1956 Navy Estimates: now the Admiralty had little faith in the survival of such concentrated forces as the Strike Fleet. Yet it remained committed to its NATO mission, and indeed Korean War experience showed that carriers would remain important in limited war. That Fall the Suez operation seemed to show once more that carriers might well be important in the future. Thus the net effect of the H-bomb was to push the Royal Navy away from considerations of general war and towards limited war; emphasis shifted from nuclear strike operations to a combination of ASW and the classical British role of peacekeeping 'east of Suez.' Emphasis on the former did contradict the general belief that the H-bomb would greatly limit the length of any future war, but on the other hand the Royal Navy had been the chief proponent within NATO of heavy investment in ASW, and found it difficult politically to abandon both ASW *and* the Strike Fleet simultaneously.

At the same time, the Prime Minister, Sir Anthony Eden, expanded the power of the Minister of Defence in the hope of establishing a long-range defense policy, which he also hoped would permit considerable economies. The necessary review was carried out by Duncan Sandys, and its results published in his White Paper of 1957. Once more, current forces were to be sacrificed for future research and development. For example, Sandys assumed that further development of manned aircraft was unnecessary in view of the future role of missiles. The reserve fleet, upon which in the late 1940s the Royal Navy had spent as much (for upkeep) as it had for research, would be discarded, on the theory that in a future war it would be destroyed before it could be reactivated. On the other hand, the Prime Minister was particularly interested in reducing the size of the British Army and its overseas garrisons without at the same time reducing British responsibilities, particularly 'east of Suez.' Meanwhile it became clear that British bases in the Third World were no longer secure: for example, the British had been unable to use their bases in Libya, Jordan and Iraq for the Suez operation. Carriers were the only possible answer, as indeed the US Navy began to argue in a somewhat different context at about the same time.

In line with his view of future general wars, and his mandate to achieve further economies, Sandys vetoed the

Admiralty's request for new carriers: even the newly commissioned *Ark Royal* was already limited by her wartime design. However, five carriers were to be retained in operation, and the British ASW mission was justified on the possibility that the initial nuclear strikes might not prove decisive. Thus a 1958 British defense statement listed naval missions as (i) brushfire war, (ii) sea control in a limited war, and (iii) the NATO general war mission. Singapore was built up as a Far East base, with a task force held in the Mediterranean ready to deploy East. The brushfire mission translated into a new interest in amphibious operations. Two light carriers had been hurriedly refitted as helicopter carriers for Suez, and in May 1957 the refit of the modern light carrier *Bulwark* as a helicopter carrier was announced. To some extent this project was inspired by US experiments. It was pressed by Lord Moutbatten, who had had considerable experience in amphibious operations during World War II. The same helicopter was selected both for troop-carrying and for ASW, which implied that the new helicopter carriers might double as ASW escorts.

Sandys' White Paper is perhaps best known for its cancellation of a wide range of existing jet fighter projects. The carriers which would be retained would need modern fighters, although in 1957 the Royal Navy was already well along in its development of anti-aircraft guided missiles, the land equivalents of which had provided the rationale for the cancellation of the RAF fighter projects. In 1957 the Navy had only one major fighter project in hand, the unusual jet/rocket SR177, which would have functioned as a point defense interceptor with a very high rate of climb but only a limited combat radius. It was expected that a combination of SR177s and Buccaneers would replace the existing Scimitars about 1963, the Sea Vixens being retained as long-range Fleet Air Defense fighters.

The SR177 project itself derived from RAF interest in an interceptor to counter an expected supersonic bomber threat, which in 1952 was expected to materialize about 1960 (Mach 1.3 to 2.0, 60,000 or even 80,000ft altitude, figures characteristic of the B-58 and B-70). At first a pure rocket fighter comparable to the German wartime Komet and launched from a ramp was envisaged, but Saunders-Roe proposed to add a jet engine, first to permit a normal landing and then later to improve overall performance. The next step was to use the jet for high-speed cruise, and the rocket for climbing, turning, and acceleration; in addition the size was increased to include a large airborne radar. At this point the SR177 was a useful naval fighter. A large design contract for a dual-purpose RN/RAF aircraft was signed in 1955; in 1957 it appeared that West Germany, too, was interested. However, the White Paper cancelled any RAF interest in the project, and the Navy version was left in limbo, the White Paper having avoided entirely the issue of naval fighters. The naval SR177 soon followed its RAF brother, although reportedly the Admiralty was sufficiently impressed with it that cancellation of the Buccaneer would have been preferable.

There was considerable discussion as to the wisdom of building any further British carriers. The existing force would suffice until about 1970, but a new carrier would have to be laid down in 1965; if the force level of five were to be maintained, four others would have to be built by 1980. In order to operate the new aircraft efficiently, they would have to be considerably larger even than the existing *Ark Royal* and *Eagle*. Lord Mountbatten himself felt that the future of navies lay in submarines, and he opposed any future carrier program. However, a staff study emphasizing the flexibility of carriers in a NATO (European) war changed his mind; carriers with steam catapults could launch aircraft quite competitive with those based on land, and the carrier task forces would be quite capable of self-defense, given the new naval surface-to-air missiles and the interceptors they would be able to operate. Nor was there any reason to imagine that the mobile air strike requirement for brushfire war would become obsolete. Moreover, there was increasing hope that the overall strength of Western nuclear forces would deter the Soviets from the all-out use of their own strategic forces, so that future wars might be relatively limited. The US Navy advanced this view at least from 1956 onwards, and from about 1960 the United States tried to make it general NATO policy, to develop limited-war (even if limited nuclear war) capabilities.

THE FINAL AXE: CVA-01

The Royal Navy formulated tentative staff requirements for a new generation of attack carriers in 1959. There could be no hope of very large production runs of specialized naval fighters and attack aircraft, so the original staff studies contemplated a single airframe which might be produced in alternative fighter and attack versions. In fact at this time the RAF and the Royal Navy jointly issued Operational Requirement 346, which bears some similarity to the US TFX project: a TSR-2 limited in weight to 50,000lb (for carrier operation). The series of conflicting requirements reportedly included the Air Force's desire for a war load of 10,000lb to be delivered over 1300 miles from short, sandy airstrips and the Navy's wish for a Mach 2.5 interceptor and strike aircraft with a landing speed of 80kts. Design approaches included variable geometry (Vickers) and a full delta wing (De Havilland DH127). Vickers claimed a CAP duration of four hours and space for a 36in radar dish which would permit search and lock-on at 60nm; the weapons bay could accommodate up to 6000lb and strike range would be 1000nm. Ultimately the elaborate dual-purpose project evolved into a specialized replacement for the Sea Vixen, the swing-wing Vickers Type 583 – which in turn was killed by the V/STOL P1154.

The P1154 in its turn was an outgrowth of the V/STOL work which would, indirectly, doom the carrier in the Royal Navy, as it became obvious that an all-V/STOL platform would be far less expensive (if also far less capable) than a conventional carrier, if only because it could be far smaller. The new aircraft would be supersonic, gaining considerable thrust by burning fuel in the forward (normally cold) lift nozzles (plenum chamber burning, PCB), and it originated in response to a NATO VTO attack specification, NMBR3. In 1962 it was proposed within the Ministry of Defence as a replacement for two ageing subsonic fighters, the RAF Hunter and the Royal Navy Sea Vixen, to enter service in 1968. Just how important VTO was for either mission is not clear, nor is it clear just what sacrifices the VTO design entailed. However, the P1154

The Saunders-Roe SR177 was conceived as a mixed-power, short-range, point defense interceptor and was derived from the earlier SR53 which employed a similar propulsion system; the SR53 proceeded to the flight stage but the SR177 fell victim to the notorious 1957 British Government White Paper. Original specifications called for a Spectre rocket motor and a De Havilland Gyron Junior turbojet (the latter also installed in the Buccaneer S1) but one design featured the RB133 turbojet instead. This artist's impression of the navalised version (SR177N) shows the rocket motor location (immediately below the vertical stabilizer, above the main RB133 jet pipe) and wingtip Red Top missiles. Also visible is the deflected exhaust (nozzles between the main gear bays) to assist landing, required because of the very light condition of the airplane when all rocket fuel had been expended. *British Hovercraft Corporation*

was ordered in two versions, a single-seat ground attacker for the RAF and a two-seat high-altitude interceptor for the Navy. As in the case of the US TFX, there was a constant conflict between the desire for economy through commonality, and the very different needs of the two services. Indeed, one British writer, Derek Wood, has suggested that the P1154 was the brainchild of Peter Thorneycroft, Minister of Aviation in 1960–62 and of Defence in 1962–64 – and an admirer of Robert S McNamara, inventor of the TFX concept.

In fact the P1154, like the F-111B, was never satisfactory to the Navy. One of the great strengths of the carrier was its steam catapult, equivalent in practice to several miles of concrete runway. To accept the costs of VTO operation was to throw away this advantage; the Navy may well have suspected that the real cost of adopting the

HMS *Ark Royal* was last British carrier, refitted on a limited scale in 1967–70 to operate Phantoms and Buccaneers. By this time the complex Type 984 was about to be abandoned, and the Anglo-Dutch three-dimensional type planned for the abortive CVA-01 and also for HMS *Bristol* had not materialized. The 'Ark' had to make do with a pair of Type 965 two-dimensional air search sets, a 982 aft, and 983 height-finders abeam her forward and after lattice radar masts. The radome abaft the superstructure, which appears similar to that of US carriers, houses a CCA set, perhaps equivalent to the US SPN-35. TACAN surmounts the central radar mast. By this time even the two Seacats aft had been removed, and the 'Ark' had no self-defense weapons whatever, although she was equipped with a quartet of Corvus chaff launchers. She was withdrawn from service in 1979; this photograph was taken in 1977. *C & S Taylor*

P1154 would be to throw away its carriers in favor of small 'air capable' ships of little real value. In any case it rejected the P1154 and in February 1964 announced that it was buying US Phantoms. Ironically, the RAF also bought the Phantom in place of the P1154, so that in fact both Services did buy very similar aircraft. The actual date of the Navy decision may have been somewhat earlier, in that the Navy arranged for US pilots to operate their Phantoms from Ark Royal during 1963. In British service the Phantom was considerably modified, with British Spey engines and with a much longer nosewheel leg which increased the effective downward component of engine thrust on take-off from a carrier and so compensated for somewhat less powerful British catapults. The limited size of British elevators was reflected in a redesign of the nose which permitted it to fold back. Even so, it took a very large refit of HMS Ark Royal to permit Phantom operation; HMS Eagle, the only other British carrier which might have been suited to Phantom operation, was not refitted. Modifications included installation of a new waist catapult and new arresting gear; the former could launch 'the largest aircraft' without wind-over-deck.

The new carrier project also included a new AEW airplane, which was to have had synchronized fore and aft radomes in place of the single radar previously employed in such types as the Gannet and the US AEW aircraft. A Blackburn project for such an aircraft was intended also as the basis for a Carrier On-board Delivery (COD) type, much as the US C-2 was derived from the E-2 Hawkeye, and the C-1 from the earlier E-1B. These designs were presumably part of a joint Anglo-French carrier AEW project, and were comparable with several French types.

In the event, there was no new carrier program. Carriers faced a variety of enemies. The RAF saw in them a threat to its primacy as the offensive strike service, particularly as the rationale for the new carrier force had included the concept of strikes against enemy airfields and other interdiction targets as much as a thousand miles from fleet center. It argued that a new generation of very large land-based aircraft, such as the TSR-2 and the US F-111, could replace the carrier aircraft in their approved 'east of Suez' role, flying out of British bases. Reportedly it was not above redrawing maps to show that the base at Gan was actually within TSR-2 range of states whose security Britain guaranteed. However, the RAF had a vital ally in the Treasury. Conventional carriers were enormously expensive, and from the outset it was clear that at least five would have to be built, the largest warships ever to be built in Britain. The advent of V/STOL suggested a face-saving way out of the dilemma, since a V/STOL airplane could fly off an extremely small platform. To a politician uninterested in details, a Phantom and a Harrier were both fighters with ground attack capability, and an 'air capable ship' supporting perhaps ten of the latter was not too different from a carrier supporting 30 or 40 of the former.

There is also reason to believe that neither the Conservative government nor the Labour government which succeeded it (and which actually cancelled the new carrier program) was really willing to build a new class of carriers, given their immense cost and the difficulty a badly rundown British shipbuilding industry would have had in carrying out the necessary design work – a problem perhaps analogous to the shortage of draftsmen often cited as an important impediment to British naval rearmament in the 1930s. The RAF argument is of current interest because it is resurrected, from time to time, by the US Air Force, and it therefore poses a danger to future US carrier construction programs.

The new carrier (CVA-01) was cancelled in a 1966 Defence Review, although in March 1967 Ark Royal began

a large refit which would maintain her in service through 1978. Of the other carriers in service at that time, Eagle and Victorious were refitted much less extensively in, respectively, 1966–67 and 1965–66. Hermes had a large refit in 1964–66 while Bulwark and Albion had been converted into helicopter assault carriers in 1959–60 and 1961–62. Centaur of this class remained unconverted and was stricken in 1971, with Albion following in 1972. Victorious was scrapped in 1969, and Eagle was laid up in 1972, cannibalized to keep her near-sister Ark Royal in service.

To a large extent the demise of the carrier force was justified by the abandonment of British commitments 'east of Suez;' the Royal Navy as a whole was re-oriented gradually to operations in the North Sea and the Eastern Atlantic. Perhaps the only bright spot in this melancholy progression was a British decision to retain some aircraft at sea in the form of V/STOL strike fighters operating from a small carrier which was initially called a 'through-deck cruiser' largely to avoid the wrath of the Labour Government (which was determined to squash this particular form of defense extravagance) and, probably, of the RAF, which had helped supply the Labour Government's ammunition. The new design fluctuated greatly in size between the first tentative announcement (in a 1967 Supplementary Statement on Defence Policy) and the order for HMS Invincible (April 1973). Ironically, it closely resembled a ship designed to escort the abortive new fleet carrier. This 'escort cruiser' would have carried the ASW helicopters otherwise normally carried by the larger ship, and thus would have improved her capability for strike and fleet air defense. In effect, had the program for a two-tier aircraft carrier fleet been carried out, the Royal Navy would have passed from what the US Navy called a CV to the combination of CVA and CVS (Support, ie ASW) which the latter operated through the 1960s. The Invincible and her sisters, then, will provide the support originally intended to permit heavier seaborne strikes – for which there will be no platform at all.

FLEET AIR ARM ORGANIZATION POSTWAR

British naval aircraft and air group development reflected the varying fortunes of the British carrier force. In 1945 the light fleet carriers operated mixed air groups of up to 21 (US) Corsairs and 18 Barracudas; the latter were replaced postwar by Fireflies, so that these ships operated all-fighter groups. The Firefly AS5 or 6 was the largest strike airplane a light carrier could operate, which fact in itself made such a ship unattractive after the adoption of the Gannet for ASW. The remaining fleet carriers operated, in addition, the Firebrand strike fighter. By the Korean War many Fleet Air Arm squadrons flew the Sea Fury, an adapted land fighter, and fleet carriers operated detachments of Sea Hornet twin-engine day and night fighters.

The new carrier Eagle commissioned with jets, Supermarine Attackers. She carried up to three Attacker squadrons, plus one ASW Squadron (Firefly AS6) and one of Firebrands. The Attackers were officially fighter-bombers rather than pure fighters. British practice was more fluid than American in the matter of air group composition; for example, within a year one of the Attacker squadrons had been landed, and the ship operated a squadron of night-fighting Sea Hornets, as well as a pair of AEW Skyraiders supplied by the United States. Later her Firebrands were replaced by a second type of jet fighter, the Hawker Sea Hawk, and the Fireflies gave way to Grumman Avenger AS4s, also a US type. In 1952 Eagle operated, too, an air-sea-rescue helicopter, and an expanded squadron of Skyraiders, for a total of 59 aircraft, her maximum, and somewhat short of the air group of a somewhat smaller *Essex*. By this time the standard jet fighter squadron, originally eight aircraft, had been increased to the twelve of propeller squadrons.

As in the US Navy, the Royal Navy now divided its air group fighters between all-weather and day types, using the latter as fighter-bombers to make up for relatively small numbers of pure strike types. Thus at Suez in 1956 *Eagle* operated 17 of the new Sea Venom night (jet) fighters, as well as 24 Sea Hawk fighter-bombers, nine Wyvern strike fighters, four Skyraiders (for AEW) and two helicopters. At this time the standard British carrier air group included eight Gannets, but in the absence of submarines it was possible to land them in favor of strike aircraft (in this case Sea Venoms). The smaller carriers were less capacious: *Albion* operated Sea Hawks and Wyverns (later replaced by Sea Venoms), as well as two Skyraiders (AEW) and two helicopters, and her sister *Bulwark* had a homogeneous air group of 30 Sea Hawks (plus two Avengers and two helicopters).

As the US Navy would discover in its transition to the CV, the eight ASW Gannets were quite expensive in terms of deck space, not to mention time in the deck operating cycle. The Royal Navy thus became an early exponent of the big ASW helicopter, which could be launched from areas of the flight deck not usable by aircraft in any case. By 1956 future air groups were to dispense with the Gannets, and long-endurance Gannet AEW aircraft would replace the American Skyraiders. For example, the new *Hermes* was to support eight of the new Scimitar day fighters and interdiction attackers, as well as nine Sea Vixen night fighters, eight ASW helicopters, four AEW Gannets, and two search and rescue helicopters – which left no room at all for specialized strike aircraft to replace the now obsolescent Wyverns. The somewhat larger *Victorious* might support twelve each of the new fighters, as well as eight Gannets (and four Skyraiders, which would soon give way to Gannet AEW aircraft). In the future, perhaps about 1963, the Royal Navy hoped to replace the Scimitars with a combination of eight Buccaneers and eight of the new jet/rocket Saunders-Roe SR177 interceptors (which in the event were cancelled), gaining deck

The Buccaneer low-altitude strike bomber, conceived as a tactical nuclear bomber, was virtually the only British military aircraft project to survive the 1957 Defence Review. Here one landing aboard the last conventional British carrier, HMS *Ark Royal*, in 1978, displays a variety of low-speed features, including massive air brakes and vents to blow air across the wings (for boundary layer control). *Royal Navy*

space by replacing the Gannets with helicopters. There was no question but that the Gannet provided more capability than the helicopter, but on the other hand flight decks were extemely constricted.

HMS *Eagle* was about 10,000 tons heavier than *Victorious*, and her future air group was set at twelve each of the new types, ten Sea Vixens, eight ASW aircraft or helicopters, six Gannet AEW and two helicopters, a total of fifty aircraft, including an 'overhead' of fourteen for AEW and ASW (with two more AEW because of her size) and a standard detachment of ten for fleet air defense (all-weather). In a more restricted ship this overhead was the limit of capability: *Centaur*, for example, could take only

With the cancellation of a variety of British naval fighter projects, the Royal Navy bought the US Phantom, suitably modified, as its last conventional naval fighter. Only HMS *Ark Royal* was modified to operate them. This FG1, flying off the 'Ark's catapult, shows clearly one of the major modifications applied to the British Phantom (F-4K in US parlance), an extra-extendible nosewheel leg which raises the thrust line of the engines and so allows them to supply some additional lift during take-off. British Phantoms are powered by the Rolls-Royce Spey 202 bypass engine; they have enlarged air intakes and auxiliary air doors aft, one of the latter being visible just over this Phantom's wing. The radome and antenna fold for more compact stowage. *Royal Navy*

Of the Western navies, only the French and the US built new carriers after 1945. This is the French *Clemenceau*, clearly reflecting British and US practice in her angled deck and in her pair of steam catapults, one of them on her angled-deck sponson and not obviously visible here. The mirror landing aid can be made out on its small sponson to port. One feature not at all characteristic of practice in the US and Royal Navies is the emphasis on a powerful anti-aircraft gun battery, consisting of eight automatic 3.9in guns, all mounted below flight deck level. *French Navy*

the 'overhead' plus a non-standard fighter detachment of twelve Sea Vixens.

Subsequent developments were almost a demonstration of the limits imposed by small hulls and AEW/ASW 'overhead'. When the high-performance SR177 failed to materialize, the Royal Navy, as we have seen, turned to the P1154 V/STOL and then to the United States for its next interceptor, but the new Phantom was so large that *Ark Royal* could operate only twelve, plus fourteen Buccaneers. The 'overhead' was cut back to seven ASW helicopters and one search and rescue helicopter, plus the usual quartet of Gannets. Even the Buccaneer imposed difficulties. For example, it could not be flown off *Eagle* at full weight, so that ship's squadron consisted of twelve strike aircraft and four Scimitars for inflight refueling.

For its new carrier the British Naval Staff had hoped to use a combined fighter/attack airframe, to limit costs by extending the production run and to achieve interdiction as much as 1000nm from the fleet center, which would have provided considerable sea room for maneuver in a European war. The price was expected to be a 70,000lb airplane (as against about 60,000 for a fully-loaded Phantom), and a correspondingly sized carrier deck; on the other hand, the new carrier was limited politically to about 50,000 tons. No air wing was ever announced, but these figures suggest a total of no more than about forty heavy strike aircraft; moreover, they suggest the importance of the 'escort cruiser' which would clear their flight decks of 'overhead'. Matters would also have been improved had the new ships operated in pairs in wartime, as in that case elements of 'overhead' such as AEW Gannets might have been shared between them.

FRENCH CARRIER POLICY SINCE 1945

After 1945 only one other nation tried to build a fleet around carrier task groups: France. Studies were made for a variety of conversions of existing hulls, including that of the incomplete battelship *Jean Bart*. Moreover, studies of new carrier designs begun during the Occupation were continued; in 1947 the French Parliament approved construction of one ship, whose design reflected a mixture of

British and US concepts as then understood. Meanwhile existing French carriers, the ex-British light fleet *Arromanches* and the former escort carrier *Dixmude*, fought in Indo-China, using ex-US aircraft. They proved their value, albeit in a scenario not envisaged by advocates of carrier construction in France. The latter estimated that France required a total of six carriers, but in 1950 a shortage of funds forced the cancellation of the single new ship. However, studies continued, encouraged by the new possibilities opened by the steam catapult and the angled deck. Meanwhile, the United States provided a pair of war-built light carriers (*Independence* class); in 1954 a carrier was approved by Parliament, which in 1955 approved a second by repeating the previous year's appropriations without amendment. Both were built, but attempts in 1958–61 to secure a third unit, which would have brought the force to six, failed. This would have been a far larger unit, capable of operating the naval equivalent of the French strategic nuclear bomber, the Mirage IV. By this time France was close to possession of a bomb of her own, and the French Navy saw in large carriers an important role in the indpendent French deterrent, not unlike that which the US Navy had secured for itself after 1950. This vision was to be transferred to the French ballistic missile submarines, leaving the two French carriers, *Foch* and *Clemenceau*, extremely useful for operations in the many former French territories, with which France maintained close relations. In 1980 both are approaching replacement age, and two new full-deck nuclear-powered carriers have been approved.

The rather ambitious French carrier program was accompanied by an equally ambitious naval aircraft program, an important motive for which was the French desire to rebuild her military industries. Like other French efforts of the 1950s, it was hampered by the cost of colonial warfare first in Indo-China and then in Algeria; the French complained later that although they received generous assistance from the United States it was all intended for such 'second line' naval missions as ASW. Offensive carrier aviation was very much a French concern, particularly since it was US policy to discourage French attempts to obtain nuclear weapons.

The 'rearmament' program of 1946 called for the construction of 70 naval fighters and 105 twin engine bomber/scouts, all of them much larger than most contemporary naval types, and all with great range. The bombers were the types designed in wartime (Nord 1500 and NC 1070); the fighter was originally the SE 582, but this type was soon replaced in the program by the unusual twin-boom pusher SO 8000 Narval, which was credited with a maximum speed of 450mph and a range of about 2160nm at 270kts. The fighters were not compatible with the first French postwar carrier project (PA25), which had to be considerably enlarged, growing by about 4000 tons to become the 18,000-ton (fully loaded) PA28, approved as the *Clemenceau* in 1947. It was to operate 22 bombers (NC 1070) as well as 5 heavy fighters (SE 582), using two flight deck catapults; another 25 SE 582s would be held in reserve in the hangar.

This was only a first generation; the French Navy soon began to order prototypes of naval jets. As part of its 1946 program it ordered three jet fighter-bombers (Arsenal VG 90, Nord 2200, NC 1080), all intended to exceed 500kts at 20,000ft, and to take off, unassisted, in about 2600ft (compared to about 800 for the heavy bomber/scouts). Four missions were envisaged: interception (two 30mm cannon), bomb attack (two 30mm plus one 1000kg or two 500kg bombs), rocket attack (three 30mm cannon plus eight 90mm rockets), and long-range escort (three 30mm cannon). The NC 1070 was converted into a twin jet (in fact, into the first French twin jet), as the NC 1071, the 'geranium pot', capable of about 430kts and with a take-off roll of about 1500ft. These were even worse than the characteristics of the original NC 1070, and indeed none of the jets ordered in 1946 was ordered into production. However, the entire program was an indication of the determination of the French Navy to embrace carrier air warfare. Financial problems, many of them consequences of the continuing war in Indo-China, caused the cancellation of all of the jet fighter projects by 1953.

A fifth project, announced in November 1947, called for a two-seat attack aircraft, both for anti-ship (torpedo, missile or rocket) and for anti-submarine (depth charge or rocket) operations. Requirements included a four-hour endurance at sea level at 160–210kts (or one hour at 380kts at 20,000ft without bombs) and strengthening for JATO launch. The combination of long endurance and a high dash speed called for a mixed power plant, a Mamba turboprop and a Nene jet engine in the tail. The result was the Br 960 Vultur, the only survivor of the postwar burst of French enthusiasm (and money). The Vultur itself fell victim to the world-wide shift in naval priorities from surface warfare to ASW. In 1952 the French Navy gave absolute priority to the ASW mission, and after studying alternative new aircraft, it adopted a modified version of the Vultur in 1953. It in turn evolved into the Br 1050 Alizé, which had a single more powerful turboprop, but no tail jet; to some extent this evolution paralleled that of the earlier Grumman TB3F/AF-2, although the Alizé is a single-package airplane, comparable to the British Gannet. Alizés serve in the Indian Navy as well as in the French.

The French Navy entered the jet age using foreign types, particularly a license-built version of the Venom which it called Aquilon. Meanwhile naval versions of the standard Air Force day fighters (Ouragan and Mystère IV) were studied but rejected during 1949–50 and 1952–53. A new series of aircraft projects began in connection with the new carrier project (PA54) which eventually produced the *Foch* and *Clemenceau*. There was no longer, in the mid-1950s, any prospect of specialized naval aircraft; the Navy would have to make do with modified versions of Air Force projects the subject of long production runs. Thus there was particular naval interest in a series of fighter-bombers designed for a 1953 NATO contest, the Br 1001 Taon and the Dassault Mystère XXVI or Étendard IIM. In each case naval characteristics were inherent in the short-field performance required by NATO. Although the Italian Fiat G91 won the NATO contest, the French Air Force and

Although it began a program of domestic aircraft development soon after World War II, the French Navy had to depend upon foreign types for its first postwar generation of naval aircraft. The indigenous Dassault Étendard IV attack bomber first flew only in 1958, and was produced in attack and also in photo-reconnaissance (IVP) versions, the latter being illustrated. Despite the age of the basic design, the Étendard IV is to be succeeded in service by a slightly improved Super Étendard with new engines and capable of delivering tactical nuclear weapons. *Richard L Ward*

Navy ordered the Br 1001, which was supposed to be supersonic at 30,000ft.

Trials were disappointing, and both the Br 1001 and the Étendard were rejected. However, Dassault proposed a single-engine version of the latter, which the Navy adopted despite its preference for the reliability of a twin-engine airplane. Dassault argued for the greater economy of the single engine, as well as for better survivability after battle damage. In 1980 the Étendard remains the standard French naval fighter-bomber, although it first flew in 1958.

The Étendard was not considered a replacement for the Aquilon fighter. That was to be a Mach 1.8 aircraft capable of carrying a tactical nuclear weapon (which the French were already well along in developing) over long ranges. Two types were proposed, the Br 1120 Sirocco and the Mirage III. Neither was adopted, and the requirement for a supersonic fighter was not filled for six years. In 1963 the French government chose the US Crusader (F-8), leaving to the Étendard the attack mission. Existing carriers were not large enough to accommodate a multi-purpose type such as the Phantom.

Another failed project was a fleet air defense fighter armed with very long range missiles, comparable perhaps to the US Eagle-Missileer concept of the late 1950s, or to the present Phoenix/F-14 combination. In French parlance this would have been the 'Talp', for 'tactique à longue portée' (or 'tactical aircraft of long range'), a subsonic Br 1170 or modified Étendard with a four-hour endurance and a large radar. This 1960 project was succeeded by a 1963–64 program for a fighter which would combine long range and high performance – and compatibility with the small French carriers. Such diverse requirements naturally added up to a variable geometry solution. The Breguet Br 120, powered by two Speys (which also power British Phantoms), was to attain Mach 2.4 at high altitude. The Mirage G, built to the same specification, flew in 1967 and attained Mach 2.5, yet was able to land at 110kts. However, it never proceeded beyond the prototype stage, as the French government consistently suffered from the high cost of other (particularly strategic) military programs.

Thus there was never a replacement for the ageing Étendard IV. In the late 1960s the French Navy considered the purchase of the US A-7 and the A-4, and in fact a special French version of the latter received the designation A-4T. It was argued that even 100 A-4s would be less expensive than 70 aircraft built in France, although the preservation of the French military aircraft industry must have carried considerable weight. There were also two French proposals: the Jaguar, an Anglo-French project, and the Super Étendard. As in the case of the interceptor, the choice was drawn out. For example, the naval Jaguar was ordered in 1968 and abandoned in 1970; in 1973 the

France never did develop a satisfactory naval interceptor; attempts to replace the Aquilon, the French version of the British Sea Venom, failed, both a Breguet Br 1120 and a navalized Mirage III proving inadequate. Finally in 1963 the French government decided to buy the US Crusader, a special F-8E(FN) version being built. Modifications for the French Navy included replacement of the US APQ-94 radar by a new APQ-104 compatible with the French MATRA R-530 air-to-air missile, which the F-8E(FN) carries; chordwise separation of the drooping wing leading edges for increased camber; flap blowing; doubled aileron and flap deflection; enlarged horizontal tail surfaces; and a 2° reduction in wing incidence travel. Thus the Crusader's landing speed was reduced by about 15kts, to permit it to operate from the small flight decks of French carriers. This example from *Flotille F* was photographed in July 1973; it does not appear to have the standard pair of fuselage missile rails, but does show the pair of 20mm cannon on each side. *Richard L Ward*

The Breguet Alizé is the sole survivor of the ambitious French naval aircraft development program of the late 1940s. Although currently employed as an ASW aircraft, it was originally conceived as the Br 960 Vultur strike-bomber, comparable, perhaps, to the US Skyraider or to the British Wyvern. The much modified Br 1050 Alizé first flew in October 1956, production machines appearing between March 1959 and July 1961. An initial order for 100 was reduced to 75 for budgetary reasons in 1958, but other navies, notably those of Indonesia and India, showed interest in the remaining 25. Ultimately the Indians bought 12, flying them from the ex-British light carrier *Vikrant*. Here an Alizé lands aboard the French carrier *Clemenceau*. *French Navy*

Super Étendard was chosen. It was a slightly modified Étendard IV with a more powerful engine and provision to carry a tactical nuclear weapon (AN-52), a capability which had first been envisaged as early as 1956–57 with the Sirocco and Mirage III, but which is only now (1981) being incorporated into the French carrier force.

One peculiarity of French carrier air groups, compared to their US and British contemporaries, is the lack of any airborne early warning capability. Nor does France operate long-range AEW types such as the US Warning Star (EC-121) or the British Shackleton or Nimrod. In 1965 France and Britain cooperated in a new carrier-based AEW project, calling for a 20-ton aircraft to operate 200nm from a force, and to remain airborne for four hours – in effect an E-2, but capable of operating from much smaller carriers. French projects included twin turboprop and twin turbojet types (Br 123A and 123B), but the program died. Some of the proposed configurations were quite unusual, with twin tail booms and synchronized radomes fore and aft in place of the typical US rotodome.

These were advanced programs, and they evince a determination to maintain a modern seaborne strike force. Indeed, before the advent of the French ballistic missile, the French carrier fleet was the only arm of the French Navy capable of strategic attack. Thus great hopes were placed in the large carrier of 1958 and in her strategic bombers. However, the reality of French naval aircraft development shows in the limited funds available for aircraft development and the great number of prototypes which never proceeded to production (and, indeed, of designs which never approached the prototype stage). The two carriers actually built were limited in size and therefore in their capacity to operate modern aircraft. Although variable geometry seemed an obvious solution to the problem of this limit, it was not well enough developed in the early 1960s to be viable, at least not for French industry. By the time such fighters had become practical, the French Navy had decided to abandon conventional carriers for its future program in favor of a combination of missile ships and helicopter carriers. This decision was symbolized by the decision to forego an advanced attack aircraft and to adopt instead a modernized version of the fighter-bomber first flown in 1958, the Étendard.

Moreover, the limited size of the two French carriers shows in the French Navy's unwillingness to accept such 'overheads' as AEW aircraft, and thus to accept very considerable vulnerability in the face of standard Soviet anti-carrier tactics. Limits imposed by carrier size also show in the small size and limited capability of the Étendard compared to its British contemporary, the Buccaneer. The effect of 'overhead' shows in a typical French air group of 1977: 16 Étendard IVM strike fighters and 10 Crusader interceptors – plus 4 Étendard IVP photo planes, 6 Alizés for ASW, 2 Super Frelon ASW helicopters and, in the Indian Ocean, 2 Alouette utility helicopters. The Étendards are now being replaced by the improved version, the Super Étendard, but it is a measure of the limited capacity of the French carriers that it was impossible for the French Navy to realize the economies inherent in a dual-purpose interceptor and ground attacker such as the F-4.

4. The Carrier and her Aircraft

Aircraft and carrier design meet at the low-speed end of the flight envelope, where the airplane lands and takes off. For the aircraft designer, the problem is to stretch that envelope so as to achieve good low-speed characteristics without paying an excessive price in drag at high speed. Low stall speed, for example, simplifies landing and indeed reduces strain on the airplane structure as the arresting gear engages. Good handling characteristics (and good pilot vision) at low speed are also important: the flight deck is narrow, and errors in approach require rapid correction. Similarly, a low take-off speed reduces the load on catapults and in effect permits an airplane to operate from smaller and less expensive ships. In an earlier era it reduced take-off roll down the deck, so that the first airplane to be launched could be placed nearer the bow, and a larger number of aircraft spotted ready for take-off abaft it.

The greater the efficiency of an airplane design at high speed, the greater, in general, the penalty paid at very low speed. Aircraft designers generally compromise between the two ends of the performance envelope by varying the geometry of their airplanes. For example, the effective lifting power of a wing can be varied by altering its angle of incidence, the angle between it and the line along which the engine supplies thrust. Flaps alter both the shape of the wing and its effective area. The lower the minimum speed required, the more the wing geometry must be altered, and consequently the greater the weight penalty of the extra flaps or other mechanism. Since naval aircraft design particularly emphasizes low-speed flight, naval aircraft generally show a higher degree of variable geometry, with corresponding penalties felt at the high (combat) end of the spectrum. For example, the 'navalized' version of the Spitfire required particularly large flaps. The F8U Crusader (later redesignated F-8) was unique in having a variable-incidence wing, hinged at the trailing edge. To some extent the nose-down attitude of the F6F Hellcat in flight reflected an angle between wing and thrust line optimized for take-off, with the high-speed penalty accepted.

The most extreme case of variable geometry is a variable-sweep wing. The first combat aircraft to have one was a naval fighter, the Grumman F10F Jaguar, which had to combine long endurance (4.42 hours, or a radius of 552nm) with a short take-off (for a jet) of 960ft with the assistance of 25kts of wind over the flight deck. Endurance in turn implied both efficient low-speed (loiter) flight and great fuel capacity, ie a relatively heavy take-off weight of 31,000lb. An unswept wing was most efficient for take-off and for low-speed cruising flight, but the wing had to be swept back for high-speed combat. Ultimately the F10F was abandoned, partly in view of its complexity, but the variable-sweep wing has been revived in the F-14 Tomcat designed for a combination of long subsonic loiter and high-speed dogfighting. It may be significant that the Soviet fighter generally reported as a candidate for carrier use, the MiG-23/27 'Flogger', also has variable-sweep wings; so does the Sukhoi Su-17 'Fitter-C', reportedly employed by a Soviet Navy shore unit, perhaps for carrier air group training.

Propellers were another candidate for variable geometry (variable pitch). At low speed the propeller is most efficient at low (fine) pitch, with the blades closest to the direction of their motion, almost perpendicular to the longitudinal axis of the airplane itself. In effect the propeller blades act as wings, and their pitch angle is equivalent to an angle of attack. As the airplane moves faster, its forward velocity adds to the rotational velocity of the blades in such a way as to produce a *relative* wind at a steeper angle to the body of the airplane; a propeller blade maintaining what amounts to a constant angle of attack must adopt a much steeper pitch angle (high, or coarse, pitch). A steeper pitch angle also corresponds to lower engine rpm: thus a variable-pitch propeller allows for more take-off power at one end of its range of pitch (higher rpm without, in effect, stalling out the propeller blades) and for lower cruise power (or more efficient cruise, or greater cruise range) at the other end. In 1933 the US Navy's General Board rejected a Bureau of Aeronautics request that the flight decks of the new *Yorktown* class carriers, then in the final design phase, be lengthened to accommodate a new generation of heavier attack planes carrying larger bombs, since it was expected that the simple adoption of a variable-pitch propeller would reduce take-off runs by 30 per cent. Even with variable pitch, some choice had to be made: a propeller optimized for take-off would not be most efficient at high speed. For example, US naval fighters of World War II sacrificed about 7 or 8mph of maximum speed to gain short take-off performance.

Another, and often conflicting, requirement is for long endurance, not merely for range but, often as importantly, for extended time in the air. For example, fighters must be kept continuously airborne on Combat Air Patrol (CAP) stations; the longer their endurance, the less frequently they must be relieved. CAP mission time now includes a considerable cruise out to station, the current theoretical standard being 150nm from the carrier, and the fighter must always retain enough fuel for combat. For strike aircraft, long range permits the carrier to operate more freely, and gains some immunity (or at least warning time) against the threat of land-based attackers. There is also the classical naval requirement that returning aircraft have a sufficient fuel margin to find their carrier. Although pilots are always given an expected carrier position, there must always be a considerable allowance for error: the aircraft may return early or late, the carrier may have to maneuver unexpectedly given wind and weather between her launch point and her expected recovery point, and she may even have to evade enemy attack. Extra endurance fuel (and, in British aircraft, an extra crewman to act as navigator) imposed substantial performance penalties on pre-World War II naval aircraft. Both the

USS *Saratoga*, about to launch her air group, about 1929, shows the victory of the air-cooled engine over the former water-cooled type in the US Navy, a victory which persisted to the end of the piston-engine era. Martin T4M-1 bombers are spotted aft (VT-2B), with Boeing F3B-1s of VB-2B forward. Like their Curtiss predecessors, each F3B could lift five small bombs.

British and US Navies developed special carrier homing beacons (respectively, the Type 72 'lantern' and the YE) which partly obviated this requirement. However, the beacon may have to be shut down in some circumstances, eg to avoid detection of the carrier.

THE FLIGHT DECK CYCLE

Aircraft endurance is intimately related to the flight deck cycle, and to the number of aircraft a carrier can usefully operate. This became particularly important with the advent of low-endurance jets flying off axial (straight) deck carriers. Such a carrier cannot recover and launch aircraft simultaneously, as an angled-deck ship can. She would generally launch and recover a group of aircraft all at the same time. As each airplane landed, it would be towed to the bow and fueled at once. As soon as the last landed, all would be towed aft (respotted) into their launch positions, the remaining aircraft would be refueled, and all would be rearmed. Alternative air group tactics could be envisaged. A maximum strike might be flown and re-covered, with no aircraft in the air while others were on deck. More efficiently, half the effective air group might be airborne while the other half was serviced; in effect the endurance time of half the air group would have to match the turn-around time on deck. Yet another alternative might be to keep two groups airborne while servicing the third, in effect halving turn-around time but only reducing the number of aircraft being turned around by a third, so that the deck crew would have to work faster or the number of aircraft in operation would have to be reduced. Tactically, the alternatives were a massive strike gaining its effect by concentration versus a continuous series of strikes blanketing the objective.

In the mid-1950s it was estimated that a jet fighter could be recovered every 0.65 minutes, and an airplane respotted every 1.5 minutes and refueled in about the same length of time. A catapult launch would take about 0.45 minutes. Generally it could be assumed that the first airplane launched would be the first recovered, and the group as a whole would have to wait both to form up and to come aboard. This group endurance (and the range at which the air group could attack) would have to be less than the endurance credited to a single airplane. The results could be striking. For example, it would take a total of 52 minutes merely to recover 80 aircraft; that time would determine the minimum mission endurance required for the carrier to operate all 80 aircraft, since the last to be launched would have to remain airborne until all of the others had been recovered. Jet aircraft were credited with an endurance of 120 minutes; if a margin of 20 were required, the standard mission would be 100 minutes. The effective turn-around would have to be even less, to leave time for forming up. How much would be required would depend upon tactics; for example, a group of forty fighters, forming up at sea level (where fuel consumption was highest), would eat away as much as a quarter of effective endurance. On the other hand, the reduction would be only about 14 per cent if the first aircraft off the carrier climbed and throttled back to allow the others to join up. If turn-around time, then, were cut to about 80 minutes, a carrier would be hard pressed to operate a total of more than about 63 aircraft in two sections. Matters would become far worse if the carrier operated with bad-weather approach radar (Carrier-Controlled Approach), in which returning aircraft would circle together for a time, and individual aircraft be 'talked down' from a considerable distance. Landing time might be as great as six minutes per airplane, and marshalling itself might consume another twenty. That would leave the effective air group reduced to perhaps sixteen fighters in two sections. Thus, although

FLIGHT DECK FEATURES

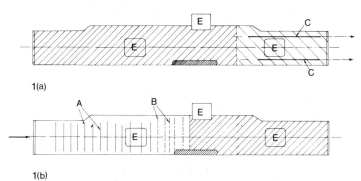

1(a)

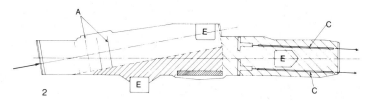

1(b)

1(a) Axial flight deck – launching layout
1(b) Axial flight deck – landing layout

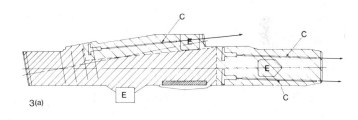

2

2 Angled deck – combined take-off and landing on 'flex-deck' system

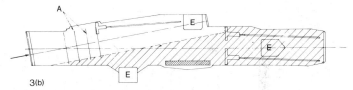

3(a)

3(b)

3(a) Angled deck – 'Alfa' mass strike, take-off layout
3(b) Angled deck – 'Alfa' mass strike, landing layout

KEY
A Arresting gear
B Crash barriers
C Catapults
E Aircraft elevators

  TAKE-OFF AREA

  AIRCRAFT PARKING AREA OR 'SPOT'

  LANDING AREA

the carrier might have stowage space for as many as ninety jet fighters, they would not represent anything like a realistic air group.

These limits can be traced directly to the fact that the axial-deck carrier could not land aircraft at the same time that it launched them. Its deck was generally divided into zones, with arresting gear aft and a crash barrier dividing the recovery area from a parking area. The catapult launch rate was too slow to permit aircraft to be launched directly from recovery, and in any case they could not be serviced nearly rapidly enough. In addition, there was always the danger that a landing airplane might bounce over the arresting gear wires, somehow miss the barrier, and hit the parked aircraft, which might best be described as a gasoline explosion waiting to occur.

The angled deck solved both problems. It was first pro-posed at a meeting at the Royal Aircraft Establishment at

US Navy practice was always to move landing aircraft into a deck park near the bows, then 'respot' them aft for another take-off. Here a Martin T4M-1 approaches *Saratoga*. The airplane shows two forms of arresting gear: the usual hook, trailing behind, and straight attachments to her main wheel axles which were originally intended to carry hooks to engage wires running lengthwise along the flight deck. They were soon abandoned. The legend '2-T-15' indicates the third aircraft of the fifth section of Torpedo Squadron Two (VT-2). When this photograph was taken, in 1932, the heavy torpedo-bombers seemed almost obsolete beside the new scout (dive) bombers; only *Saratoga* retained them.

Bedford on the problems of operating undercarriageless aircraft and the compatibility of heavy (30,000lb) aircraft with the 800ft flight decks of the new *Ark Royal* and *Eagle*, 9 August 1951. The meeting was chaired by Captain Dennis R F Cambell, then Assistant Chief Naval Representative to the Ministry of Aviation, who later became first captain of the *Ark Royal*, the first British carrier to have an angled deck. The deck itself was first tested aboard the light carrier *Triumph*, which had a 10° angled landing path painted on her flight deck. Touch-and-go landings were made aboard her and also aboard the USS *Midway*; in both cases arresting gear and barriers were oriented to the original axial deck. However, between September and December 1952 the *Essex* class carrier *Antietam* was modified with a true angled deck incorporating arresting gear, and the *Ark Royal* was modified while under construction. The angled deck was also applied to the new *Forrestal*, one of its advantages being the restoration of a conventional island superstructure in place of the retractable type required by the original flush deck design.

Ironically, both the *Forrestal* and her design predecessors, the abortive *United States* and the US fleet carrier of 1945, incorporated a type of angled deck in their designs. However, where the British angled deck was intended to separate the landing zone from the launch zone of the flight deck, the earlier US concept was no more than a means for catapulting more than two aircraft simultaneously. The two bow catapults were supplemented by waist catapults sponsored out to port and starboard; aircraft still

A carrier is the least automated of warships, and her efficiency depends very largely on the skill of her flight deck crew. Here deck crewmen manhandle a newly landed Hellcat into the forward deck park of an *Essex* class fleet carrier during Japanese attacks on Task Force 38.3, 24 October 1944. The pilot has not yet climbed from his cockpit. He was probably among the last of the air group to land, since some of the aircraft of the deck park are already being prepared for movement aft to take-off positions (note the jeeps at the tails of the Avengers in the background). The Avengers show the unique Grumman 'Sto-Wing' first devised to fit Wildcats into the constricted spaces of Royal Navy carrier hangars. The pivoted design permitted wing-folding without any structural break in the main wing spar; it remains in use in the massive E-2 Hawkeye. *USN by courtesy of Norman Polmar*

landed along the centerline of the ship, and safety barriers were still required to separate them from parking and launch areas forward along the centerline. Indeed, as modified, *Forrestal* (and all later US carriers) included waist catapults in their angled-deck sponsons, the operation of which would interfere with landing operations.

In the British angled deck, the landing area was physically separated from the launch area by being angled away from it. The triangular 'dead space' thus formed was an ideal parking and servicing area, into which landing aircraft could be fed and out of which aircraft could move on to the catapults. With the connection between turn-around

time for an individual airplane and air group size broken, a carrier might operate in a variety of modes, including a continuous stream attack. For example, typical current US practice is either a massive strike for maximum impact ('Alfa' strike) or a continuous cycle of small groups of aircraft (the 'Flex-Deck' concept). These two extremes trade off carrier and aircraft vulnerability. The 'Alfa' strike limits aircraft losses over a defended target, but takes considerable time to prepare, during which time the flight deck is crowded with aircraft and weapons, all of them presenting a fire and explosion danger. On the other hand, the small sections represent little explosion or fire damage, but are relatively vulnerable as they stream over a target area at, perhaps, 5- or 10-minute intervals, two or three airplanes at a time. A carrier operating at maximum pressure, 24 hours a day, might launch one 'Alfa' strike every eight hours. On the other hand, there is a natural deck cycle keyed to aircraft endurance, perhaps 1.5 or 1.75 hours. If the carrier must turn into the wind for aircraft operations, the continuous stream is cut down to such intervals. One problem aboard a carrier operating both short-legged jets and long-endurance aircraft (such as ASW S-3s and AEW Hawkeyes) is that the latter must generally operate at intervals of the standard deck cycle, even though their endurance does not match such a figure.

Through the 1950s the Royal Navy developed the angled deck by increasing its angle to the keel, thus increasing the parking area which determined how many aircraft could be operated simultaneously. A steeply (8.5°) angled deck carried structural and topweight implications, and it could not be applied to small carriers such as the wartime light fleets; the latter, if they were modified at all, received 'interim' (5.5°) decks, which amounted to little more than moving arresting gear wires and painting a new approach path on deck. Operating experience suggested a flaw in the angled deck concept: a pilot approaching a carrier first sees her wake, ie the line of her keel. If her deck is sharply angled, he must then make a rather sharp turn just as he descends. The abortive CVA-01 design therefore incorporated a new deck configuration, a landing deck very nearly parallel to the launching deck, leaving a much enlarged

The *Essex* reconstruction program ultimately combined the three elements of jet carrier equipment: the angled deck, the mirror (or lens) landing aid, and the steam catapult. This is *Shangri La* in June 1955, newly completed to SCB-27C configuration. Her six arresting pendants and her nylon crash barrier are clearly visible, as are the after elevator (folded) relocated from the centerline to the starboard side to clear the landing area aft. Another deck edge elevator is visible at the fore end of the angled deck. It would appear that no mirror aid had as yet been fitted, as an LSO platform can be seen abaft the arresting gear wires. Note, too, the gun battery, still quite heavy at this time, with twin 3in/50s right aft and mounted on the two 5in/38 sponsons and abeam the bridge, A SPN-8 CCA radar is mounted at the after edge of the island, but there was as yet no dedicated search ('marshalling') radar for blind landing. *The Floating Drydock*

parking area abaft the catapults and alongside the landing area. One advantage of this arrangement was that the front end of the recovery area could be moved forward on the hull, so that *total* flight deck length might be reduced without loss of operating capability, an important point on a hull limited by political fiat. Even so, parking area would so sharply increase that all operational aircraft might remain on the flight deck. Another feature of the design was a very substantial 'Alaskan Highway', a ramp outboard of the island along which aircraft might be moved to the catapults forward. There were, to be sure, disadvantages of the new arrangement. For example, it required an even larger overhang, and thus even more unbalanced weight far out to port, than a conventional angled deck.

As for the endurance issue, that too was subject to considerable postwar development by the aircraft designers. Piston aircraft can achieve long endurance because their engines are most efficient over the wide range between 60 and 80 per cent of full power; variable-pitch propellers greatly improve things. Jets are another matter. A jet engine is a gas turbine, efficient only over a very narrow range of power. Gas turbine-powered ships have the same problem; generally they attain useful cruising efficiency by using several engines for maximum power, shutting down all but a few to cruise at the maximum power of the cruising engines. The British Gannet was analogous. It used two turboprop engines, but geared both to a common propeller shaft in order to avoid asymmetric thrust when one was shut down for cruising. Although it was not designed to achieve great endurance this way, the US Banshee (F2H) fighter built a good reputation for long endurance on CAP station because in practice its pilot could generally shut down one engine and cruise on the other.

THE FLIGHT REGIME

Modern naval jet engines have two basic modes of operation: normal thrust and maximum thrust with an afterburner cut in. In the most sophisticated installations there may be several gradations of afterburner firing, for alternative levels of boost. The basic engine provides power for subsonic flight, and the afterburner blasts the fighter through the speed of sound. Generally it is fired only for short periods, although the engine may be rated for extended use. For example, the J79-GE-8 of an F-4B Phantom II is rated at 10,300lb of static thrust at sea level; its military rating is 10,900. With the afterburner cut in, it produces 17,000lb of thrust, and it is intended to be used for no more than half an hour below 35,000ft or two hours above. In its 'clean' configuration, carrying four semi-recessed Sparrows, the Phantom can fly at 597kts at 25,000ft; its average cruising speed is 505kts and its combat radius 410nm. With the afterburner cut in, however, the Phantom fights at 1290kts at 40,000ft. However, the 410nm radius is based on a flight including only five minutes (out of a total mission time of about 103 minutes) at maximum speed, plus a few seconds to climb to combat ceiling.

In effect, then, the Phantom operates in two very different flight regimes, but only rarely in between. As in the case of a propeller plane, it requires some degree of variable geometry, in its case in the air intakes. The engine itself does not vary in flight. The next step may be to vary the geometry of the engine itself, for example by means of variable-incidence compressor blades, to achieve some range of efficient operation. A current program for a 'variable-cycle engine' (Pratt and Whitney) has this goal. From the shipboard point of view, the price would be increased complexity and therefore an increased maintenance load, where the load is already almost unbearable. On the other hand, a true variable-cycle engine might be employed by a sufficient variety of naval aircraft actually to reduce the maintenance cycle through a reduction in types of engines.

For now there are only compromises. The F-14 was designed to achieve a very long loiter, ie good subsonic fuel economy, and yet to dogfight to near-sonic and supersonic speeds. It employs a turbofan, the TF-30, originally developed for the F-111 and used (without afterburner) in the A-7 Corsair II, combined with a complex, five-zone afterburner. Even full power is considered somewhat insufficient, and in fact the F-14 program began with the intention of developing a new engine, tentatively designated F401, for refit into what would become the F-14B. At military power, it would provide power equal to that of the TF-30 with Zone 3–4 afterburners lit, at about a quarter of the fuel consumption, due to its turbofan design. However, cost escalation in the F-14 program ended F401 development, and it is not clear whether the full potential of the F-14 airframe will be realized. In that case the low-speed loiter represented by the basic turbofan will remain as perhaps its most important capability. To some extent, too, the Navy decision to operate F-18s optimized for air combat alongside its F-14s suggests a two-airplane solution to the problem of two operating regimes.

TAKE-OFF ROLL

Carrier aircraft operate in a regime very different from that of their land-based relatives. By a combination of her motion through the water and the prevailing wind at sea, the carrier produces a constant wind-over-deck (WOD), which adds to the wind generated by the motion of an airplane along the deck, either self-propelled or catapulted. Indeed, early aircraft required almost no deck run at all; Grand Fleet light cruisers, for example, were fitted with 14ft runways for fighters, for use with a 34kt WOD. It was necessary only to provide a clear deck height beyond the end of this runway to permit the airplane to dip slightly. The heavy monoplanes of the late 1930s and World War II required far more. For example, in 1937 the Imperial Japanese Navy demanded that its new fighter, which became the Zero (A6M), take off in 70m (about 230ft), with a 27kt WOD. At the outbreak of war the British standard was 300ft in a 20kt wind, which was a severe problem for the aircraft designer. By 1942 it had risen to 350ft, but even that was far from enough. In particular the Royal Navy had to accept high-performance RAF types with relatively poor low-speed characteristics. In December a special Joint Committee on Aviation Arrangements in HM Ships proposed a new standard of 500ft with a 30kt WOD; the speed was later cut to 27kts on the theory that even a carrier rated at 30kts might take some considerable time to work up to full speed. The US Navy, on the other hand, was able to buy specialized aircraft. In 1944 it asked for a deck roll of 200-250ft (WOD 25kts) for new fighters such as the Grumman Bearcat (F8F). This level of WOD was easily attainable by a 32kt fleet carrier, and even by an 18kt escort, given a light wind.

All of these figures had considerable consequences. Take-off roll set, first, the absolute minimum of flight deck length an airplane might tolerate. For example, at 18kts most US escort carriers could barely launch an FM-2 Wildcat, an airplane retained in production specifically for their use, after a full-deck run. However, effective carrier operations required multiple launches, and that in turn required aircraft warming up on deck. Rolling take-offs were preferred over catapult launches because they were much faster. However, they required the first airplane to be positioned far aft – and further aft as the war progressed and aircraft operational weights grew. For example, the original Hellcat design, the F6F-1, was to have had a gross weight of 10,512lb and a take-off roll of 283ft (WOD 25kts); in 1945 an F6F-5 with a drop tank (and a different engine) took off at 13,797lb and required 384ft of deck. Every few feet of deck cost several aircraft. Thus, when the Royal Navy decided on a standard of 500ft of deck-roll rather than the previous 350, that implied a great loss of striking power. For example, in *Implacable* only 17 aircraft (40ft long and 50ft in span) could be accommodated on deck, although matters could be simplified somewhat if only the first six aircraft on deck were spread, and the others folded to a width of 27ft, for a total of 19. On this basis the loss of 150ft would be equal to at least three aircraft. The US Navy tended to fold most of its aircraft on deck to achieve much tighter spots, and it considered any loss in effective deck space far more serious. A US commander writing in 1944 estimated that every foot of deck was equivalent to 1/1200 of an airplane; presumably he meant every square foot: 'It has always been our operating procedure in the US Navy to pack the deck full. The clearances are small. In our initial arrangement of airplanes to spot very frequently the criterion of clearance is just the span of a hand. There are many features which affect the number of planes you can get aboard in a given length of deck; the span of the aircraft folded, the wheel tread which is of importance when you put one wheel next to the outboard waterway of the deck and allow the wing to overhang. Another aspect of importance is whether you place the tail under the stub

THE CARRIER AND HER AIRCRAFT 97

wing. Very frequently you can increase the deck capacity
by having the tail of one aircraft underneath or behind the
wing tip of the other two behind it. There must always be
clearance in the spot for the rotation of the propeller . . .
Very frequently the most outboard part of the airplane in
the folded design is the folded tip of the propeller which is
bad, so realizing the deck capacity is of the greatest importance and the fact that normally the fighters are stacked
forward on the deck and take-off run is most important
from the capacity standpoint . . .'

One factor in the difference of views in the two navies
may have been the use of power wing folding in US naval
fighters, so that the airplane might remain folded until the
point of launch. On the other hand, British fighters such as
the Seafire, derived from high-performance, thin-winged
RAF interceptors, could not afford such an addition of
weight or of wing volume. The need for manual unfolding
in turn made for a much looser and hence less capacious
deck park, and one which did not take full advantage of the
folded dimensions of British aircraft. Nor does it appear
that the Royal Navy was quite as willing as its US counterpart to edge aircraft close to the side of the deck.

CATAPULTS

Almost from the first, there was an alternative to the
normal rolling take-off: a catapult, which the Royal Navy
called an accelerator. The US Navy fitted catapults to its
two big carriers, *Lexington* and *Saratoga*, primarily to
launch floatplanes. Although the catapult was cumber-

Most carrier aircraft wings fold upwards, as in this Demon starting up on
the catapult of USS *Coral Sea*, March 1961. The catapult bridle is just
being attached, and the towing hook disconnected; the deck towing-
tractor sits under the fighter's wing. Shoes under the wing proclaim this
to be a Sparrow-carrying missile fighter (F3H-2M).

some and slow to operate, it was considered preferable to
the alternative, a wheeled trolley supporting the float. The
Ranger received no catapult, but consideration was given
to a hangar-deck type which would permit her to launch
simultaneously from flight and hangar decks, and thus
increase the size of a strike group. Flight and hangar-deck
catapults actually were installed in the next three classes
(*Yorktown*, *Wasp* and *Essex*). All of these units were
intended to launch wheeled aircraft. Instead of a car,
which would have been adaptable to the contours of a float,
they used a simple wire bridle to pull along an airplane by
attachment points in its wheel wells. Catapults were not
particularly popular in the prewar US Navy; for example
in the entire 1940 Fiscal Year USS *Enterprise* used hers
only 55 times, while in FY41 this figure fell to 21. The
cross-deck catapult on the hangar deck was unique to
American practice; it permitted the carrier to launch even
with her bow crowded with aircraft or, presumably, even
as she recovered her air group. Perhaps the chief value of
the catapult, on either deck, was that it permitted an
aircraft to be launched with zero WOD, perhaps even with
some negative WOD, so that a carrier would not have to
turn into the wind for only a few airplanes. However, the
power of the cross-deck unit was limited by available

This VF-211 F-8J Crusader shows the variable-incidence wing which gave the airplane a combination of excellent supersonic and low-speed (landing and take-off) performance. The catapult bridle is visible just abaft the nosewheel, and the crewman is giving the 'thumbs-up' for launch (USS *Hancock* in the South China Sea, May 1972). In a sense, this photograph is symbolic of the limits the carrier imposes on her aircraft: *Essex* class carriers such as the *Hancock* could not operate the heavier Phantom; the Crusader had to be re-manufactured to maintain them in service. Thus the F-8J was a re-manufactured F-8E (F8U-2NE); the F-8E in turn was the first Crusader to incorporate substantial all-weather capability, with its APQ-94 search and fire control radar, and a separate infrared seeker, visible above the radome. There were two underwing hard points, and a hump on the wing center section enclosed electronics for Bullpup air-to-surface missiles. Remanufacture generally added boundary layer control (for low-speed performance) and strengthened landing gear.

beam: the aircraft limited the acceleration it could impose, so that it was generally emloyed, in the prewar carriers, only to launch light observation planes of perhaps 5000lb, such as the Vought O3U Corsair.

The Royal Navy followed a rather different path. It saw accelerators as a means of launching floatplanes, and for this purpose developed an elaborate cradle with four attachment points. Although HMS *Courageous* and *Glorious* had their flight decks stiffened for catapults as early as 1929, no such units were installed until 1935–36. In wartime they and their successors in all later British classes proved extremely useful for quite another purpose: flying off defensive fighters even when the carrier was not heading into the wind. British operating practice was to keep the carrier within the screen. In order to avoid altering the course of the entire formation when only a few aircraft were being launched (eg, to attack a shadower), they employed their catapults, which a contemporary US observer described as designed to permit launch at full load, and at a maximum angle to the wind. On the other hand, rigging that catapult (then designated ATOG, Assisted Take-Off Gear) normally required about half an hour, 'during which the use of the flight deck for take off would be somewhat hazardous'. This justification changed in wartime: in December 1942 the Admiralty's Joint Committee reported that often during the six or seven minutes it took a carrier to turn into the wind fighters could be catapulted off and in this period could climb to 20,000ft. By this time the Royal Navy had dispensed with its complex catapult car and had adopted the US-type bridle, so that the sacrifice in time due to a catapult launching was only about 10 seconds per

launching, compared to an average of 20 seconds for a free take-off.

In the US Navy, the catapult first became popular aboard short-deck escort carriers. Without it, they were effectively limited to low-performance observation types such as the OS2U Kingfisher, and to lightweight fighters such as the Wildcat. Even with a completely empty deck, an escort carrier at 18kts might barely launch an Avenger without a torpedo, and with only two-thirds of its fuel. However, with a catapult the same airplane could be launched with its torpedo and with full tanks; moreover, the flight deck could be filled with other aircraft. In larger carriers aircraft weights (and therefore take-off runs) rose, as did the number of aircraft, which in turn reduced deck length available for rolling take-offs. By late in the war, some carriers were making 40 per cent of their launches by catapult, clearing the deck until enough length remained for the faster rolling take-offs. In 1945, the Bureau of Aeronautics could list among the virtues of the catapult its independence of WOD, which it considered important in cases of battle damage. At night, the catapult could be used without deck lights, which otherwise would be necessary to prevent swerving on a narrow deck. As in the Royal Navy, catapults permitted cross-wind take-offs. At Samar, for example, they were credited with saving the escort carriers, which otherwise would have had to turn *towards* the enemy to launch. After the Gilberts invasion, it was estimated that two days of fuel had been saved by catapulting search planes during the run from Hawaii. Finally, catapults ensured that the carrier would be able to launch even after flight deck damage. For example, a deck holed forward would be inoperable unless the carrier backed down to launch.

The effect of the catapult on deck spots was quite impressive. For example, an *Essex* could spot 47 Avengers on her flight deck, allowing 450ft take-offs at a WOD of 30kts. A reduction to 25 would cost 25 aircraft, to allow another 150ft of deck. However, an Avenger could be catapulted off even at 3kts.

Catapults also made possible the delivery of land-based fighters by escort carriers; similar deliveries kept the fast carrier task force (Task Force 38/58) at sea by providing a steady stream of replacement aircraft. The first such delivery occurred during the North African invasion, when paratroopers captured an airfield, and the technique was particularly common in the Pacific. Thus by the end of the war all Mustangs and Thunderbolts assigned to the Pacific received their (removable) catapult fittings on the assembly line. The United States continued to use escort carriers for aircraft delivery postwar, and indeed continued to experiment with catapult fittings for land jet fighters. However, by the early 1950s even light fighters required such powerful catapults that existing transport carriers had to be reduced to carrying their aircraft cocooned on deck, and all had their catapults removed in 1952.

Of the three major carrier navies of World War II, Japan alone never installed catapults in carriers. The Japanese Navy was well aware of the need for some form of assisted take-offs, given the increased wing loading of its aircraft, particularly the bombers and torpedo-bombers. Work thus began on a flight deck catapult, apparently similar to the British type in its use of a heavy carriage. Problems included the lack of rigidity of the flight decks (which, as in US practice, were not strength decks and thus incorporated expansion joints) and the great weight of the catapult itself, about 30 tons. However, the design of the armored carrier *Taiho* showed two flight deck catapults, and installations were planned for other ships. The project was dropped in favor of rocket-assisted take-off, generally using two 1540lb thrust powder rockets firing for 3 seconds, attached to the sides of an airplane's fuselage. The Royal Navy also used rockets to launch aircraft from many of its carriers, including fleet units equipped with catapults. They were particularly useful postwar, when the Navy wished to test jet fighters whose take-off requirements were beyond the capacity of existing hydraulic catapults. American use of this system appears to have been less common, though by no means unknown. For example, Neptunes from from *Midway* class attack carriers in postwar tests required rocket-assisted take-offs.

Thus in 1945 catapults were a necessity for small carriers, but a convenience for the larger ones. However, the new jets combined relatively low take-off thrust with high-speed design, which made for unacceptable deck runs. For example, the first US naval jet fighter, the McDonnell Phantom (FH-1) was barely carrier-compatible, with a rated take-off run of 785ft at 25kts WOD. In its successor, the F2H-1 Banshee, this rose to 815ft, still barely acceptable. On the other hand, the F2H-2 required 1300ft with tip tanks (865ft without, but that would reduce combat radius from 715 to 455nm). The next Banshee, the F2H-3, passed entirely beyond the deck launch range: 1944ft 'clean', 3848ft with tip tanks. Even the most favorable of these figures were unpleasant. Moreover, a jet warming up immediately in front of other airplanes would tend to knock them over with its jet blast. If jets were launched only from catapults, special jet blast deflectors could be raised behind the limited number of catapult starting positions. Such a procedure was simplified by the fact that, unlike piston powerplants, jet engines could be started and run up to full power very rapidly.

After 1945 the combination of aircraft weight growth and design optimized for very high speed flight began to outstrip the capacity of existing catapults at realistic levels of WOD. There were two different kinds of limit on future catapults. First, deck design limited total catapult length. In British armored deck carriers, the catapult had to be mounted forward of the armored section, which could not be slotted to receive it. In US practice, the flight deck was not a strength deck, and therefore was broken by expansion joints: catapults could not extend across them. In turn, the acceleration a catapult might apply was limited by a combination of the strengths of the airplane

and the pilot's body. Typically, the pilot might withstand about five times the acceleration of gravity (5g). Wartime aircraft could accept something over 3g; for example, the US Navy's standard was 3.375. More recently, 4g has sometimes been accepted; combat jets can withstand far more, given the violence of their maneuvers at high speed. On this basis a catapult smoothly accelerating at 4g reaches 100kts in a length of about 111ft. However, acceleration in general is not perfectly smooth, and the ratio of maximum to minimum acceleration may be as great as 1.4:1 in a modern steam catapult. Then the effective average acceleration might be closer to 3g, and the length for 100kts as great as 140ft. Even these figures can be attained only if the catapult is provided with sufficient energy, and with the appropriate mechanism with which to release it.

THE STEAM CATAPULT

This issue of mechanism provides the second set of limits. The earliest US carrier catapult was a flywheel type designed by Carl Norden, later of bombsight fame. It could not store much energy, and the US and British catapults of World War II employed instead a hydraulic system. Press-

The British-developed steam catapult was the key to carrier jet operation, as it provided sufficient power to launch the postwar generation of heavy aircraft. In this 1951 photo the experimental steam catapult dwarfs the light carrier HMS *Perseus*, which had originally been completed as an aircraft maintenance ship. Aircraft on deck are two Sea Hornets, a Sturgeon, a Sea Fury fighter and an Avenger, with a Firefly just abaft the island. The BXS-1 catapult is mounted atop a built-up section of deck, and trials in British waters began in August 1950. It underwent tests in the United States in December 1951 through about February 1952, and was standardized for US service as the C-11; at the same time the larger C-7, which had been designed as an explosive catapult, was redesigned for steam operation. *MoD(N)*

An F-4J of VF-31, USS *Saratoga*, is prepared for steam catapult launch in the Mediterranean, aboard the carrier *Nimitz*, August 1975. The catapult watch booth is visible in the foreground, as are the wire bridle which actually pulls the airplane forward and the jet blast deflector. Steam is already rising from the catapult slot.

ure was built up in an accumulator; it drove a piston over a relatively short distance. A system of wires and sheaves magnified this motion and transmitted it to the catapult shuttle proper. More power required, at first, no more than a larger piston and accumulator. However, the wires and sheaves also had their limits, which the US Navy reached in the H-8 catapult of rebuilt *Essex* class carriers (SCB-27A). The H-8 project actually predated the heavy attack projects of 1945, and the Bureau of Aeronautics had to look elsewhere for catapults for the new heavy carriers it was designing from 1946 on.

The Bureau sought a direct-acting device, a catapult without wires and sheaves and thus without either the losses they imposed or the structural weaknesses they represented. At first it appeared that the ideal would be a simple powder catapult, a long slotted tube with an explosive charge at one end. Development did prove less than simple, and merely storing the special cartridges (not to mention bringing them to the catapult breech) presented considerable problems. Commander Colin C Mitchell, Technical Director of Brown Brothers & Co Ltd of Edinburgh, solved the problem by devising a steam catapult; trials aboard the British maintenance carrier *Perseus* began in August 1950, and the ship sailed for the United States in December 1951. All modern Western steam catapults are descended from Mitchell's BXS-1, which was built under license in the United States as the C-11.

The steam catapult consists of a pair of slotted cylinders below the flight deck, each with a piston. The pistons are joined by a connector, attached in turn to the car which pulls the airplane. The great issue in the design is sealing the slots to prevent the high-pressure steam from escaping, while at the same time permitting the car to move freely. Mitchell's innovation was a flexible metal strip extending the length of the cylinder and held under tension. Fittings fore and aft of the piston pull it out of the slot to allow the piston to pass, then stuff it back in; in a sense it acts like a zipper. The entire system is quite simple and also quite amenable to enlargement. In the United States its only significant challenger was an internal combustion type proposed for the nuclear carrier *Enterprise*, perhaps

on the theory that nuclear-generated steam had to be kept in the machinery area. In fact the ship received steam catapults. Probably the major complaint against the steam catapult is the drain it imposes on boiler steam: with any sustained rate of catapulting there is associated a reduction in ship speed.

The steam catapult is so firmly associated with carriers that when Admiral Zumwalt set out the specifications of the gas turbine-powered Sea Control Ship he provided no catapult. Similarly, it is often said that a gas turbine ship such as HMS *Invincible* is inherently unsuited to catapult operation. However, hydraulic catapults were quite successfully installed aboard diesel-powered escort carriers during World War II. The internal combustion type was considered inferior to the steam catapult, but it was certainly a workable proposition. Finally, there is JATO, jet (rocket) assisted take-off, in effect an accelerator associated with the airplane rather than with the structure of the ship. The rockets do require special handling and stowage, but they also provide many of the advantages of a catapult with far less impact on the design of the ship.

ARRESTING GEAR
Arresting gear is the opposite of the catapult: it absorbs roughly as much energy as the catapult pumps into the airplane. Generally it consists of a series of wires ('pendants') stretched across the flight deck, one of which the landing airplane engages with its tail hook. As the wire stretches, an arresting 'engine' absorbs energy – for example, it may pump hydraulic fluid out of a cylinder. Earlier systems employed friction brakes or even weights. Typical installations on angled-deck carriers comprise three wires and a barricade, which stops aircraft missing the wires or unable to lower their hooks. A landing jet may stretch the wire it engages as much as 350ft, and this distance plus the usual distance from the after end of the flight deck to the point of touchdown (perhaps 180ft) largely determine the length of the angled deck. Provision must also be made for wire spacing, about 40ft, and for barricade stretch and aircraft turn-around after stopping, perhaps 95ft. Generally the airplane touches down between the first and second wires, and engages the second. Thus the total recovery length for a modern US carrier landing-on aicraft at a WOD of at least 20kts might be as great as 670ft. As in the case of a catapult, the arresting gear stretch-out is determined in part by the level of deceleration the airplane and

US carrier design is nowadays predicated on very intense operations, in which the ability to launch several aircraft simultaneously is essential. Here the nuclear carrier *Nimitz* launches a Vigilante from her waist catapult while one of the two bow catapults still steams from the previous launch and an Intruder prepares to take off from the other bow catapult. A Corsair II is being moved into position for launch on the port catapult. The enormous length of the bow catapults is evident both from the length of the steaming slot and from the position of the jet blast deflector behind the A-6. Although both bow catapults and one of the waist catapults can be used almost simultaneously, the two waist catapults cannot; they are designed so that an aircraft can warm up on one while the other operates. Here an F-4 is visible on the second waist catapult, its jet blast deflector already in place for take-off. By this time carrier self-defensive armament had been reduced to a few Sea Sparrow launchers, such as the one visible at the break of the starboard sponson. The primary protection for a ship such as the *Nimitz* is a combination of her fighters and missile escorts such as the nuclear cruiser *California*, steaming in the background. Both were part of TF-60, in the Mediterranean, September 1976.

A steam catapult often requires no wind-over-deck to launch aircraft: this VF-151 Demon is flying from USS *Coral Sea* moored at Yokosuka, 13 March 1962.

Early naval aircraft required little special gear for carrier operations. Arresting gear was designed primarily to hold the landing airplane down to the deck, so that it would not tip over the side. This Douglas DT torpedo-bomber, taking off from the experimental carrier *Langley* (March 1924) shows the earliest such gear in US service, a series of hooks suspended from the landing gear axles to engage fore-and-aft wires. The bar under the engine protected against nose-overs; it was soon abandoned. Note the split undercarriage, designed to accommodate a torpedo. Four similar DTs of the Army Air Corps made the first around-the-world flight in 1924; they were designated DWC, for Douglas World Cruiser. *USN by courtesy of Larry Sowinski*

Quite soon it became evident that the only important function of arresting gear was to stop an airplane within a short distance. The Royal Navy, using the whole length of its flight decks for landing, considered this unnecessary, although upward slopes were incorporated into British flight decks to aid in braking. The US Navy, on the other hand, used a combination of arresting wires and barriers to divide its flight decks into landing and parking zones. Here a Grumman FF-1 lands aboard USS *Lexington*, February 1933. The wire has just been engaged, the airplane is stopping, and deck crewmen rush forward to disengage the hook so that the airplane can taxi into the deck park in preparation for the next landing. Further wires are visible in the background.

its pilot can tolerate; the rate of energy absorption by the arresting engines also enters. It seems noteworthy that acceleration by catapult requires substantially less length, perhaps about 200ft or less, so that the catapult operates at a higher level of acceleration.

One of the great advantages of the angled deck is that a pilot making a very bad approach can apply power and fly around for a fresh approach without endangering the aircraft parked forward. It follows that in an axial carrier design the consequences of bouncing over the wires were far more serious, and this is reflected in the complexity of earlier arresting gear installations. For example, as rebuilt for SCB-27A, an *Essex* class carrier had no fewer than thirteen pendants, before which were a series of barriers, different ones for propeller and jet aircraft. This array compared with the original *Essex* design, which incorporated only eleven principal pendants and consumed a somewhat shorter length of deck.

The value of such gear is obvious enough for jets landing at 100kts or more, but early naval aircraft landed at speeds little above the net WOD. On the other hand, they had no brakes, and they had to be kept steady as they slowed. Thus the earliest British and US schemes included both lengthwise and athwartships wires, the former to steady the airplane and also to slow it gradually by pressing down on special axle hooks. In some cases a landing airplane knocked over blocks or cross-deck panels to lose speed and energy. At first airplanes were far too fragile to hook a

single wire to stop. However, by 1929 the US Navy had adopted much the modern system, with athwartships wires only. It had also evolved its standard operating procedure, in which the barrier protected the deck park forward. Aircraft landing procedure was also affected, and that in turn influenced the design of the aircraft, particularly their ruggedness.

One pecularity of American practice was that arresting wires were provided forward as well as aft, and indeed the arresting gear was designed by two-way operation, over bow or stern. The original concept was that aircraft might be landed-on forward without disturbing the deck park further aft, but it was also noted that in a very high wind the carrier might steam into the wind so as deliberately to reduce the WOD; in that case aircraft would be landing over the bow wires. Under some circumstances the carrier might be unable to steam into the wind for fear of encountering enemy warships, or perhaps part of the after flight deck might be destroyed by enemy action; here, too, she might have to land aircraft forward. Ultimately it was demanded that the carrier be able to land-on aircraft over her bow while steaming astern, and in the *Essex* class a sustained speed astern of 20kts was called for. Indeed, these carriers were almost fitted with turbo-electric machinery for just this reason. The complication of forward wires was not dropped until the design of the *Midway* class in 1942, and the wires themselves were not removed until 1944, by which time the Royal Navy, too, had adopted them, although perhaps without the two-way feature.

Arresting gear design set requirements on the aerodynamics of the flight deck itself, for example on the extent to which landing aircraft could tolerate the eddies set up by the end of the deck and by the island structure. Thus a wartime Admiralty report on deck airflow remarked that 'in general the Americans seem to have done very little work in an attempt to get good airflow over their carriers and seem to regard a carrier as a suitable hull with as large as possible a rectangular platform on top and with an island designed from every point of view but that of aerodynamics. But, and this is the major difference, their carrier planes are so designed as to use a different landing technique from ours; the planes come in at a speed well above the stalling speed and at a steeper angle than ours do normally, and literally fly into the deck. Owing to the design of their undercarriages, which are very strong with a long travel and good energy absorption, their planes can do this without either bouncing or breaking their undercarriages as ours would. Representative figures are about 75 per cent energy absorption in the oleo, 25 per cent in the tyre, for the Martlet, whereas they are 20 per cent in the oleo, 80 per cent in the tyre for the Seafire. Thus, in a Seafire, 80 per cent of the impact energy is available for the rebound. As a result, they can land nearer the stern than most of our planes owing to their higher angle of approach, and due to their greater margin of speed above the stall they can land satisfactorily after passing through greater wake disturbance than would be possible with an aircraft flying just above the stalling speed . . .' In other words, the US Navy designed its aircraft to land aboard carriers whose designers had been able largely to disregard issues of airflow over their decks. At about the same time, US officers described their landing technique as 'we come in hanging on the prop, with the power set for level unaccelerated flight, as near to the stall as we can get it. In that condition the engine is warm, and it will accept a burst of power if you get into difficulties . . . We can accept higher and higher landing speeds, providing we have adequate control aft and near the stall . . . That factor is the equivalent of about 10 miles an hour if the pilot knows he has to land, and he can control his stall . . .'

All of this was consistent with the US drive to achieve maximum aircraft operating rates by restricting the zone of flight deck in which an airplane would land, so that landed aircraft could be safely parked forward, for respotting aft and turn-around for a new sortie. The forward park did not have to be quite as capacious as the aft park for launch, because no allowance for propellers turning was necessary, but its mere existence meant that arresting gear was indispensable, even if the airplane could normally be expected to land within a fraction of the flight deck.

British prewar experience was quite different. Arresting gear was invented not to divide up the flight deck into zones, but to permit an airplane without brakes to come to a stop somewhere on a relatively smooth deck; land airplanes generally benefited from the roughness of a grass field. Thus in 1931 a British naval pilot wrote that 'although there were occasions when wires prevented aircraft from going overboard they also in about 9 cases out of 10 turned a moderately good landing into a bad one.' By the late 1920s, then, the Royal Navy had completely abandoned arresting gear, trusting in good low-speed flying characteristics. For example, aircraft landing on HMS *Glorious* in the early 1930s were generally brought to a stop by their handling crews, only the single-seat Nimrods having brakes. The carrier's deck also sloped upward from the stern. Carrier operating practice, not only between the wars but also through the early part of World War II, was for each airplane to be struck below as soon as it landed; the flight deck was not cleared for another landing until this had been done. Thus the British developed much faster elevators than did the US Navy: in 1944, for example, the standard British cycle was said to be 12 seconds (for one hangar), compared to 45 for the US carriers.

There were, to be sure, tactical costs. For example, the captain of HMS *Courageous* remarked in 1931 that arresting gear might be justified 'if it reduced the very serious tactical restrictions at present imposed on aircraft carriers . . . Carriers are now very often required to steam 20 or 25kts on an arbitrary course into the wind for three-quarters of an hour or more when landing their squadrons in order to create a relative wind of 25 to 30kts over the deck. If arresting gear will reduce these figures by even 5kts, we have gained something very important . . .' US observers noted that the experimental gear installed in this ship was quite far forward, 'ie, it is installed solely for tactical reasons and not to increase the operating or stowage capacity of the vessel in the manner that an after location would . . . It is not intended to employ the gear at all times but only when tactical considerations dictate.' Trials with the new arresting gear were evidently successful, so that by about 1935 it was fitted aboard several carriers. It was favored, for example, because it permitted operations with a combined roll and pitch which previously would have been nearly impossible. Many believed it was useful largely because it permitted operations with higher-performance aircraft, ie with aircraft with higher landing speeds.

US naval observers believed that the revival of arresting gear in the Royal Navy was largely due to publicity concerning the *Lexington* and *Saratoga*. It appears, too, that the movie *Helldivers* had a considerable influence on British naval aviators. However, although in 1931 the British Director of Naval Construction had recognized in arresting gear the means of operating more aircraft from a single-hangar carrier (and thus, in a 60-airplane, 32kt carrier, save about 2200 tons in standard displacement on a total of about 21,000), his views were not widely known. In 1935 the US Naval Attaché could write that 'the value of arresting gear for increasing carrier capacity and

In the rigors of wartime flight deck operations, it was all too common for an approaching aircraft to miss the wires altogether. This returning Hellcat pilot overshot aboard the light carrier *Bataan* (18 January 1945), but lived. *By courtesy of Larry Sowinski*

operating speed is not a conception which exercises any governing force in Britain, if indeed it has been reached at all ... This is undoubtedly due to the fact that the most important carriers are the double-deck type which does not lend itself to these advantages, but on the contrary, provides a definite limit to speed of operation in the elevator speed. The statement has been made over and over again to the writer that although the arresting gear was probably a step in advance, no real value could be seen in it on ships which had a long enough flight deck to permit clear deck landings in safety.' Deck parks were impractical because the arresting gear was considered unreliable: the tail hooks of British aircraft were provided with a special latch, holding them up: 'Due to the hook rebound before a cross wire is engaged, so many airplanes miss the arresting gear entirely that operations with aircraft parked on deck ahead of the gear are considered out of the question.' The latch was not to eliminate the problem of hook retrieval by the deck crew, but rather to minimize tail rise after it was engaged by the wire. Indeed, the British wondered how the US Navy could operate with freely trailing tail hooks. One US writer suspected that the division of responsibility between Navy and RAF was the root of the problem: the Navy told the RAF how much space it could use to land and to take off in, but the RAF designed the airplanes, and space was an issue of negotiation between the two.

Thus what might seem at first blush a rather arcane issue – the design of arresting gear and tail hooks on naval aircraft – exerted a considerable influence on the ability of a carrier to operate her air group, both as to the numbers to be operated and to the operating tempo. Even after the Royal Navy accepted arresting gear, it continued to strike down each airplane as it landed, and consequently accepted considerable inefficiency, at least in US eyes. The barrier came later; in 1940, for example, US observers were still finding 'some concern [among] flight personnel who have not accustomed themselves to the thought of flying into an arresting gear with a protective barrier ahead of them.'

On the other hand, landing without arresting gear allowed for a considerable range of judgment by the pilot. British practice was generally to glide in with the engine throttled back. Wartime US observers were impressed by the casual British view of landing and noted that many unhooked landings had been made by pilots entirely without carrier experience. Thus the landing of a Hurricane on HMS *Furious* 'was considered far more of an exploit by an experienced US observer than by the British'. The key was probably the deck park, which converted the carrier landing problem from one of coming down onto a relatively short field to one of coming down precisely amid the wires; after all, the penalty for landing too far forward in a British carrier might be no more than a shorter run to the elevator for the ride down to the hangar, where in a US carrier it might be a flight deck crash and fire.

British deck practice came to approach that of the US Navy during World War II; in any case, as aircraft

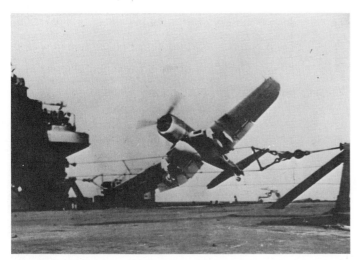

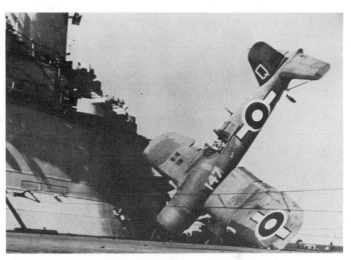

Although the arresting 'pendants' could generally be relied upon, the safety of the deck park demanded some positive barrier forward of them. Here a British Corsair, having bounced over the pendants, is finally stopped by the wire barrier stretched across the flight deck just abeam the island. Its markings are those adopted by the Fleet Air Arm in the Pacific in 1945–46, blue-and-white roundels surrounded by white and provided with white bars. This particular aircraft was flown by Lt P S Cole, Senior Pilot of 1830 Squadron aboard HMS *Illustrious*, 13 April 1945; he had just missed the first of the two barriers. *By courtesy of Richard L Ward*

The standard wire safety barrier was ill-suited to jet aircraft: instead of wrapping itself around a propeller, it would ride up over the smooth nose of a jet, perhaps decapitating its pilot. The British nylon safety net, shown here stopping an A-4 aboard USS *Oriskany* (20 November 1967), was the solution. This particular pilot, Lt J G Denny Earl, had just had both his legs shattered by North Vietnamese anti-aircraft fire, and could not have made a second pass at the arresting gear.

FLIGHT DECK FEATURES

KEY

1 Jet blast deflectors
2 Deck cooling panels
3 Catapult
4 Optical landing systems
5 Aircraft elevators
6 Bomb elevator
7 Barrier
8 Arresting wires
9 LSO platform
10 Torpedo elevator

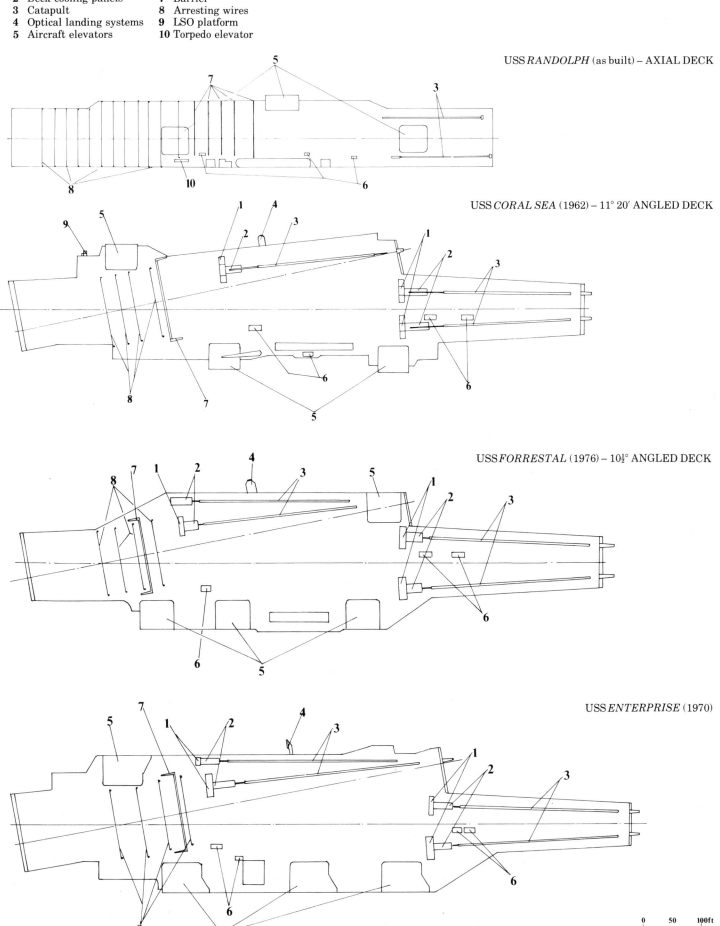

USS *RANDOLPH* (as built) – AXIAL DECK

USS *CORAL SEA* (1962) – 11° 20′ ANGLED DECK

USS *FORRESTAL* (1976) – 10½° ANGLED DECK

USS *ENTERPRISE* (1970)

0   50   100ft

performance advanced, the concept of a hookless landing became less and less tenable. Certainly no modern jet can land without its hook, and, indeed, without the use of massive arresting gear 'engines' which in themselves exact a considerable space and weight penalty on the carrier designer.

Japanese policy appears to have differed from that of the US and Royal Navies. Early arresting systems were not particularly satisfactory, as indicated, perhaps, by the upward slope worked into the flight decks of the first large Japanese carriers, *Akagi* and *Kaga*. However, the French developed a very efficient arresting gear for their *Béarn*, and sold it to Japan. Its adoption in turn made possible the use of a much smaller flight deck. By the late 1920s Japan was permitted to build only 27,000 tons of new carriers, given her existing fleet; the French gear, which employed transverse wires and a crash barrier, permitted the design of the *Ryuho*, which was originally to have displaced about 7000 tons. Despite the introduction of the crash barrier, her aircraft capacity was still determined by her hangar capacity, and when the Naval Staff asked that it be doubled, she had to be given an extra hangar; she was commissioned in 1934 at about 8000 tons, but proved top-heavy and ultimately came to about 10,000, as reconstructed twice to improve her seakeeping and her structural strength. All later Japanese carriers had arresting gear, but the persistence of double-hangar designs suggests that they were not intended to operate with deck parks.

DECK LANDING AIDS

The American style of carrier operations required a Landing Signal Officer (LSO) to tell the pilot whether he was properly lined up for landing and even when he had to cut his engine. The LSO became more and more essential as aircraft performance increased and the margin for pilot error shrank, particularly if the tempo of operations was to be kept up. On the other hand, the prewar Royal Navy considered the LSO a convenience, and required the pilot to make most of the relevant decisions. For example, even after LSOs had been well established, they did not signal the pilot to cut his engine: that was his decision, based on his perception that he had engaged the arresting gear, or that if he had not, he would be able to brake in time and therefore should not try another circuit. The Japanese Navy did not employ LSOs at all. This was another issue, only marginally relevant to the carrier designer (who had to provide a small platform for the LSO alongside the flight deck), but vital in determining the tempo and character of carrier flight operations.

As in so many other aspects of carrier operation, the advent of jet aircraft greatly complicated matters. The LSO no longer had time to judge the speed and altitude of an incoming airplane, just as his margins for error shrank considerably. At the same time the pilot could no longer respond nearly as easily; for example, a jet has a far slower throttle response than a piston engine. Nor, at a much higher approach speed, did the pilot have nearly as much time to watch the LSO. A British exchange officer at the US Naval Air Test Center, Commander H N C Goodhart, concluded that the pilot needed a mirror image of his own approach, so that he could make his own corrections as fast as possible. This became the mirror landing system, the basis of modern optical landing aids.

The jet lands at a constant sink rate, with full power on; that is, it flies down a straight line into the deck, and does not turn off its engine until it has been hooked. This simplifies the mirror problem and contrasts with the older type of landing: flat, with a last-second flare controlled by the LSO; in a jet, the flare (to stall out) would either bolt the airplane off the deck or else crash it. The mirror system,

then, had to indicate to the pilot whether he was following the appropriate glide path all the way in; it had to show him both his angle of glide (his angle to the deck) and whether he was following in the centerline of the deck.

A light near the end of the flight deck shines on a mirror up the deck, from which it is visible to the pilot. The resulting 'meatball' is the pilot's altitude signal. If he is on the glidepath, the meatball appears to be centered on the mirror. If he is high, it appears to be high; if he is low, it appears low. In effect the source light is reflected by the stabilized mirror as though it is shining from a point further up the deck, precisely along the appropriate path. Lines of green lights on either side of the mirror indicate the middle of the mirror, as a reference. Although there was no longer a human LSO in the traditional portside position, there was still an observer monitoring each landing and capable of waving-off an erring pilot, now by means of a bank of flashing red lights along the top of the mirror. Early mirror systems also included green lights which could signal 'cut' for propeller aircraft: jets landed all the way on full power. Generally the pilot himself is responsible for his angle of attack, ie his approach airspeed. The system was first tested aboard HMS *Albion*, and the first US mirror landings were made aboard USS *Bennington* in 1955.

The advantages of the new system included much higher visibility, particularly at night. The mirror was stabilized, and tests in rough weather showed that it permitted much faster and safer recoveries. Different aircraft require different glide angles: the mirror could be tilted to provide them. In effect the mirror places the pilot's *eye* on the glide path, and different aircraft thus require different mirror heights. This, too, is controllable. There were some problems. It was impossible to stabilize the mirror to cancel out all ship motion in a heavy sea; generally the mirror was set to provide a stable reference point about 2500ft out, and the pilot had to average out ship motion closer in. From the ship designer's point of view there was some complexity in a system consisting of a large stabilized mirror with a source light about 173ft further aft, which had to focus on it.

The current US system replaces the combination of mirror and source lights with a bank of five Fresnel lenses, each with three lamps behind it, one lens above the other. In effect each is set at a different angle, so that a pilot landing at the proper angle sees a horizontal bar across the projector, which is high if he is high, low if he is low, and which appears to move continuously up and down the face of the Fresnel lens unit. As in the mirror, there are green datum lights in a horizontal row on either side, with vertical red wave-off lights. Instead of an adjustable mirror, there are three separate units to offer a proper range of eye heights. Advantages include a reduction in deck personnel, as the lenses are controlled from the 'Pri-fly' control position in the superstructure; and at night the lens does not blind flight deck crews, who might otherwise have to look into the mirror's source lights. Even so, light intensity is greater, and thus the pilot can see the lens at a greater range, for example under low visibility. Nor is the lens affected by variations in sunlight or reflection from the sea. Finally, there was the problem of ship warping and flexing in a heavy sea, distorting the light path between mirror and source light.

CARRIER-CONTROLLED APPROACH

It seems noteworthy that although the mirror was originally introduced to overcome the problems inherent in all carrier jet landing operations, in fact it was enthusiastically accepted because it permitted much more efficient operations in heavy seas and at night. The two great

From the mid-1920s until the late 1950s, carrier landing in the US Navy was the province of the Landing Signal Officer, the LSO; the Royal Navy adopted the same system in the late 1930s, calling its LSOs 'batsmen'. Here a US Banshee flies over the LSO who had just landed it, April 1957.

Given the higher landing speeds of jets, something which could react far more quickly than an LSO was needed. The mirror landing aid allows a pilot to see for himself how well he is landing. This is one of the earliest installations, aboard HMS *Albion*, 23 September 1954. *Conway Picture Library*

thrusts of postwar US carrier development were the desire to operate more and more powerful jets, including heavy bombers, and the desire to extend that portion of the time carriers could operate, particularly in rough Northern waters. The last explains both the enclosed bow, adopted in the mid-1950s, and the stabilized mirror/Fresnel lens. Neither of the latter, however, could overcome one other limitation: low visibility. That required a radar-based system, which became known as CCA (Carrier-Controlled Approach). It was developed out of wartime experience

with bad-weather ground controlled approach (GCA) systems.

The basis of any CCA system is a very accurate radar which can indicate to the LSO exactly how fast the approaching airplane is moving and in precisely which direction. If more than one airplane is involved, it is also necessary to 'marshall' the approaching aircraft, feeding them one by one into a glide path: after all, in very bad visibility they cannot see each other. The combination of marshalling and one-by-one radar-controlled landings goes a long way to explain the very long delays associated with CCA in the mid-1950s study of air group size vs jet endurance already cited. At that time US systems generally consisted of a medium-range air search radar specifically for marshalling control (then SPN-6, now SPN-43), a precision radar for guidance from 6nm down to within a minimum of 200ft from touchdown (SPN-8), and a doppler airspeed indicator (SPN-12, later replaced by SPN-44). There is also SPN-41, which transmits glide slope and azimuth errors to the approaching pilot. Data from these radars was displayed in the carrier Combat Information Center, and the pilot talked down by an LSO. In theory the LSO would become visible at the last moment, and the pilot would be able to correct his path at that time. Later it was automated, and data was transmitted directly to the autopilot of the approaching airplane. More recently, all US carriers have been fitted with a large approach radar, PSN-35, housed in a big radome abaft the island. It determines aircraft range and height to within, respectively 60 and 20ft on final approach, for final hand-over to a Fresnel lens system or to SPN-10, the automated successor to SPN-8 (and now replaced by SPN-42). British carriers were similarly fitted: HMS Ark Royal, for example, had SPN-35.

All of the CCA radars face aft, and all require clear arcs. They also require operating spaces and displays in the carrier's Combat Information Center, but these are relatively minor design issues. However, they also represent unique sources of radar emission, which an enemy can use to identify a ship as a carrier: many ships share similar air search radars and even, in the US Navy, similar height-finding radars, but a radar like SPN-35 is mounted only aboard carriers. It has only a short range, and in fact the air itself soon absorbs its radiation. However, it must be visible to a sensitive receiver at some considerable distance. Having introduced CCA to enable its carriers to approach launch points off, for example, the Soviet coast in almost all weather, the US Navy is faced with the possibility that using this equipment will, in turn, permit the Soviets to mount successful anti-carrier assaults. Nor can it be argued that in any case the approach equipment would be required only at the conclusion of a successful strike: carrier operations now demand continuous fighter air cover, and hence frequent launch and recovery of Combat Air Patrols. CCA operation, then, is associated with the larger issue of whether a carrier should attempt to survive by stealth (eg by shutting down radars) or whether she should employ her radars continuously, trusting in an active defense such as that provided by fighters. To a minor extent this issue can be resolved by transferring the CCA function (at least in part) to a carrier-launched airborne radar platform, an airborne early warning aircraft such as the Grumman E-2 Hawkeye. Although the airplane, too, has a very distinctive radar signature, its location does not quite match that of the carrier, and at the least it may be able to take over the marshalling role.

ELEVATORS

Hangar design and the layout of the elevators reflect flight deck practice. In a straight-deck carrier, for example, the forward elevator was generally used to move recovered aircraft down to the hangar, whereas the after one fed into the deck spot awaiting take-off. An intermediate elevator amidships could perform a dual role, depending upon flight deck practice: it could feed into the take-off spot, increasing the rate at which aircraft could be moved up from the hangar, or it could strike aircraft below while others landed, given sufficiently reliable arresting gear and safety barriers. In US practice, the only aircraft struck below during a normal recovery were those requiring maintenance and those which would not be used for the subsequent sortie. They would have to be pulled out of the landing line while the other recovered aircraft were parked forward, and thus it was important for the amidships elevator, which permitted this practice, not to block the flow of airplanes forward. Thus it was offset to starboard in the Yorktown (CV5) class and the flight deck widened to port opposite it. The deck-edge elevator introduced in the Wasp (CV7) class interfered even less with deck operations, and has since been characteristic of US carrier practice. Indeed, wartime carrier operators found the amidships deck-edge elevator so useful that in 1945 it was proposed that the forward elevators of Essex class carriers still under construction be replaced by deck-edge installations. That, however, proved impractical: the elevator requires vertical tracks on which to run, and the form of the Essex hull forward precluded that. For its part, the Royal Navy presumably did not trust its arresting gear to protect an amidships elevator during landing. One was fitted to Ark Royal, probably to move aircraft up to the flight deck more rapidly. Subsequent armored flight deck carriers were limited to two centerline elevators at the ends of their hangar, a choice quite logical in view of the impossibility of armoring the elevator itself.

Postwar changes in operating procedure also changed the roles of the various elevators aboard a carrier. A ship with her catapults forward, using only catapults to launch aircraft, uses her forward elevator to feed aircraft into the catapults, ie to lift them off, where previously that same elevator would be the one striking them below after landing. The elevator located as far aft as possible, to feed aircraft into a deck spot without losing much of the flight deck, would no longer be particularly useful. Some elevator closer to amidships would be able to strike landed aircraft below, but once the carrier was fitted with an angled deck the conventional portside location would be directly in the path of the landings. Postwar-designed carriers, then, show forward elevators feeding their centerline catapults, and after elevators, at the starboard deck-edge, to strike aircraft below. This was the arrangement of the French Clemenceau class and also of the abortive British CVA-01. Angled-deck conversions of Essex class carriers also retained their original deck-edge elevator, which now formed the fore end of their angled decks. In the Forrestals, designed postwar, centerline elevators were entirely eliminated in favor of four deck-edge units, one to port at the fore end of the angled deck, and three to starboard, distributed fore and aft of the island, out of the way of landing aircraft and, incidentally, of the parking area. In later units the portside elevator was moved to the after end of the angled-deck sponson. In this position it could feed the pair of catapults on the sponson without interfering with landing operations.

Landing and take-off are not the only considerations in the elevator arrangement. In modern carriers the hangar itself is generally divided into bays. Its contents are, to say the least, highly inflammable, and such a division at least restricts the damage a fire can do. Each bay must be served by at least one elevator, which means that a carrier should have at least two. There is also the issue of survivability.

Naval aircraft are always limited by the dimensions of elevators and hangars. Here a folded Swordfish rides the elevator of a British escort carrier; note how the method of wing folding leaves the rigging undisturbed. *Conway Picture Library*

The more widely dispersed the elevators, the less the chance that one lucky hit will disable the carrier by eliminating all of her elevators. Thus there should be at least one starboard and one port elevator, and the elevators should be widely spaced fore and aft. Current US practice calls for two separate hangar bays, each with two elevators, which explains the total of four: ideally, both bays should be accessible from one side, which reduces interference with landing operations, but there should be at least one elevator to port, not only to deal with battle damage, but also to operate at times when wind and sea make operation on the other side impossible. This applies not only to aircraft operation, but also to underway replenishment, since the large side openings required for the elevators are also the ones through which stores and ordnance are brought aboard.*

The US Navy originally favored the deck-edge elevator because it did not interfere with flight-deck activity. It was light and simple, and less susceptible than a conventional centerline type to the effects of hangar deck explosions – a very great preoccupation in the Kamikaze days of 1944–45. In an armored flight deck carrier, moreover, it presented no important weak spot. From the constructor's point of view, it represented no cut in the strength deck, which might be either the hangar or flight deck. Although the Royal Navy succeeded in designing carriers with centerline elevators which employed their flight decks as strength decks, such designs would become increasingly difficult with advances in aircraft size and weight. Even on the hangar deck, a centerline elevator presented problems. Its structure descended deep into the ship, and the elevator well presented difficulties of drainage. Moreover, to devote a large space in the middle of an increasingly restricted hangar deck to an elevator was to accept a considerable loss of capacity in an already cramped ship.

There were counterarguments. The deck-edge elevator requires a large opening in the side of the hull, which in itself presents structural problems and is, moreover, difficult to seal against wave action in high seas. The elevator

*In carriers without side elevators underway replenishment could be to the flight deck, with the consequent loss of time as stores were struck below before the carrier might resume flight operations.

and its mechanism are subject to sea damage, particularly if they are located well forward. Thus the Royal Navy preferred to retain a centerline elevator forward in its CVA-01 design, as did the French Navy in its *Clemenceau*. They were not without allies within the US Navy. Operating in very rough seas, given the change in emphasis toward attack on Soviet targets, US carrier commanders found that in many cases their ships were quite steady enough to launch and recover aircraft – but that elevators could not be operated. The choice to continue to use deck-edge elevators, then, was a choice for maximum aircraft capacity and operating tempo, even if that might somewhat restrict the number of days per year that the carrier could operate – a restriction the US Navy ultimately evaluated as marginal.

FUEL STOWAGE

The aircraft designer affects the carrier designer through the size and weight of his aircraft, but those are matters of compromise. Fuel is not. Until well after 1945 the single most dangerous substance aboard a carrier was high-octane aviation gasoline, or avgas. How much of it the carrier could accommodate determined the operating endurance of her air group, in a period of thirstier and thirstier aircraft. For example, the *Essex* class was designed in 1940 to operate about 74 aircraft, each of which might be expected to consume 37 gallons per hour, up to 8 hours per day, or 21,900 gallons per day. She was expected to be able to steam about 10,000nm at 25kts, or 16 days, of which the aircraft might operate two-thirds of the time, perhaps 10 days, using 219,000 US gallons. None of these assumptions was characteristic of the war the *Essex*s actually fought. For example, the standard fighter, the F6F-5, required about 75 gallons per hour on average. The Avenger burned about 45, and the Helldiver about 50. The tempo of operations was far higher than had been envisaged, and the air group far larger. In 1945, for example, the standard for an *Essex* was a total of six deck-load strikes, each employing half the air group, each strike day. Each airplane, then, would fly three times, and that would consume perhaps 117,450 US gallons per day, assuming a late-war air group of 72 Hellcats, 15 Avengers, and 15 Helldivers, and providing drop tanks for the Hellcats only. Even the new *Midway*s, at about 350,000 gallons, could not support this kind of effort for more than three days. The abortive US fleet carrier study of 1946 combined a flight deck of *Midway* proportions (and, therefore, an air group comparable with *Midway's*) and 500,000 gallons of avgas stowage. The Royal Navy faced much the same problems, but perhaps more painfully: during World War II it almost doubled the size of its air groups by adopting US-style deck parks, and at the same time progressed from relatively low-performance (hence fuel-economical) types to very high performance US Navy and ex-RAF types. It was possible to increase the avgas stowage of some existing carriers, but the end result of such modifications fell far short of US standards, even allowing for the smaller British carrier air groups.

The great problem of avgas is that it forms an explosive vapor. An effective stowage system, then, must prevent the formation of empty spaces above the mass of gasoline. In the event of battle damage, the gasoline must not spread out of its tanks, where it can burn or form its explosive vapor. On the other hand, it must be piped up to the hangar and flight decks for refueling: the earliest British carriers stowed their avgas in small cans, which were poured directly into aircraft, but that was recognized as impractical even in 1920. Ultimately British carriers employed a water displacement system, in which seawater both surrounded the gasoline and poured into the tanks to force it upward. In US carriers, on the other hand, gasoline tanks were surrounded by seawater tanks; nitrogen under pressure was pumped above the gasoline to prevent the formation of explosive vapor. In general, the US Navy was willing to accept a lesser standard of protection for gasoline than was the Royal Navy, as reflected in British alterations to US-built escort carriers, in which avgas stowage was reduced by about three-quarters in the interests of better protection. In either case, avgas had to be stowed within an armored box already crowded with substantial magazines, elevator machinery and the propelling machinery itself. Although some expansion was possible, eg in the postwar *Essex* conversions, not too much could be done: it was fortunate that jet fuel required far less effort.

Japanese practice was to build gasoline tanks as part of the hull structure; generally the gasoline was surrounded by carbon dioxide, which in an emergency could also be pumped into the space above the gasoline. However, these precautions proved inadequate, and in wartime the top and side gas spaces were filled with concrete. One peculiarity of Japanese systems was the use of two separate grades of fuel: high octane for starting up and for bursts of speed, and lower octane for cruising. Carriers generally were provided with tanks fore and aft, divided into two sections, and piping for both fuels was provided at each fueling point, on the flight deck and both hangar decks.

At first, jet fuel was handled with avgas; indeed, early US jet engines burned a mixture of gasoline and kerosene, the latter being quite non-explosive. As early as 1947 the Bureau of Ships investigated the possibility of a 'mono-fuel' carrier which would burn jet fuel in her boilers, but when the *Forrestal* was designed in 1951 she was provided with 750,000 gallons of protected avgas stowage. Gradually the practice of mixing fuels was discarded; current types such as JP-5 behave like standard Navy bunker fuel, and can therefore be stowed outboard of the armored box in the usual wing tanks. Carrier boilers can be adapted to burn JP-5, albeit at some cost in efficiency, so that in effect there is no longer any specific aviation fuel capacity for a jet carrier. Rather, the carrier's captain can trade off between carrier endurance fuel, jet fuel, and escort endurance fuel.

Nuclear carriers are a special case. In a conventional carrier, the fuel carried in wing tanks serves a dual purpose: it provides torpedo protection as well as endurance. The nuclear carrier needs this level of protection just as much as does its non-nuclear counterpart, and therefore needs a very similar series of full and void wing tanks. However, all of them can be devoted to a combination of aircraft and escort ship fuel. In the design of the *Enterprise*, for example, so much capacity was gained this way that ammunition stowage was enlarged to balance the increased number of sorties the ship could fly – thanks not to any desire to enlarge her, but rather to the need to protect her against torpedo attack. This experience impelled the Bureau of Ships to seek a new and more compact protective system, if only to reduce the size and weight penalty associated with nuclear power. Moreover, a carrier is volume-critical even without internal avgas stowage, and reductions in the volume consumed by underwater protection are welcome. Ironically, the first application of the new compact system was to the non-nuclear carrier *Kennedy*, CVA67.

AIRPLANE MAINTENANCE
Aircraft also impose large maintenance loads, which require large areas of hangar deck devoted to shops, and in turn force up carrier complements. Extended operations are particularly costly in spare parts and in technicians. This is not a new problem. For example, as it operated in the Mediterranean in 1935–36 in the expectation of a war with Italy over Ethiopia, the British fleet found itself in dire need of maintenance facilities which were not available in the area. The response was a specialised 'Fleet Air Arm Supply and Repair Ship', HMS *Unicorn*, which was to support a squadron of three armored carriers. She was supplied with a flight deck and catapult, so that repaired aircraft could fly off. Thus she developed into a carrier rather than a classical depot ship, but she was still too slow for first-line use, and in fact it was expected that at the outbreak of war maintenance requirements would quite occupy her time. Later a series of light fleet carriers were converted for similar work; the US Navy preferred to use a network of shore bases and a more traditional sort of fleet train.

Such specialized ships merely reflect the cost and size of the maintenance organization actually aboard ship, particularly to handle electronic equipment. For the carrier designer, shop space on the hangar deck, ie adjacent to the aircraft, shrinks the hangar itself, and also requires doorways through the fire-tight screens which divide the hangar into bays. On the other hand, to place shop spaces elsewhere in the ship is to require more elevators and, ultimately, more wasted internal volume. To some extent, too, requirements for quick underway replenishment translate into maintenance requirements, since much underway replenishment is required to provide sufficient spare parts to keep aircraft flying. This is a particularly difficult issue given the range of aircraft *types* aboard many carriers, and consequently the limited number of spares of any one type which may be available aboard ship.

Current practice includes elaborate automated testing devices, specialized for each aircraft type. Formerly the shops themselves were built into the ship, so that a radical change in air group (as envisaged under the CV concept) might have required considerable reconstruction. The current thrust, then, is to build such equipment into vans or onto pallets which can be tied down in maintenance spaces, but removed rather quickly when changes are required. In principle this practice should also simplify carrier construction and carrier refits, since maintenance spaces would merely be emptied of their vans or pallets at refit time. It is also claimed that the Navy can afford to buy fewer sets of maintenance vans than there are carriers, since ships under refit can transfer their vans to operational units.

Carrier landing requires good low-speed performance but combat efficiency requires the best performance at high speed and, generally, high altitude. To avoid a crippling compromise, the aircraft designer generally employs some form of variable geometry, ranging from unusually large flaps to variable incidence wings or variable wing sweep. This F-111B prototype, photographed in July 1968, displays several high-lift devices including wings extended at minimum sweep angle and movable 'glove' sections. In the production version underwing pylons for fuel tanks and Phoenix missiles would have swiveled against the angle of the wing to remain parallel to the fuselage. Despite a combination of high-lift devices and a series of intense weight improvement (reduction) programs, the F-111B was rejected by the Navy; a modified version of its weapons system and its turbofan engines remain in the current F-14 Tomcat.

DESIGN CONFLICTS

Just as the aircraft exact a considerable penalty on the ship designer, he in turn imposes requirements on the aircraft designer, and land-based aircraft which are 'navalized' usually accept some performance penalties. The most fundamental limits are dimensions: length and wingspan (folded) are limited by carrier elevators. Length is perhaps the most important of the two, since it determines how effectively a vertical fin of a given size will promote directional stability. The larger the fin, the greater its drag, so that designers generally prefer a smaller fin and a longer fuselage. The Curtiss SB2C Helldiver, for example, suffered from directional instability due, ultimately, to a requirement that two Helldivers fit on a standard carrier elevator, for quicker transfer to the flight deck. In the Vought F4U Corsair, a restriction on length was countered by increased wing dihedral. However, there is a drag penalty associated with a wing which meets the fuselage at an angle. To some extent the Corsair's gull wing was a way around this problem.

Then there is hangar height. Prewar US carriers had unusually deep hangars, partly because of a requirement that they carry spare aircraft (initially equal to 25 per cent of their operating air groups, and never counted in nomi-

nal aircraft capacity) triced up between the flight deck girders. With 17ft 6in of headroom, the aircraft designer could simplify wing folding by folding his wings directly up, as in the Corsair and the Helldiver. The Royal Navy had shallower hangars, and when it adopted the Corsair had to clip its wingtips. In a double-hangar carrier, hangar depth contributed greatly to topweight: some smaller Japanese carriers could afford no more than 10 or 11ft of clear deck height, and consequently their aircraft could not be folded, at least not as completely as was common at the time in US and British practice.

The elevators and the flight deck impose weight limits, the latter in view of the landing load: at 3g, the airplane imposes a temporary load of three times its weight. Sometimes the margin is quite narrow. For example, the Grumman S2F (later S-2) Tracker was originally designed to operate from *Commencement Bay* class escort carriers, but it could ride their elevators only minus its three crewmen.

Wing folding in itself adds weight. For example, where a conventional wing gains strength from the entire continuous structure from tip to root, the folding wing has only a few strength joints. Often there must also be a power folding mechanism. There is, then, an incentive for the designer somehow to avoid folding entirely, and the Douglas A-4 Skyhawk was so small that it omitted this feature. At the other end of the scale, the North American AJ Savage was so marginal for carrier operation that normal wing folding was deleted. It would normally ride the flight deck at all times, but provision still had to be made to bring the Savage below for maintenance. This operation entailed removal of the tip tanks and attachment of a special folding mechanism; it took about 15 to 20 minutes to stow an AJ below. Moreover, the AJ was not cleared to land aboard a carrier until it had expended all of its bombs and nearly all of its fuel. The new generation of swing-wing fighters finally does away with the weight penalty of wing folding, since the wings can be designed to stow in a 'super-swept' position.

Finally there is a weight penalty due to the greater structural strength demanded of a carrier airplane, for example to take the shock of arrested landings ('controlled crashes' in US naval terminology). This penalty is less important than formerly because modern jet fighters experience far greater stress in normal maneuvering than they do in such landings, but it is extremely significant and still applies to many less violently flown aircraft. In general, too, a naval fighter or bomber requires greater range than a landplane, if only because the carrier's operating cycle may demand it. It is difficult to specify the effects of these penalties, because naval aircraft adapted to land service are rarely simply 'de-navalized.' Certainly the Phantom and the Crusader performed effectively as land-based fighters without any redesign. When the Sabre was 'navalized,' the difference between F-86F and FJ-2 Fury was about 1000lb on a total of about 18,000, but on the other hand the FJ-2 had 20mm cannon whereas its land counterpart had six 0.5in machine guns. Stalling speed increased by 4mph and maximum speed fell by 8mph at sea level, or 2mph at 35,000ft, both marginal figures quite overshadowed by differences between individual aircraft. On the other hand, in order to avoid severe losses in performance, the Seafire could not be strengthened sufficiently for naval service, and was, therefore, notoriously subject to landing accidents.

5.Strike Warfare

Modern US carrier design is dominated by the requirements of strike warfare: high-intensity flight operations sustained for a few days at a time, to deliver the maximum possible weight of munitions in minimum time, for the greatest possible impact. The sortie rate itself is determined, first, by the arrangement of the flight deck, which in these ships permits continuous launching while aircraft are being recovered. Moreover, since rearming and servicing take far longer than launch and recovery, it is essential that both be possible during flight operations. Another factor is the rate at which weapons can be delivered to the flight and hangar decks. Rearming is still largely a manual operation, but the arrangement of a bomb elevator on the flight deck will determine how easily the weapons it lifts can be brought to aircraft awaiting them, and how much of the time it may obstruct air operations. Flexibility demands that aircraft loads can be changed to reflect changing circumstances in the target area, and that in turn requires that weapons be returned rapidly to the magazines. Otherwise they accumulate on deck and come to be a hazard, as the Japanese learned at Midway in 1942.

A carrier's ability to sustain strike operations depends, first, on the size of her magazines. Volume is far more important than weight, because weapons tend to be relatively light for the volume they occupy. The combination of magazine capacity and sortie rate determines how often a carrier operating continuously must pull back to replenish, or how long a carrier can maintain a single series of strikes. To some extent, however, crew and particularly pilot fatigue are also determining factors. In any case, the length of time which must be wasted in underway replenishment during continuous operations is determined by the rate at which ammunition can be taken aboard, and in part by the rate at which it can be struck below.

NUCLEAR, CONVENTIONAL AND SUSTAINED STRIKE

Current practice envisages three very different modes of strike warfare. In the nuclear strike role which shaped the US Navy of the late 1950s, the carrier launches an intense strike as quickly as possible, bearing in mind the possibility of counterattack, then moves on. A typical Navy statement of the mid-1950s envisaged a carrier task force attacking three widely separated targets on three consecutive strike days, then withdrawing from the war zone to replenish. A much-publicised drawing showed the task force, with three carriers, moving about 500nm per day, and attacking at a range of 1500nm, presumably with A3Ds. In such tactics the rate of launch is very important because it determines the extent to which the carrier is exposed to enemy attack. Munitions consumption is relatively low, because each attack airplane carries no more than a few weapons of perhaps a ton each. Thus the reported 165-ton nuclear capacity of the *Forrestal* would suffice, assuming a strike combining long- and short-range attack aircraft.

As the US and the Soviet Union approached nuclear parity, the Navy began to emphasize conventional operations. Once more a hit-and-run operation was envisaged: typically a two-day run-in, a three-day high-intensity strike, and then a similar run-out, assuming that the carrier task group would be able to reduce speed and perhaps replenish at the far end of that 700nm run-out. In a single operation of this type modern naval aircraft can quite exhaust a carrier's magazines. For example, an A-6 or A-7 carries over 5 tons of bombs on a typical flight, and it can fly at least three sorties per day. Then each airplane, if it is not lost, expends more than 45 tons of bombs, and a typical air group of 36 will expend over 1620 tons. Reportedly the conventional weapons capacity of the *Forrestal*, as designed, was about 1650 tons. These figures do not include expenditures of air-to-air weapons, bombs carried by fighter-bombers, or weapons deemed not suitable for the targets at hand but nonetheless normally carried on board.

Finally there is the sustained strike, a series of short strikes carried out end to end, with short periods of underway replenishment in between, not merely to replace expended ammunition but also to reduce aircrew fatigue to a manageable level. Again, a useful average figure might be three days of air operations followed by one day of replenishment outside the immediate battle zone. It seems

The US Navy's great contribution to the art of strike warfare was the dive-bomber. Here a Vought SB2U-3 displays its 'displacement gear', the crutch under the center section which carried the single heavy bomb clear of the propeller, permitting bombing from a dive as steep as 90°. In the design of the Douglas Skyraider weight was saved by replacing the crutch with explosive bolts which blew the bomb free of the diving airplane.

TYPICAL FLIGHT PROFILES

A3D-2 Skywarrior

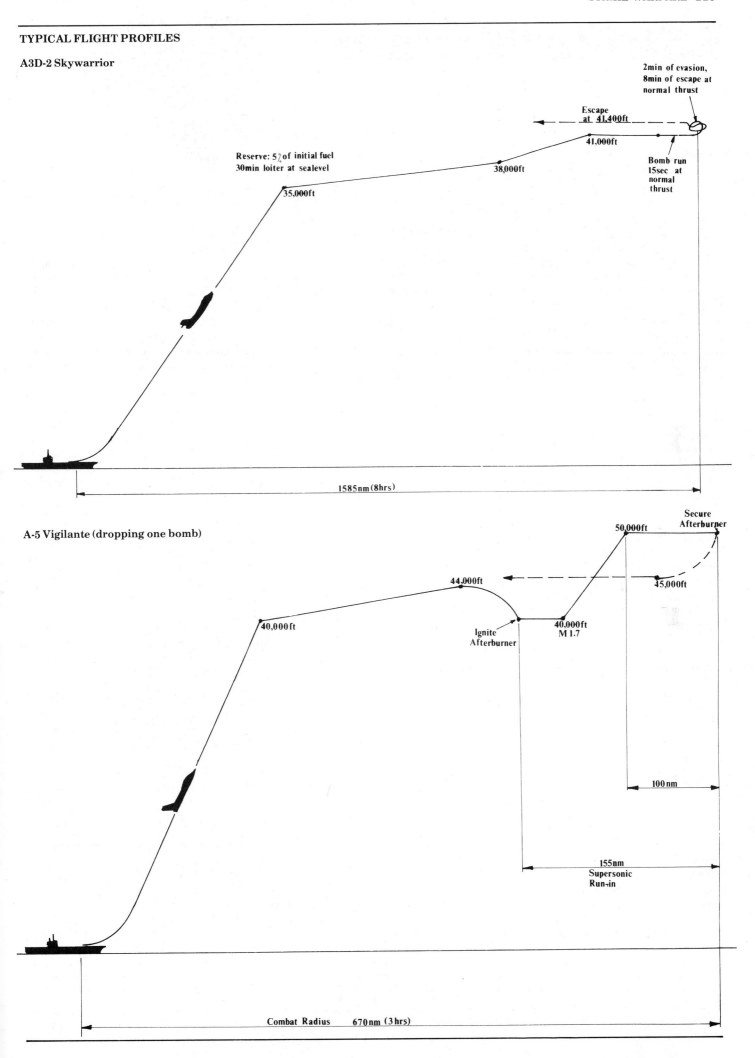

2min of evasion,
8min of escape at
normal thrust

Escape
at 41,400ft

41,000ft

Bomb run
15sec at
normal
thrust

Reserve: 5% of initial fuel
30min loiter at sealevel

38,000ft

35,000ft

1585nm (8hrs)

A-5 Vigilante (dropping one bomb)

Secure
Afterburner

50,000ft

45,000ft

44,000ft

40,000ft

Ignite
Afterburner

40,000ft
M 1.7

100 nm

155nm
Supersonic
Run-in

Combat Radius   670nm (3hrs)

The AD (later A-1) Skyraider was designed in 1944 but fought in Korea and then in Vietnam. This is the last A-1J built, painted up in the colors of VA-215. Underwing it carries drop tanks and an M76 'subcaliber' practice bomb. There were also practice bombs designed to be dispensed from a tank-like Aero 4B practice bomb dispenser, and subcaliber bombs which duplicated the ballistics of the low-drag Mk 80 series of weapons.

noteworthy, incidentally, that this schedule applied not only to Vietnam but also to the sustained carrier operations off Okinawa and five years later to Korea. It may, then, be a measure of human rather than mechanical endurance, and it may be used to set carrier magazine requirements. For example, typical World War II maximum strike practice was to fly three sorties per airplane per day. In 1945 British carriers were designed to provide nine loads for each attack airplane, and an Admiralty report on carrier endurance called for enough fuel to fly each airplane a total of 7.5 sorties of four hours each.

CARRIER DESIGN AND MAGAZINE REQUIREMENTS

Carrier magazines are now the single largest consumers of volume within the armored box which protects the vitals of the ship. They share that box with the machinery spaces, which must be spread out for survivability; when carriers operated piston-engine aircraft, avgas stowage also had to be accommodated within the armored box. Thus the *Forrestal* originally accommodated 750,000 gallons of stowage protected both by armor and by layers of sea water, fore and aft within her protected length, below the waterline, and this stowage of course reduced space available for munitions. In practice the survivability requirements of magazines and of machinery are quite different. No hit in the machinery spaces can itself sink a carrier, but the loss of all power will ultimately lead to the ship's loss, presumably by other means. On the other hand, the ammunition requirements of modern carriers are so massive that a single penetrating hit can, in theory, touch off an explosion quite sufficient to destroy the ship. In fact it can be argued that the destruction of a mass of explosives equal to half or even to a quarter of a magazine will destroy a carrier.

It seems likely that in practice hits on a ship will be distributed about their mean point of aim. In World War II,

when weapons were unguided, that aim point was roughly amidships. Guided weapons should aim at a variety of points. For example, a radar-homing missile will either seek the 'centroid' of its target, which again should be roughly amidships, or it may be attracted by corners, which are particularly bright radar reflectors. Depending upon the angle at which it approaches, then, the radar homer may seek the edge of the carrier island, or perhaps the forward edge of a sponson. A heat-seeking weapon will make for the island with its hot uptakes, although in practice ships are often fitted with devices to reduce their infrared signatures. Television-guided weapons present more complex possibilities. Typically, they are either 'centroid' or 'edge' seekers. In the former case they operate roughly as do the radar seekers, except that under some circumstances the carrier may not provide enough contrast from the sea. Where an edge-seeker strikes depends very much upon the angle at which it approaches the carrier: from above, it will probably lock onto the contrast between white wake and dark sea, and so may be a near miss; from the side, it will seek, perhaps, the edge of the flight deck or the bow or stern. Torpedo hits will generally show peaks amidships and aft, where homing torpedoes seek the propellers.

The sheer size of the carrier, compared to the volume of such vitals as magazines, makes direct hits relatively improbable, as long as the magazines are not situated precisely at any point at which the distribution of hits will peak, eg dead amidships and above water. On the other hand, the sheer size of magazines in a large attack carrier implies that they will consume a large fraction of the limited volume within the hull that can receive maximum protection, including torpedo protection. With the elimination of aviation gasoline, their only major competitor for this volume is the machinery: consequently the choice of magazine arrangement depends very much on the arrangement of the machinery spaces, which in turn depends upon the type of machinery and the requirements for uptakes. For example, US steam plants are concentrated in a single block consisting of two sets each of two independent units (boilers plus turbine) separated, for survivability, by an auxiliary machinery space. In theory

a single magazine might be provided at one end of this array, but volume towards the ends of the armored box is so limited that such an arrangement would be impractical. Moreover, the magazines must feed aircraft on the flight deck, and standard US practice is to provide bomb elevators for both the forward pair of catapults in the bow and the combination of waist catapults and parking area roughly amidships. Hence the typical arrangement of two magazines at the ends of the machinery space.

Moreover, it seems likely that in practice hits on a ship are distributed almost randomly over her length, so that two widely separated magazines may attract almost twice as many hits (which in any case are not too probable, given the small size of the magazine as compared to the length of the ship) as one larger one. The choice of magazine arrangement, then, depends in large part on the arrangement of the machinery spaces. In a steam plant the desire for wide dispersal must be balanced against the need to concentrate uptakes in a single compact island, and the usual choice is two plants separated by auxiliary machinery spaces. In theory a single magazine might be placed at one end of this array, but volume towards the ends of the armored box is so limited that that would be impractical. Moreover, the magazine arrangement must suit the needs of the flight deck: most carriers, then, have a pair of magazines fore and aft.

On the other hand, a nuclear plant requires no uptakes, only a reasonably clear area overhead for recoring once every decade. It is, therefore, possible to separate nuclear plants quite widely. In the *Nimitz* class the number of separate plants is reduced to two. The former standard magazine locations, at either end of a continuous machinery box, are now pushed out towards the ends of the hull, where there is less internal volume; on the other hand there is another possible magazine location between the two machinery spaces. The designers of the *Nimitz* chose to dispense with the after magazine, but had to retain the forward one to serve the pair of bow catapults.

An A-4E of VA-23 attacks Viet Cong with 2.75in folding-fin rockets. Originally developed for air-to-air use, these weapons proved effective against ground targets, and were generally carried in pods with a capacity of 7 or 19; one such, with head and tail fairings blown away, is visible under the Skyhawk's wing. There are also a 5in High Velocity Aircraft Rocket (HVAR) with fixed fins, carried externally on zero-length rails, and a 5in folding-fin (Zuni) rocket carried in a four-round Aero 10D launcher.

The flight deck places its own requirements on magazine location. A modern US carrier has two pairs of catapults: forward in the bow, and amidships in the forward portion of the angled deck. Only the bow catapults can launch even while aircraft land aboard; thus if a carrier is equipped with two catapults more powerful than the other pair, the most powerful units are in the bow. Similarly, if she must maintain aircraft on ready alert, they will sit on the bow catapults. For example, when the heavy carriers were assigned the deterrent (prompt nuclear attack) mission in the 1950s and 1960s, A-4s carrying nuclear weapons often rode the forward 'cats'. These positions in turn required a bomb elevator to service them. A second elevator, or sometimes a second group of elevators, services both the waist catapults and the parking/rearming area in the triangle formed by the inboard edge of the angled deck.

There is also a requirement that bombs and other weapons be deliverable to the hangar deck, although it is current policy that aircraft are armed only on the open flight deck. This is easily met, as at least the after bomb elevator shaft passes through the hangar and can be opened there. Doors in the bulkheads separating the hangar into bays permit the free movement of weapons, so that it is never necessary to provide one bomb elevator per hangar bay.

Generally, a modern carrier also requires substantial spaces for weapon assembly. Streamlined bombs, assembled, take up far more volume than their unstreamlined predecessors, but their explosive content is far smaller than their total size. Thus it is possible to store bombs

Losses of attack aircraft to ground fire in Korea led to the development of the Martin Bullpup air-to-ground stand-off missile (AGM-12). The pilot of the attack aircraft keeps the tail flare in sight, using a joystick to steer the missile. Here an FJ-4B Fury of an experimental squadron ('X' in tail code) carries four Bullpups over the Point Mugu test center, April 1958.

knocked down, with only a fraction of their total volume consuming valuable magazine space. Missiles are generally stowed without their fins, again to make more efficient use of space. In some cases, too, a weapon may have several seeker or warhead options, and once again working space for assembly between protected stowage and the airplane is required. Space on the hangar deck is at such a premium that it cannot be so used, and the flight deck is crowded enough by men hoisting weapons onto aircraft racks.

Modern guided weapons require maintenance and check-out spaces: they are not yet 'wooden rounds' which can be pulled from a magazine and fired without test. In addition, some weapons require special fuels or liquids, such as hydrogen peroxide and liquid oxygen. If one were to break down the internal volume of the carrier and assign part of it to strike operations, these non-magazine spaces would have to be included.

ORDNANCE

Historically, carrier strike operations and ordnance have gone through three distinct periods. Before 1945, loads were relatively small, no more than about a ton per sortie. Weapons were unguided, but on the other hand their targets, primarily ships, could be destroyed with relatively few hits. Since a carrier could only mount a limited number of sorties, it was vital to achieve the greatest possible effect per flight, and navies far more than land-based air services emphasized special tactics such as dive-bombing. For most of this period, too, carrier magazine capacity far exceeded the requirements of any particular operation, and magazines were a relatively small component of total hull volume. Hits on a magazine were generally not fatal, because the inrush of sea water due to a hit would quench any fire that hit started in the magazine itself. In this sense carriers were more like cruisers than like capital ships, which could be destroyed by magazine hits. Only with the very intense strike operations of 1945 did carrier magazine capacity begin to be approached by the requirements of a single series of consecutive strikes. Thus throughout this period the primary limit on carrier operating endurance was avgas stowage. It

might, however, be argued that because both avgas and munitions had to be accommodated within the armored box, they competed for the limited hull volume at the ends of the concentrated machinery spaces.

During this period the primary threats to attack aircraft were shipboard guns and fighter interceptors, and a major means of overcoming the former was a diving attack. As long as guns were not equipped with proximity fuzes, the bomber diving almost vertically was extremely difficult to hit, even though he had to keep his diving speed down to about 280kts to avoid inaccuracy. Typical US dive-bomber tactics envisaged visual target acquisition from about 15,000ft, then a dive down to 7000, at which altitude the pilot would begin his near-vertical dive to a release point at about 2000 or 2500ft; he would escape at low altitude. The near immunity of the dive-bomber to anti-aircraft fire or even to fighter attack made it useful as a companion to torpedo-bombers; in theory the first torpedo would arrive with the last bomb. In each case it was the accuracy of the attack, not the number of weapons expended, which decided the issue. However, when Task Force 58 struck Tokyo in February 1945, it was attacking area targets which could not be destroyed without the expenditure of large numbers of individual bombs. Thus the carrier aircraft failed to do net damage nearly proportionate to the investment in manpower they represented.

The second period, from about 1946 on, was the era of jet aircraft, nuclear weapons, and far heavier bomb loads per aircraft. Nuclear weapons required special storage and, at least in the case of early systems, special assembly spaces. Reportedly the earliest naval atomic bombs could take as much as 24 hours to prepare for use, which made a nuclear attack a deliberate affair indeed. Even so, the first postwar carrier, the *United States*, was designed primarily for nuclear strike, with a secondary conventional strike capability. However, conventional operations with her designed air group required a far larger magazine capacity than did nuclear strikes. Similarly, the *Forrestal*, designed in 1951 with the ability to launch strategic attacks in almost any weather her principal characteristic, reportedly accommodated 1650 tons of conventional ordnance – and 160 of nuclear. She was, to be sure, officially a dual-purpose carrier.

Through the 1950s the lifting capability of jet fighter and attack aircraft continued to increase, so that about the turn of the decade it could be said that magazine capacity was becoming as much of a limit on sustained air opera-

tions as was fuel stowage. At the same time there was an increasing recognition of the dangers of heavy anti-aircraft concentrations around prospective targets, and of the rising number of Soviet surface-to-air missiles. Programs for stand-off weapons such as Bullpup and the abortive Corvus were begun, complicating magazine design and requiring specialized maintenance facilities. However, strike aircraft themselves remained simple, apart from the all-weather A-6 and the supersonic, very long range A-5 Vigilante.

The natural reaction to increased target defenses was a much higher speed approach to the target. Jets could not be used for dive-bombing because they had extremely high terminal velocities; they could gain some accuracy, however, by glide-bombing, ie by approaching the target in a shallow dive. However, like level bombing, such a technique suffers badly with any degree of pilot error. The faster the airplane, the greater the consequences of small delays in pilot reactions, eg in bomb release. With improvements in electronics, one response to this problem was to automate the bomb release mechanism – in effect to arrange for the computer to sense aircraft speed and diving angle; the pilot aims the airplane, and the automatic bombing system does the rest. It is a modernized and automated equivalent, in terms of accuracy, of what dive-bombing did. In dive-bombing, the pilot could aim the airplane directly. Now there must be some intervention to correct for the fact that the airplane cannot dive vertically at its target. Such bombing systems exist in most modern attack bombers such as the A-7.

PRECISION GUIDED MUNITION (PGM)
The bombing computer helps, but it cannot entirely solve the problem of hitting a small target very accurately. Moreover, it cannot solve the pilot's problem of avoiding enemy anti-aircraft fire while diving towards his target.

The A-7 Corsair II will be the standard US naval day bomber until its replacement by the McDonnell Douglas F/A-18 sometime later this decade. Here an A-7 loaded with bomblet dispensers (cluster bomb units, or CBU) and Shrike anti-radar missiles for SAM suppression awaits launch from USS *Ranger*, January 1968. Sidewinders for self-defense are carried on the two fuselage rails immediately underwing and the Shrikes are outboard. This unit, VA-147, was the first to employ the Corsair in combat, from December 1967 onwards.

Experience in Vietnam showed that, no matter how good the bombsight, conventional attacks were largely unable to hit point targets in the face of strong anti-aircraft fire. The answer selected at the time was the Precision Guided Munition (PGM), generally a bomb fitted with some type of homing device which could be activated and locked on from the cockpit. Often it was a television, although laser designators were also used. Results were sometimes spectacular: a whole bridge, which had survived hundreds of conventional attacks, might be brought down by a single weapon delivered by a single aircraft – which, moreover, had been able to attack from a distance that made it immune to local anti-aircraft fire.

The term PGM, and its equivalent, the 'smart' bomb, now apply to a wide range of guided stand-off munitions and missiles; the third period of strike operations is characterized by the widespread adoption of PGMs. The features of this period are not yet entirely clear. One reason an A-6 is designed to lift up to 18,000lb of bombs for a single brief sortie is that it must drop many bombs merely to be sure of making a few hits: the entire load may be required to gain hits on a single pre-planned target. Indeed, the airplane is generally limited to a single target or target area, given its finite endurance (in miles) and its very limited airborne endurance (time). Thus it might be argued that a bomber armed with a PGM would never profit from carrying very many of them, since it would not be able to engage more than one or two targets, with one or two weapons per target, per flight. In might follow that the

Carrier strike efficiency depends as much on the abilities of the deck crew and of the ordnance men as on the characteristics of the attack aircraft. Here ordnancemen of VA-85 load 500lb bombs onto an A-6A aboard USS *America*, May 1968.

general adoption of 'smart' weapons would lead, first, to a generation of far smaller bombers, and also to a considerable reduction in demands on carrier magazine space, since the magazine is essentially sized to support a given number of sorties by the total air group, not a given number of tons of high explosive.

Thus the wholesale adoption of PGMs as a primary means of attack would tend to favor, too, a transition of V/STOL aircraft. The latter are generally poor weight-lifters and have little endurance, but then again a television-guided PGM makes almost no demands on the airplane which carries it, and indeed even the explosive portion can be reduced somewhat on the theory that it will arrive far closer to the target. Indeed, one might go further and suggest that only the wholesale adoption of PGMs can make current forms of V/STOL viable as a means of projecting sea power into coastal states. There is, too, the attraction of wholesale reductions in carrier size, as smaller aircraft (V/STOL) require less deck space per airplane, less fuel per sortie, less magazine volume per sortie, in theory still obtaining the same level of effective damage over a period of strikes. Even if V/STOL itself is unattractive for other reasons, it might be argued that a transition to PGMs would automatically allow a considerable shrinkage of attack aircraft (and carrier) size.

There are, however, some important counterarguments. First, not all targets are point targets. For example, a factory is spread out over a considerable area, and cannot be considered disabled unless much of that area is hit. It might be considered an assembly of point targets, but to engage them one by one with PGMs in any reasonable length of time would be entirely impractical. A beach under the threat of amphibious assault is somewhat similar. It may be subjected to area bombing in order to force defenders to remain under cover. Once again, there is actually an array of point targets, but that array is far too rich for an airplane which can drop one PGM at a time to

engage a single target. Far better to drop a pattern, and hope that shock and noise effects will overlap to neutralize the large number of defenders.

The other issue is target acquisition. A PGM attack requires, first, that the target be seen and only then that the PGM seeker be 'locked on'. In poor visibility the initial detailed acquisition may be entirely impossible; if the pilot knows roughly where it is (using, for example, a high-resolution radar as in the A-6), he may get far better results by taking his chances with a pattern of bombs. Target acquisition must be particularly difficult for a pilot flying at very low level and at high speed to avoid detection and destruction; he just has not enough time to carry out his own reconnaissance.

Most current PGMs are guided on the basis of either an optical or an infrared image of the target area. Although not vulnerable to decoying, many of these seekers cannot function at all in heavy smoke or fog, or perhaps even rain. For example, in Vietnam it was standard practice to drop a PGM, then make a second pass with another. It was soon discovered that the dust and smoke of the first prevented the second from locking in (in this case to a laser beam reflected off the target), and thus the second round would 'go ballistic' and be wasted. In general, the PGM, whatever the character of its seeker, is by definition vulnerable to some countermeasure, whereas the 'dumb bomb' is not. Moreover, it can be argued that by putting the sophistication in the airplane, the maker of the automated bombing system is also providing a higher degree of protection from ECM than is available in any unmanned system. In any case, a naval air force redesigned entirely on the basis of the promise of the PGM might find itself very much the victim of countermeasures, the success of which would render it very largely useless, since reduced weight-carrying would reduce the total capacity of the air force below that required.

At least in its present form, the PGM makes for a very slow rate of engagement of different targets, as each must be lined up and the weapon locked on, generally before launch. Electro-optical (EO, or television) systems can be locked on at launch, with the seeker trying, for example, to stay on a sharp line in or on the target. However, laser semi-active types require the launcher to remain in the area until the missile or PGM hits, continuously shining its laser on the target. Thus it is conceivable that the appropriate tactical countermeasure to a PGM-armed force is the concentration of large numbers of potential targets, their tight bunching limited only by the requirement that a PGM hit on one does not destroy too many neighbors. Such an array might be quite vulnerable to a carpet attack by conventional bombing, but it might exhaust the sortie capacity of a PGM force. These problems are particularly relevant to a carrier which can support a limited, albeit large, number of sorties in a limited period of time.

The PGM is usually unpowered. Its brother is the stand-off ground attack missile, which can be fired from outside enemy defenses and which must use some form of guidance to balance off its relatively small warhead. It may have a data link back to the launch airplane, permitting it to be locked on well after launch, eg well after it has cleared the horizon. For example, the abortive Condor could fly about 60nm, and could be guided into a target by means of a television camera in its nose. Harpoon, on the other hand, is self-guiding, given some initial target data. From the point of view of the carrier, such weapons are so heavy, compared to their warhead size, that they seem rather poor candidates for V/STOL armament. They suffer from most of the ills of the PGM, but cannot be replaced by any conventional form of bombing because of the level of

enemy defenses. Since an unpowered PGM generally gains some range because it glides on its guiding wings, the line between PGM and stand-off missile is at best a vague one.

One important issue is the high unit cost, and consequent low production rate, of PGMs and stand-off weapons compared to simple bombs. Experience in warfare in the Middle East suggests that wartime rates of ammunition use will far exceed budget-driven peacetime estimates, and thus that most stocks of PGMs will be expended quite early in a war. After that new production is unlikely to match usage rates, particularly as many PGMs will undoubtedly be wasted or lost as the result of aircraft losses. This possibility bears on proposals to reduce the size and cost of naval attack aircraft by reducing sharply both their bomb loads and the sophistication of their bombing systems, both of which would be consonant with greater reliance on target-seeking weapons guaranteeing a very good chance of killing a target with a single weapon. Another argument against excessive dependence on PGMs is the possibility that some enemy countermeasure will cause them to fail catastrophically, thus in effect disarming the PGM-equipped force; in Northern Europe, of course, that countermeasure may be no more than winter fog or snow. In such a case the only alternative will be brute force, a carpet attack – albeit perhaps with new and more efficient bombs, such as bomblet dispensers. Thus the retention of large, heavy, expensive naval attack aircraft – and, by extension, large, heavy carriers – is to preserve at least the potential for a retreat from the era of the PGM. It is an option probably denied any navy adopting the current generation of V/STOLs.

BACK-UP

In 1945 the strike power of a carrier was simply expressed: she had one bomber and one torpedo-bomber squadron, one double squadron of fighter-bombers, and a few photo-reconnaissance aircraft for strike planning and evaluation. With the rise of air defense systems, however, much more has been added. US Navy practice is to accompany a strike with a specialized jamming airplane, usually a Grumman EA-6; the EA-6s of course add to the complexity of the flight deck and crowd out aircraft more conventionally understood as offensive. Generally, too, strike aircraft benefit if they can fly at higher speed over enemy territory. That reduces their endurance, and since the late 1950s carriers have accommodated specialized tankers: first modified Savages, then KA-3s, now KA-6s. During the Vietnam War, special A-3s were fitted both with ECM gear and with inflight refueling equipment; they were referred to as TACOS (Tanker and Countermeasures aircraft).

All of the specialized aircraft of course require more shop space and more technicians. Moreover, since the late 1960s there has been a drive towards greater round-the-clock

Current US practice is to fly specialist jamming aircraft with strike groups. These two EA-6B Prowlers were assigned to VAQ-137 aboard USS *Enterprise*; they were photographed early in 1975.

The long reach of carrier air power is due both to the range built into the aircraft and to the airborne refueling capability of the carrier. That includes both specialized tankers and tactical aircraft equipped for 'buddy' refueling from underwing tanks. This FJ-4B carries tanks with self-contained pumps powered by the small propellers in shrouds at their forward ends.

capability. In the A-6 this is reflected in new programs: forward-looking infrared viewers as well as high-definition ground-mapping radar, to permit the pilot to lock his airplane onto a radar target for an accurate ballistic delivery. The A-7, originally conceived as a very simple clear-air attack bomber with maximum payload at minimum cost, is now capable of night operation, particularly if it is accompanied by an A-6. The net result of these changes is to permit a carrier conducting 'Alfa' strikes to use the eight night hours to effect, so that the previous typical level of two per day (with A-6 sorties at night, but at a lower intensity) can now be increased by 50 per cent. The cost is more complexity and more maintenance effort.

In World War II the chief targets of naval stikes were, at first, enemy warships each of which could be disabled by a few relatively small weapons. After the war there was an emphasis on nuclear attack, again by a relatively small number of weapons. In Korea and Vietnam, however, the emphasis was on large tonnages, and carriers were used to deliver attacks against extended land targets such as Hanoi. At present the chief scenario of US military planners is a ground war in Western Europe, in which the targets will be thousands of Soviet tanks and other military vehicles. In theory the carriers will be used largely for sea control and for attacks around the NATO periphery. However, in practice it seems likely that much of the land-based air power of the NATO alliance will be destroyed early in such a war, and that the carriers will have to deal with those thousands of point targets. The sheer size of the array of targets militates against reductions in carrier magazine volume, although advocates of the PGM may argue that there should be a trade-off between the number of carrier aircraft and their unit size, if only to increase the number of carrier-based bombers which will survive Soviet tactical air defenses.

6. Carrier Airborne ASW

As compared to strike operations, carrier ASW operations make very different demands both on the carrier and on her air group. A strike is an intense operation delivering a maximum tonnage of ammunition over a very limited period of time, after which the carrier either withdraws entirely or else replenishes in a relatively safe area. An ASW carrier, on the other hand, generally provides sustained 24-hour-a-day coverage which requires only a relatively low sortie rate. Munitions, too, are expended relatively slowly, as the carrier aircraft do not fire unless they detect a submarine. Thus although the low sortie rate is balanced by the length of the cruise, ASW requires far less magazine space than does a strike mission; nevertheless, it stresses sophistication in weapons and in airborne sensors, and so may require more maintenance per airplane and per flying hour, at least where avionics are concerned. Indeed, the size of ASW aircraft is driven far more by sensor requirements than by the need to carry heavy weapons or to achieve high performance. In many cases sensor data must be processed aboard ship: ASW stresses command and control far more than does a strike operation, although not more than does fleet air defense. In another context, it has been suggested that the volume of data generated by the prosecution of one submarine contact may be comparable to that generated by an air defense system during a raid, although the time scale of the latter is far shorter than that of the former.

These differences explain why ASW aircraft can often co-exist with strike aircraft aboard a single carrier, as in the British postwar air groups, and in the current US Navy CVs. Above all, they do not compete for scarce magazine volume within the armored box below the waterline. Indeed, when the US Navy designed specialized ASW carriers in the early 1950s and again in the 1960s, it was easy to provide for a secondary strike mission: magazines were designed to accommodate weapons sufficient for the secondary mission, because ASW weapons, for the primary mission, required only a fraction of the magazine volume. On the other hand the size and weight of such ASW aircraft as the S2F (S-2) Tracker set definite and quite substantial lower limits on the size of the flight deck and on the power of the catapult such ships had to have. In fact it was the lower limits set by postwar ASW aircraft which restricted many of the wartime escort carriers to non-combat roles postwar; at best they might be recommissioned to operate helicopters.

The central problem in ASW, be it air- or seaborne, is detection: wide-area detection, far too imprecise for any attack, but sufficient to cue ships or aircraft for a search; the usual submarine detection, the result of such a search, and in the modern airborne sense not yet quite close enough for an attack; and localization, sufficiently precise for a kill. The first is the most difficult, but it is the basis for any offensive ASW strategy. If submarines can be placed within efficiently searchable areas, it makes sense to scour those areas. ASW efficiency may then reduce to the rate at which an area of hundreds of square miles can be searched. The alternative is defensive ASW: the area through which a convoy or task force is to pass or in which it is to loiter (for example, to carry out a series of strikes) can be searched and 'sanitized'. Since the survival of the convoy or the task force is the objective, defensive operations generally suffice. In principle they are inefficient because they must be mounted whether or not any submarines happen to be in the search area. Thus offensive ASW, *if* it can be prosecuted, is far more efficient in effort expended per submarine destroyed. Moreover, it is the only strategy which can counter a threat such as the ballistic missile submarine – if it can be made effective through a suitable wide-area detector. There is one intermediate choice. An examination of the locations of enemy bases and probable wartime submarine operating areas may reveal restricted areas through which enemy submarines must pass; this recognition is in some sense equivalent to the operation of a crude wide-area detector, and the offensive ASW force can set up a barrier across such 'choke points' to inflict losses as the enemy transits to and from his bases. To some extent NATO strategy, at least since the late 1950s, has been a combination of offensive ASW based largely on SOSUS (Sound Surveillance System) and SOSUS-like schemes, plus barriers in areas such as the Greenland-Iceland-UK Gap. Escort forces, which prosecute defensive ASW, have been drawn down as the efficiency of the wide-area detectors has improved. On the other hand, some targets, such as carrier battle groups, are just too attractive and too valuable to be left without considerable defensive ASW cover.

The airplane is the ideal vehicle for offensive ASW. Contacts are generally fleeting; every delay in beginning the search merely expands the area of uncertainty which must be searched, as once contact is lost the submarine may be anywhere within an area whose dimensions are proportional to its speed. The airplane can reach the point of lost contact very rapidly, and, if it has an efficient search sensor, it can search at high speed. Just how well that can be done depends upon the effective range of the sensor, ie upon the *width* of the strip the airplane can search at a given speed.

The efficiency of the carrier as a vehicle for offensive ASW depends in part upon the relative ranges of wide-area detection and of shore-based aircraft. In World War II, for example, the principal wide-area system was a combination of radio direction-finding and code-breaking. The German U-boat offensive was tightly controlled from a shore headquarters, which arranged 'wolf-pack' concentrations by sending coded messages. In effect, then, code-breaking was an ocean-wide submarine detector, or at least an ocean-wide detector of the intentions of the German submarine force. On the other hand, it was imprecise at best, as submarines were assigned fairly large patrol areas. For their part the submarines had to report to base, and their signals could be detected by ship- and shore-

based direction-finding (D/F) equipment. Perhaps most significantly, a U-boat gaining contact on a convoy would transmit so that other boats of the same 'wolf-pack' could home on the convoy for a mass attack. Thus the destruction of the transmitting boat was of particular significance and, moreover, particularly urgent. Although shore-based aircraft could be used to find and sink submarines in the open ocean, attacks in mid-Atlantic, particularly those directly supporting convoys, were more often made by carrier aircraft flying from nearby. In addition, the search width of World War II ASW aircraft was such that often shore-based aircraft could not efficiently overcome the uncertainties associated with very distant contacts.

Postwar shore-based ASW aircraft were larger and had better onboard sensors. They therefore suffered from progressively less disabling uncertainties, and the area in mid-ocean which required carrier coverage shrank. Thus although the US ASW carrier force of the 1950s and early 1960s was primarily concerned with area offensive ASW operations in support of SOSUS, that task has now passed to the P-3 Orions. By the mid-1960s, what had previously been a secondary task – direct support of carrier task forces or vital convoys – had become the single greatest concern of the specialized ASW carriers. As these ships wore out, and as the US Department of Defense was increasingly unwilling to pay for replacements, their function was transferred to the attack carriers themselves, in the form of ASW aircraft supplementing their normal air groups. This CV concept, or multi-purpose carrier concept, was adopted in 1970 and is now standard.

SENSORS AND WEAPONS
The size and complexity of the specialized ASW aircraft has grown in response to an increasingly potent threat. Until the wholesale appearance of snorkel vessels in 1944, submarines might justly be described as surface ships capable of brief submergence for concealment. They had little mobility when submerged, and in fact any mechanism which forced them from the surface could greatly reduce their efficiency. The first ASW search sensor, then, was the eye, and the measure of effectiveness of much airborne

After 1945 the advent of snorkel-equipped fast submarines considerably complicated the airborne ASW problem, as submarines no longer spent any considerable fraction of their time on the surface. The only standard radar effective against a snorkel was the APS-20, developed for airborne early warning, which required a dedicated airplane. Grumman developed a pair of Guardian ASW aircraft, the AF-2W 'hunter' (foreground), with APS-20, and the AF-25 'killer', with a much smaller APS-31 attack radar and a variety of attack weapons which might include internally-carried homing torpedoes. The 'killer' also carried a powerful searchlight under its port wing for target identification, and sonobuoy dispensers could be carried underwing. *Grumman History Center*

An alternative hunter-killer pair better suited to fast carriers was developed from the Douglas Skyraider. The 'hunter' element was the standard airborne early warning variant, carried in any case for the fleet air defense mission; the 'killer' (illustrated) had a radar pod under one wing and a searchlight pod under the other. A homing torpedo could be carried in a special heated centerline pod, in effect duplicating the internal stowage of the Guardian, and sonobuoys were carried in the rear section of the searchlight pod. These AD-4NLs were photographed in October 1951. *By courtesy of Larry Sowinski*

The Grumman S2F (later S-2) Tracker combined the hunter and killer functions into a 'single package'. Here an S-2B shows both the search radar (APS-38A) and the Magnetic Anomaly Detector (MAD) boom extended; the 70 million candlepower AVQ-2 searchlight is visible in the port wing. The radome over the cockpit carried ECM (radar search receiver and D/F) gear, and each engine nacelle could carry ten SSQ-2 sonobuoys. Although it was not a large airplane, the S2F could carry a considerable variety of weapons, including a 'Lulu' nuclear depth charge in the bomb bay and four homing torpedoes (Mk 43 or 44) and two HVAR aircraft rockets underwing. *USN by courtesy of Norman Polmar*

ASW in the early part of World War II was that it forced submarines down. A natural next step was surface search radar, which might be supplemented by a high-intensity searchlight with which an object on the surface might be detected. The combination of visual search and radar continues to be extremely important. However, with the advent of the snorkel a submarine could operate continuously submerged, with only a periscope or a snorkel showing, and that only intermittently. The reduction in target size was disastrous, since search widths could be kept up only by going to far more powerful radars, which in turn required far larger aircraft to carry them. For example, the wartime APS-2A, mounted in such aircraft as the twin-engine Harpoon, would be reduced to about 1nm range, and it would take a heavy airborne early warning radar such as the APS-20 to get a theoretical 26nm. By way of contrast, the APS-3 was credited with a range of 10nm on a submarine awash.

It was expected that a submarine sighting an airplane would dive immediately. Similarly, a submarine would probably have electronic intercept gear (ESM) mounted on her snorkel mast or periscope, and so would detect the approach of a radar-equipped search plane; she, too, would dive immediately, and in either case there had to be some means of re-establishing contact and then attacking a rapidly evading submarine. At first the magnitude of the problem was not appreciated, and indeed there was a celebrated operations research study which showed that depth bombs dropped on a diving submarine had to be set to explode at a very shallow depth, because only those U-boats caught either on the surface or just in the act of submerging were likely to be hit. The next step was a homing weapon, which became the 'Mk 24 Mine' used with great success by the Royal Navy and US Navy from 1943 onwards. It could be dropped over the point at which contact had been lost, and home passively on submarine propeller sounds. Its one great flaw was low speed, about 12kts, traceable, presumably, to a requirement for light weight for aircraft use.

The Mk 24 had an acquisition range of about 1500yds,

and arguably a submarine diving at high speed from periscope depth after detecting an aircraft radar might evade it. However, by late in World War II there were also passive sonobuoys, which might be dropped in a pattern to detect propeller and other noise. They were particularly effective because snorkeling submarines were particularly noisy, and by 1945 the standard AN/CRT-1 was credited with a maximum range of about 3nm. It was not, however, a wide-area search device: no aircraft could carry enough expendable sonobuoys for that. Rather, it represented an intermediate step between radar detection and attack. Thus in a typical attack in March 1945 a British Coastal Command Liberator detected a snorkel on its surface search radar and dropped five buoys in a pattern, over a 3nm square. One buoy detected the submarine, and the Liberator then searched again with its radar; in any sea state radar detection was at best spotty. Finally it dropped two homing torpedoes which killed the U-boat.

There was one other wartime attack sensor: MAD, the Magnetic Anomaly Detector. A submarine is a large chunk of metal in the earth's magnetic field, and the disturbance it creates, although quite weak, is detectable. For some reason the Royal Navy found MAD less attractive than did the US Navy, and both during and after World War II preferred to rely on sonobuoys. However, despite its very short range, MAD has the great advantage of overcoming both silencing and such anti-sonar techniques as special absorbent coverings. In addition, like radar, it is a continuous search sensor which requires no ejection of limited expendable stores, and, like a passive sonobuoy, it gives no warning to the submarine. MAD therefore remains in the airborne ASW armory. It is generally used to confirm that a sonobuoy target is in fact a submarine, and to provide location data good enough for an attack.

Beside the homing torpedo, the other great wartime ASW weapon was the rocket. Where the torpedo made up for uncertainty due to the submarine's dive upon sighting or detecting an approaching airplane, the rocket reduced the diving time available to the submarine. It permitted an airplane to attack from a much greater distance, before the submarine had time to dive. It was also a far simpler weapon than a homing torpedo. Moreover, the complex torpedo had a sufficiently poor performance that its existence had to be kept secret; once known, it would be far too easy to evade. Thus, for example, aircraft were forbidden to attack pairs of submarines with Mk 24s, for fear that one would survive and carry back the secret. There was no such problem with the rocket.

Wartime ASW measures were effective because wartime submarines, for the most part, operated on or near the

surface. The appearance of the fast, deep-diving Type 21 submarine suggested that this state of affairs could not last, and in 1945 it was clear that the future submarine threat would be something far worse, perhaps a submarine able to operate continuously submerged, never showing even a periscope. The imminence of the atomic submarine was already clear. An airplane buys its high speed by staying well clear of the ocean surface; it can perform a wide area search only with some sensor which can penetrate that surface without touching it – a non-acoustic sensor such as MAD. Other postwar candidates included the Sniffer, which could sense the exhaust gas from a snorkel (but which was not too useful downwind of coastal industrial cities), and which is still in use; and a thermal wake sensor, to detect the small difference in surface temperature due to the rise of water from a depth as it is churned up by a submarine. The latter has had a checkered career, although it did appear in a recent James Bond movie, as a sort of ultimate ASW detector, quite capable of achieving the old dream of making the ocean 'transparent'. The great problem of all such non-acoustic devices is that a submarine is a very small object in an extremely large ocean, and sea water is notoriously opaque. In some oceans a shallow submarine can be seen by the naked eye before it can be detected by any sophisticated device; but that is not the problem.

SONOBUOYS
The only signals the ocean transmits easily are acoustic ones, and the principal line of postwar ASW development was toward sonobuoys of increasing effective range. Instead of continuously searching strips of ocean, an airplane with long-range sonobuoys can, in theory, lay a pattern at high speed, then loiter high overhead monitoring the entire field. Effective search rate, then, depends upon the probability that this field will detect a submarine passing within it. If the buoys are very far apart there must be some means of converting a very long range detection into information specific enough for an attack, and the airplane must be able to move fast enough to localize its contact and strike.

Sonobuoys are no more than miniature sonars suspended well below the surface. Their performance depends upon a combination of their own acoustics and the sophistication of the data processing, just as the ability of a hull sonar to detect a submarine depends not only upon the strength of its signal but upon the way the returned echo is processed to distinguish it from the surrounding noise. The

The same airframe formed the basis for three standard US carrier aircraft of the 1950s: the Tracker, the Tracer airborne early warning aircraft, and a carrier onboard delivery airplane, the C-1 Trader. Here Tracers and a Tracker line the flight deck of USS *Intrepid*, March 1972. They formed part of Carrier Anti-Submarine Air Group 56 (CVSG-56), with the tail code 'AU'. The S-2E illustrated differed from the earlier S-2A through S-2C in that it incorporated a new and more capacious bomb bay, a new APS-88 radar, computerized ASW equipment, and provision for the Julie-Jezebel active-passive explosive echo-ranging system. ECM antennas were relocated to the wingtips, and a much greater variety of sonobuoys could be carried, sixteen per nacelle.

only way to go beyond the kind of performance achieved during World War II, and thus to restore the kind of rapid area detection previously possible with airborne radars, was to introduce more and more complex signal processing. However, that was not possible given the restricted space aboard ASW aircraft limited by carrier decks and catapults: thus the US S2F incorporated a special data link, and by the 1960s any carrier operating such aircraft had to have a specialized ASW Command and Control system aboard. The development of micro-electronics permitted the design of a computer which could fit aboard the newer S-3 Viking, which thus gained a certain independence of operation – and, perhaps more importantly, which thus greatly reduced its minimum demands on a host carrier. This, too, was presumably a vital element of the CV concept.

There are several types of sonobuoys: first omnidirectional passive, then directional but still passive, then active but effective for range only, and then active and directional, like a full miniature ship sonar. In principle a fully passive field of buoys should suffice to locate a submarine, since the details of when sounds arrive at widely separated buoys should be available. In practice, aircraft generally lay fully passive fields for the same reason that aircraft radar was not an unmixed blessing: an active 'ping' alerts the submarine and gives it too much time to flee, before an attack can be set up. Current tactics generally call for the airplane to use its active buoys to refine target position, and then set up the attack using MAD.

The US Navy tried an alternative in the late 1950s: explosive echo ranging. The airplane might not be able to dip a sonar into the ocean while flying overhead at 300kts, but it would drop a small explosive charge. Sound waves from the explosion would be picked up by a pattern of passive sonobuoys. Among the claimed advantages of this 'Julie' system were its ability to pick up a silenced or stopped submarine. Requirements on the airplane

The Lockheed S-3A is the successor to the S-2, serving aboard multipurpose carriers rather than aboard specialized ASW ships. This VS-41 Viking is shown in flight off San Diego, with its MAD boom extended.

The sonobuoys bay of an S-3A Viking; buoys are pre-loaded into the tubes and dropped to form patterns which the aircraft can monitor. Given improvements in sonobuoy reliability and also in weapon lethality, the S-3 carries many fewer weapons (torpedoes or nuclear depth charges) per sonobuoy than did the S-2.

included a specialized data recorder/plotter and, of course, stowage for the small explosive charges.

Compared to a surface ship, then, an airplane can (in theory) perform the same detection function as can the surface sonar, and indeed under some circumstances it might be argued that a sound head several hundred feet underwater has some advantages over a sonar under the keel. Of course the small sonobuoy cannot provide anything remotely like the signal strength or the directivity of the big shipboard sets; the airplane has to compensate with its speed, which permits it to lay an elaborate pattern and then to correlate the signals the pattern picks up. There is one other limit. A surface ship can be fitted to detect a submarine resting on the bottom in relatively shallow water, such as would be encountered in the North Sea: it can move over the area of the suspected submarine, examining the bottom in detail. All the airplane can do is pass over using MAD gear, and with that it may well detect a wreck rather than a live submarine.

Aircraft weapons have developed directly from those of 1945. Current US ASW aircraft still carry 5in high-velocity aircraft rockets, as well as greatly improved homing torpedoes and a high-explosive depth charge, the latter presumably to counter a bottomed submarine which would not provide sufficient noise for a homing torpedo. In addition there are nuclear depth bombs, with a lethal volume probably not too different from the effective acquisition volume of the homing torpedo. The great advantage of the nuclear depth bomb is its immunity to countermeasures. The airplane (or even the helicopter) can, moreover, drop it with impunity, whereas a surface ship has to fire a nuclear depth charge from a considerable distance and even then must be designed to withstand the resultant underwater shock wave.

From the late 1950s there was, however, an additional

requirement, as the Soviets began to deploy submarines armed first with ballistic and then with long-range cruise missiles, both of which had originally to be fired from the surface. It followed that the destruction of a surfaced submarine was once more an important goal; moreover, that had to be a very prompt destruction indeed, given the effect of a delay. Patrol aircraft were thus armed with Bullpup guided missiles. Later, Harpoon was developed partly to attack surfaced Soviet submarines firing the SSN-3 (Shaddock) cruise missile. Although SSN-3 can be launched very rapidly, it requires a data link back to the launch platform, so that the destruction of the submarine even some minutes after launch remains worthwhile.

Also from the late 1950s there was a fear that the considerable effectiveness of ASW aircraft would bring about a defensive reaction on the part of the submarines. To some extent this prediction was verified by the development of the Vickers SLAM submarine defensive system, which reportedly is actually fitted to some Israeli submarines. At first blush such a weapon might seem futile, as the same opacity which shields submarine from airplane should operate in the latter's favor. However, an airplane or a helicopter is quite noisy, and its sound penetrates the water. It is not clear that a submarine can locate an airplane very precisely in this manner, although it may be worth remembering that sound location was the predecessor of radar in land air defense systems. However, any submarine defensive weapon must act as a deterrent, particularly if aircraft tactics call for flying almost directly overhead in a final MAD pass before attacking. Thus from time to time over the past quarter-century there have been calls for ASW stand-off weapons to counter the potential threat. Presumably they would add to the loads already imposed by the ASW mission, and total weapon loads would have to be reduced.

THE SPECIALIZED ASW AIRPLANE
In World War II a single airplane often sufficed to carry out the entire ASW mission. If visual search was being used, the pilot or lookout could spot the submarine, and the same airplane might carry a depth bomb or rockets. In fact US carrier doctrine called for ASW patrols by torpedo-bombers or scout (dive) bombers carrying a depth bomb which was a staple of the carrier magazine: in the Pacific, with Japanese submarines few and far between, these same weapons were generally dropped on land targets. However, existing single-engine carrier aircraft could not generally accommodate both a load of sonobuoys and homing torpedoes, and by the end of the war it appeared that future carrier ASW practice would require pairs of aircraft, one to search and the other to attack. This was particularly clear when the heavy APS-20 radar, originally developed for airborne early warning, was adopted as the primary anti-snorkel radar.

Thus the postwar US ASW carriers operated two versions of the Grumman AF Guardian. The AF-2W was unarmed, but it was equipped with a big APS-20 in a belly radome. It was intended to guide a companion AF-2S into an attack. The latter had a smaller APS-31 radar under one wing, and a high-intensity searchlight under the other, to help in target identification. In accordance with wartime procedures, the AF-2S had to be able to regain contact on a dived submarine (or on a snorkeler which had gone deep) and therefore it carried six sonobuoys to establish target position. The attack proper would be made with a single homing torpedo, and there were also six rockets (or four rockets and four depth bombs). There was no MAD gear.

The combination of aircraft was awkward, and in 1949 the Bureau of Aeronautics issued a requirement for a

'single package' type; not too long afterwards the British Gannet was redesigned for a similar mission. In the US case a key to this development was a much more compact ASW radar, designed specifically to detect snorkels, the APS-38A. It could perform both the wide-area search and the precision attack functions. However, the S2F operated from specialized ASW carriers which generally also operated airborne early warning aircraft carrying the APS-20 or its successors, and which automatically passed their radar data back to the carrier, providing part of the area search formerly assigned to the AF-2W. The S2F also benefited from evolving electronic technology. Originally two homing torpedoes had been desired, to achieve a reasonable probability of a hit, but the S2F had to be operable from an escort carrier (*Commencement Bay* class), and so could lift only one Mk 34. However, a much smaller torpedo was soon developed: Mk 43, the forerunner of the present Mk 44/46 family. Two could be carried, as well as twenty sonobuoys – which were now beginning to present an area search potential of their own. As development continued, the bomb bay was blistered to permit the Tracker to carry an atomic depth charge, or else up to four torpedoes. In addition it was given another non-acoustic sensor: an ECM receiver and homer. Submarines, too, had radar, and it was possible to use both their radar and, perhaps, their radio emissions to detect them.

By the late 1950s the US Navy no longer operated escort carriers, and it was possible to relax restrictions on S-2 weight, given the larger (*Essex* class) carriers from which it would operate. New non-acoustic sensors included a sniffer and an increasing array of direction finders; late model S-2s could carry as many as six torpedoes, or one nuclear depth charge, four torpedoes and two rockets. A typical mission might carry the airplane 300nm from its carrier on a seven-hour flight, which is indicative of the tempo of CVS operations. By the 1960s effective sonobuoy field operation required data relay back to the carrier for processing, and very long distances required the additional complication of an airborne relay, such as a helicopter closer to the carrier.

The Tracker had two fundamental defects, both of which affected the carrier operating it. First, it was increasingly alone as a piston-engined airplane in a world of jets. This was not an annoyance as long as it operated from specialized ASW carriers whose air groups consisted largely of Trackers. However, by the late 1960s new carriers were

From the late 1940s onwards, the United States Navy operated specialized ASW carriers, and restricted ASW aircraft aboard fast carriers to very small numbers. At first the specialist ships were war-built *Commencement Bay* class escort carriers; this is USS *Badoeing Strait* with Sikorsky HO4S helicopters of HS-4 aboard for West Coast exercises, 27 July 1954. Although not operated from such ships, the Grumman S2F was designed within the limits imposed by the *Commencement Bay* class. ASW modifications to these small carriers were considerable, including a new standardized island structure that was also fitted to reconstructed light fleet carriers. *Badoeing Strait* shows HF/DF gear at her fore, with a YE homing beacon below it, dipoles for ship-to-air communication, surface search radar, an SP height-finder for air control, SPS-6B for air search, and a pair of DBM radar direction finder radomes. Both the HF/DF and the DBM were, in effect, non-acoustic submarine detectors, using the submarine's communications and radar emissions for detection.

being built entirely without avgas stowage; in any case avgas always represented a fire and explosion hazard. It was tolerated because piston engines made for great efficiency on long missions far from the ship. However, the development of turbofans made a jet ASW airplane a practical proposition. It would be compatible with other modern naval aircraft and this compatibility was an important factor in the success of the CV concept.

The other defect was the Tracker's need for a dedicated carrier-borne command and control system, which in itself limited the distance from the carrier at which it could operate. In addition, it limited operational flexibility – which, again, was only a minor problem as long as Trackers always operated from a dedicated ASW carrier. However, even before the demise of the special carriers, there was pressure from the Fleet for a more modern replacement. Fleet commanders of course buttressed their arguments with indications of the shortcomings of the existing Tracker, but much of its equipment could have been replaced. However, it could not be stretched into the independence of the carrier. Moreover, jet engines provided a dash speed which made long range more useful, given the increasing power of wide-area detection systems. Interest in such distant ASW operations increased partly because of the growing range of Soviet submarine-launched anti-ship missiles. The jet replacement for the S-2 was the current S-3 Viking, a very highly automated aircraft. Among its features is a forward-looking infrared (FLIR) viewer which obviates the previously standard searchlight.

Even the S-3A is hardly without ship impact; it is just that the impact has been shifted. Highly developed auto-

The next step was to transfer uncoverted *Essex* class carriers from attack to ASW roles. They were redesignated CVS, support, carriers; their role included ground attack in support of amphibious operations. Here USS *Valley Forge* and the destroyer *Eaton* (DDE510) fuel from USS *Pancatuck*, AO-108, June 1959. One effect of the existence of dedicated fast carriers was to eliminate any requirement for specialist ASW aircraft aboard fast attack carriers, thereby increasing their capacity for pure attack and fleet air defense types.

mation is often recognized as equivalent to highly developed maintenance problems. The US Navy developed an automated test system, VAST (Versatile Avionics Systems Test), which was to service a new generation of more complex aircraft, including both the S-3 and the F-14. Difficulties with VAST itself have led to a general loss of confidence in the S-3, but it seems unlikely, in 1980, that a US Navy concerned with area ASW and with the ASW security of carrier battle groups threatened by Soviet submarines armed with long-range submerged-launch weapons will be able to give them up.

THE ASW HELICOPTER

Since the early 1950s there has been another line of ASW aircraft development: the helicopter with a dipping active sonar. It was early recognized that if the passive sonobuoy were to become a search rather than a localization device, it would be of distinctly limited value in the immediate neighborhood of a noisy task force. On the other hand, destroyers 'pinging' actively were subject to long-range torpedo attack. Helicopters could hover long enough to lower a substantial sonar transducer into the water, 'ping', listen, and move to another station in an aerial version of the 'sprint-and-drift' technique. The Royal Navy found them so attractive that it abandoned its Gannet ASW aircraft in their favor, and indeed still operates them from ex-aircraft carriers. The US Navy did not consider the two systems in any sense equivalent, and it had the luxury of operating a large number of specialized ASW carriers which could accommodate mixed air groups of helicopters (for close-in screening) and Trackers. One great advantage enjoyed by the helicopters was the ability to dash out to a screen position, to help prosecute a nearby contact. On the other hand, they could not have either the endurance (in time) or the load-carrying ability of a more conventional airplane. In effect the combination of airplane and helicopter might be described either as a defense in depth for the carrier battle group, or as a means by which the carrier

group can 'sanitize' an extended area of ocean while at the same time defending against submarines 'leaking through'.

When the US Navy abandoned its specialized ASW carriers, it included in the new mixed air wing a combination of fixed- and rotary-wing ASW aircraft, the latter dipping helicopters. It was argued, indeed, that under some sonar conditions the helicopters can still search usefully with their active sonars, whereas the passive sonobuoy field is useless: sound just does not travel far enough for the usual necessarily sparse field to pick up a submarine passing through it. On the other hand, closely spaced helicopters booming out strong signals constitute an effective barrier.

These heavy helicopters are only very loosely related to frigate- or destroyer-borne lightweight types such as LAMPS (Light Airborne Multi-Purpose System). LAMPS, for example, is intended to prosecute a sonar contact at the first or second convergence zone, perhaps up to 80nm from the ship, where precision is quite insufficient for the destroyer to launch a weapon (which, indeed, it does not have); the helicopter flies out, redetects, drops sonobuoys to localize, tows its MAD, and then attacks. Much of its data processing must be done aboard ship *à la* Tracker; it is severely limited in weight and in size because it must operate from an extremely constricted helipad.

FUTURE DEVELOPMENTS

ASW continues to be a critical area of naval warfare. What is most remarkable in any review of the progress of airborne ASW over the past forty years is the dearth of major changes, and the death of many promising non-acoustic concepts. In theory there should be some non-acoustic submarine signature, clearly visible (if only one knew how to look) on the surface of the sea, perhaps even from the fastest vehicles of all, in space. There is no shortage of candidates, and usually the verdict is not that they are totally impossible, but rather that they are so weak that as yet there is not quite the data processing power to separate them from the inevitable background noise. Presumably if success ever came in this endeavor, and submarines could be reliably and accurately detected from space, carrier ASW (at least in the United States) would be abandoned in favor of some gigantic land-based missile system. That day seems, to put it mildly, remote.

It is difficult to say just how intractable the problem is.

Certainly a submarine snorkeling at periscope depth on the high seas runs a serious risk of detection, and that fact alone must tend to inhibit submarine commanders and thus to reduce their mobility. Certainly, too, acoustic detection works rather poorly in crowded seas, and even a rather unsophisticated submarine might be quite successful against modern airborne ASW weapons in some waters with very poor sonar conditions. The sea is, after all, penetrable by light down to below periscope depth in some areas, so that the human eye is still an effective sensor, and some years ago the US Naval Research Laboratory publicized experiments in which blue-green laser light penetrated several hundred feet into the sea. These considerations suggest that although the submarine has by no means been driven from the sea, it may find shallow operation difficult, at least in patrolled waters. However, a modern nuclear submarine can attack from some considerable depth, using sonar information alone. At present the only airborne counter is a field of sonobuoys, and detection depends upon the relative efforts of data processors (both aboard the sonobuoys and in the aircraft or ship) and of submarine builders improving the silencing of their products, or perhaps introducing coatings which will absorb active sonar 'pings' – in which case signals will be far weaker, demanding more processing by the sonar operator and by the acoustic torpedo which will ultimately seek the submarine.

One interesting current development is the use of a V/STOL fighter such as the Harrier to plant sonobuoy fields at long range from a carrier. Although the Harrier cannot loiter over them, they can probably be monitored by helicopters. The combination of Harrier and dipping helicopter does not quite match that of S-3 and heavy helicopter, but on the other hand it does place a far smaller burden on the carrier, since the Harrier requires neither catapult nor arresting gear. In a sense this is a return to the original Tracker concept: the Harrier is available both to plant a field and, later, to attack – assuming that some-

The Royal Navy had no special ASW carriers of any description postwar, and ASW aircraft constituted an 'overhead' expense which became more onerous as the attack and fighter aircraft became larger. Here HMS *Eagle* shows four Gannets aft, with the four Skyraiders of her airborne early warning detachment alongside. Ranged amidships are her strike aircraft, seventeen Sea Hawks, and eight Sea Venom night fighters. This 'overhead' issue first motivated the Royal Navy to abandon fixed-wing sea-based ASW in favor of helicopters, and then to seek a better solution in a separate limited platform, the air-capable 'escort cruiser', which ultimately evolved into HMS *Invincible*. *Conway Picture Library*

how the typical US intermediate step of localization/classification can be foregone. That may actually be practical if the field is smaller and denser than has up to now been common. Harriers were tried in this role during the US Interim Sea Control experiments aboard the USS *Guam* in 1974, and they accompany helicopters in the air group of the British carrier *Invincible*. They are usually thought of purely as fighters or perhaps fighter-bombers, but *Invincible* is far more allied to the old US CVS than to a British carrier of the 1950s and 1960s. Moreover, the Harrier is sufficiently well armed to represent an immensely valuable addition to the air defense umbrella already provided by the surface-to-air missiles of the British surface force.

Such a use of V/STOLs is interesting even in the context of a big US carrier. Perhaps the single greatest flaw in the CV concept is the mismatch between the ideal deck cycle times of the ASW aircraft and the strike aircraft; the helicopters, which can take off from any unused part of the flight deck, present no particular problem. In theory a V/STOL ASW airplane would present similar benefits. In the case of the Harrier, loitering time would be replaced by a combination of quick landing/launching and a high-speed dash out to the area of interest. The use of a fighter such as the Harrier preserves, too, some air-to-air capability even if the flight deck is severely damaged, whereas a specialized ASW V/STOL, which is often proposed, would have no such secondary ability.

7. Fleet Air Defense

A carrier and her defensive fighters form a weapon system, analogous in some ways to the weapon system of a surface ship. In each case there are early warning sensors, whose data must be interpreted. There is some means of assigning defensive weapons to the attackers the sensors detect, and that assignment must be conveyed to some mechanism for fire control. Finally there are the defensive weapons themselves. In a surface ship all of these elements are located aboard the same hull, wired together in a fixed geometry, which greatly simplifies the operation of the system as a whole. In a carrier the analogous elements are very widely distributed, their relative positions vary rapidly, and the wiring is largely replaced by radio data links. The carrier's defensive weapon system extends over a very large area, too: typically, for example, the weapons themselves are aboard Combat Air Patrol (CAP) fighters orbiting 150nm from their ship, and their Phoenix missiles may reach about 50nm further out.

The development of the carrier's defensive weapon system has been in the direction of increasing automation and extension to meet ever faster attackers carrying weapons of greater and greater range. Of course the carrier is generally part of a wider fleet air defense system which includes ship-borne missiles, but in important ways she can be treated as a separate unit. In practice a fleet air defense commander will assign a missile free-fire zone, outside of which the long-range fighters operate: despite all of the automation, no one is willing to assume that the weapon controllers aboard ship will never fire at a friendly fighter. Such a scheme fails only when the fighters must return to land, but modern Soviet saturation tactics imply a short, sharp battle rather than an extended one.

TACTICS

The defensive fighter tactics of World War I carried over to the new carriers commissioned postwar: fighters, which had long endurance, would orbit over the area to be defended. There were no long-range sensors to inform them, but on the other hand speeds were relatively low, and a high-altitude position guaranteed sufficient warning time. Moreover, the attackers had to approach their targets quite closely and, until the advent of dive-bombing, their chance of disabling a carrier was slim. Thus the individual defensive fighter combined all of the elements of the weapon system: early warning by observation, evaluation (perhaps by the flight leader), fire control (eyeball), and weapon (machine gun).

This arrangement became increasingly unsatisfactory as aircraft speeds increased. At 120kts an airplane is making only 2nm per minute, so that if it is spotted at 6 miles, that is three minutes' warning – a long time. However, by the late 1930s many aircraft made twice that speed. Not only did that reduce warning time, but in addition it increased the distance from a ship that a bomber could drop, since the bomb or torpedo would carry on through the air with almost the speed of its bomber. The US response

was the aerial scout, which could orbit as much as 40nm from the carrier, to report incoming raids. In addition, destroyer pickets would report aircraft observed overhead. The sensor was still the eye, but now the system of sensors was more widely distributed and had to be linked by radio. It was also necessary for the volume of incoming information to be filtered, so that the relatively small number of fighters might be used most efficiently.

To some extent warning *time* decided fighter tactics. As long as it remained very short, the only fighters which would be able to engage enemy bombers before they attacked would be those already in the air, on CAP. However, CAP was an inefficient use of pilots and fuel, both in short supply aboard ship. Ideally, an incoming raid would be detected so early that fighters held on deck (deck-launched interceptors, or DLI) would be able to rise and vector out to meet it. Given the very limited total capacity of a carrier, and the fact that attacking aircraft (particularly if they were land-based) might be extremely numerous, DLI was extremely attractive. Depending on fighter endurance and turn-around time, CAP at best employs half of all serviceable defensive fighters, since there must always be a CAP section waiting to relieve the one airborne. However, if turn-around time is long or fighter endurance very short (eg as the price of very high performance), the ratio may be even worse. In this context the issues are fighter and attacker performance, and the distance at which the attacker may be detected.

For example, the F6F-3 Hellcat of World War II was credited with the ability to climb to 15,000ft in 7.7 minutes. From the moment of decision to launch against an incoming bomber, as much as five more minutes might elapse: the pilot would have to be briefed, would have to get to his cockpit, warm up his engine, and so on. Perhaps 13 minutes would be required, and during the climb the fighter might make an effective speed of as much as 240kts outbound, a distance of about 32nm. During the same 13 minutes an incoming bomber at the same average speed would make good a distance of about 52nm towards the carrier. Leaving a two-minute margin of error (8nm), the decision to launch would have to be made when the bomber was about 92nm from the carrier. Such figures were far beyond the reach of the prewar visual system, but they made the DLI a practical proposition when radar early warning appeared. DLI must have been particularly attractive to a Royal Navy which had been forced to adopt high-performance, short-range RAF fighters such as the Seafire.

The figures now go very much the other way. An attacker carrying a stand-off missile must be shot down before he can fire. The fighter can attack the missile itself, but that is a far more difficult target. Moreover, if it can destroy the bomber and the bomber's elite crew, then over the length of a campaign the carrier's security will improve. Otherwise the sacrifices made by the fighter pilots will merely worsen matters, as the enemy's force

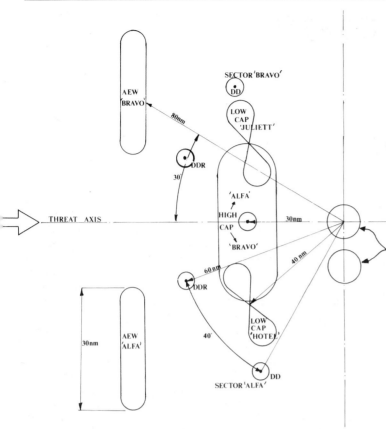

AEW AND CAP STATIONS

These stations are for an air defense exercise in the Seventh Fleet, December 1956 (Task Group 77.4). In this exercise, CAP aircraft were FJ Furies (model not specified). High CAP aircraft cruised in the large 'racetrack' pattern shown to conserve fuel, while low-altitude CAP operated on the two stations shown.

This is a *typical* US disposition. A more modern arrangement would include a SAM defense zone around the carrier, with aircraft operating zones beyond that. Current CAP practice, as reflected in Standard Aircraft Characteristics, is for CAPs to operate 150nm from the carrier, AEW aircraft, 200nm (50 rather than 30nm 'racetrack'). This extension towards the incoming threat reflects considerable Soviet progress in air-to-surface missile technology, as the 1956 formation was designed against bomb and torpedo attack from short range.

EACH CIRCLE REPRESENTS ONE CARRIER AND TWO DESTROYERS (ONE A DDR); THE DDR IS TO INCREASE THE PROBABILITY OF DETECTING LOW FLIERS LEAKING PAST THE OTHER PICKETS

will remain largely untouched while the carrier loses efficiency. A typical air-to-surface missile may have an effective range of 150nm, so that the bomber must be attacked outside that range. A Phantom carries Sparrows with a nominal range of about 10nm and a speed of about Mach 4, perhaps 40nm per minute at high altitude. It climbs to combat altitude in about two or three minutes, and runs out the target area at about 500kts, so that to reach 150nm takes it about 18 minutes. If the bomber approaches at a similar speed, the 10nm Sparrow can be fired at a range of about 12nm, so in fact the Phantom must only reach a firing position about 140nm from the ship, 17 minutes out. At the moment of launch, then, the bomber is about 300nm from the ship, and matters become even worse if leeway is left for pilot briefing or warm-up or even for turning the carrier into the wind to launch. Modern radars are, at best, marginal under such circumstances. Hence the decline of DLI tactics.

Typically, a carrier maintains several CAP stations, with two fighters per station. Fighters are relieved on station to avoid any gap in coverage, and the relief aircraft must be maintained ready on deck. Thus a carrier with a Phoenix-CAP squadron of twelve F-14s can generally maintain two stations, with four ready reliefs, and four other aircraft being maintained. These stations are purely defensive, but in Vietnam attack carriers typically operated CAPs over the strike target areas (TARCAPs) as well as barriers off the Vietnamese coast to prevent enemy aircraft from mixing with returning strikes, or from attacking shore-bombardment ships spread about off the coast (BARCAPs). Under such circumstances several carriers typically joined forces. Presumably in future the F-18 will be employed on strike escort and TARCAP/BARCAP missions, while the less numerous (but more capable) F-14s remain on defensive CAP.

THE ROLE OF RADAR

The mere existence of shipboard radar did not solve the early warning problem. A radar scope shows a 'blip', indi-

cating the direction of some unknown object at one instant of time. However, a fighter is directed at the *future* location of an incoming bomber; in order to estimate that location, the radar operator must maintain a file of successive locations, then draw a track along them. Some radars are designed to track a particular target continuously, but then they are dedicated to that single target and do not see any others which may appear. The problem is that in practice there is almost never a single target or a single 'blip'. Not only must the operator connect up the 'blips' which happen to represent one target of particular interest – he must also identify all of the others, at least to the extent of deciding which one are of interest. Again, almost from the origins of operational radar there has been an automatic means of accomplishing this task (IFF, or Identification Friend or Foe), but also again it has its limits. When IFF is working properly, it does permit friendly fighters to be excluded. However, it does not indicate which unidentified 'blips' are enemies, nor does it indicate which ones present the most immediate threats to the carrier or to the fleet.

This last issue might seem relatively unimportant in the event of a single massive enemy air raid, as often occurred in the Mediterranean during World War II. However, US carriers in the same sea in peacetime are on constant alert against surprise attack. After all, land-based bombers armed with stand-off missiles are the primary Soviet anti-carrier weapon, and an unopposed attack would be quite damaging. On the other hand, the Mediterranean sky is filled with civilian, neutral, and friendly air traffic, most of which does not reply to naval IFF interrogators. Some analysis of observed radar tracks is then the chief means of identification.

In effect, then, the carrier radars operate in a 'track-while-scan' mode: they continuously scan to pick up new targets, while maintaining track data (hopefully good enough for fighter control) on targets deemed of particular significance. Such operation demands relatively precise location data from the scanning radar, and there is a

From the first, carrier radar was the key to effective fleet air defense, as it alone could supply sufficient early warning to permit the carrier to launch her fighters in time. This late-war view of USS *Ticonderoga* shows both the long-range air search 'mattress' of SK and the pencil-beam 'dish' of the fighter-control set, SP, before it. A second search set, an SC-2, was mounted on one side of the funnel but is not apparent here. Forward of both radars is a mounting for a radar countermeasures receiver (SPR-2).

The SK shows an IFF antenna on its upper edge, essential for fighter control; an IFF transponder is mounted outboard of the funnel. The only important air control antenna not visible is the homing beacon (YE) atop the mast. Other radar antennas visible here (Mk 12 and 22 on the Mk 37 director) controlled 5in guns firing proximity-fuze ammunition, itself an application of radar principles. *The Floating Drydock*

Radar on board ship has only a limited range against low-flying aircraft due to its low height above the surface, and therefore its close radar horizon. From 1942 onwards the United States Navy sought to develop an airborne search radar, first to observe enemy ships at a great range but then, far more urgently, to detect low-flying aircraft such as Kamikazes. The result was Project 'Cadillac', represented here by an Avenger with an APS-20 search radar in its belly and a data link down to a 'terminal' aboard a carrier or a radar picket ship. AEW aircraft became a fixture of US fast carrier operations from the late 1940s onwards, and 'Cadillac' also produced a series of land-based 'airborne CICs', long range aircraft which could cooperate with the Fleet at sea. The first of them were converted Flying Fortresses (PB-1Ws), but they were superseded by the familiar WV-2 Super Constellations, some of which operated during the Vietnam War. These aircraft had much the same function as the present AWACs. *Grumman History Center*

trade-off between radar range and precision. That is, the radar sends out a stream of pulses, and there is a probability, varying with the range, that any particular pulse will be reflected off the target and then detected by the radar. The more pulses the radar sends in any given direction, the better the chance that it will pick up a target located there at any given range. The radar beam itself has a width, within which it cannot tell target directions apart. The wider the beam, the longer, in effect, that it looks in one direction – and the less precise its data. One might imagine that the solution would be to use a narrow beam but many more pulses. However, that, too, limits the effective range of the radar. If the pulses come too close together, a target may reflect one pulse after the next has already been sent out, and the radar will be unable to decide which has been reflected. In effect the time interval between pulses sets a limit on the range to which the radar is usable; in practice radars rarely perform this well.

'Track-while-scan' introduces another issue as well: the rate at which the radar scans – in effect, how often it observes in any given direction. Tracking is most accurate when the radar checks back on a target after it has moved only a short distance. Thus, the faster the target, the faster the radar should rotate. However, the faster the scanning rate, the fewer pulses hit the target, and thus the lower the probability of detection in the first place. For example, where wartime US air search radars scanned at about 4.5rpm (providing a second look every 13 seconds), postwar

Many fast carriers operated AEW versions of the Skyraider, and AD-4Ws were operated by the Royal Navy as the Skyraider AEW4. This AD-5W of VAW-12 is shown landing aboard the *Essex*, then designated an ASW carrier, in June 1960.

models scanned at about 15 (with a new look every 4 seconds) to counter the faster jets.

Many wartime carrier installations also included a tracking radar which could provide precise data on a particular target. For example, the Royal Navy generally provided its carriers with two air search sets, a Type 279 and a shorter-wave 281. Together they could cover the volume around the ship more effectively, given the patterns of signal fading associated with each set. Perhaps more importantly, the 281, which had a very wide beam and therefore provided only imprecise scanning data, had an alternative precision tracking mode. In US carriers precision tracking was the province of the dish-shaped SP or SM, which could provide height as well as range and bearing. Fighter interception required all three, since a fighter vectored to the wrong altitude (and particularly to too low an altitude) would be unable to complete an interception. Thus the Royal Navy used an additional specialized height-finder, Type 277, or else a US SM.

Quite early both navies discovered that the proper processing of radar data was as important as the raw radar capability itself. 'Track-while-scan' operation demands a memory, and before the age of computers that memory had to be a plotting board marked with observed aircraft positions. Fighter control required plotting and computation to vector the fighter, far from the path of the incoming target, into the target's path. Non-radar information, for example radio messages from other ships in the task force, would make track identification more reliable. Moreover, effective performance of the carrier/fighter system in battle demanded decisions as to which enemy attackers should be engaged first, and by whom; these decisions were particularly critical, given the relatively small number of CAP fighters airborne at any time. They could be made only on the basis of a comprehensive picture of the evolving air battle, ie a picture based on all available radar and non-radar information.

These considerations were the origin of the Combat Information Center, CIC; during World War II the standard British term was Action Information Organisation (AIO). To some extent CIC might be considered the natural counterpart of the plotting station maintained aboard surface ships, displaying a running picture of a battle derived from lookouts, range-finder data, and reports. The heart of CIC was generally a vertical plot, synthesizing radar and

other data, and maintained by hand. In some British ships the plot was horizontal, and a tracking radar (281) could provide an automatic plot of a particular target. However, there was no means of transferring radar data directly from scope to plot, and that was the great drawback of wartime and early postwar CIC systems.

That is, in a simple radar, it is the operator who decides whether a point of light on the scope face is or is not a valid target. Returns from real aircraft are mixed with considerable amounts of noise. Moreover, given the scale displayed, the 'blip' on a radar scope is in many cases even less precise than the radar beam itself. In the wartime CIC, the radar operator would call out his judgment of the 'blip' location, which the CIC plotter or plotting team would transfer to the master plot. Errors crept in at both ends, and the rate of error would increase as more and more targets appeared, or as the radar scanned more rapidly, producing more frequent 'blips'. Postwar experiments showed, too, that CIC plotting accuracy would degenerate far more rapidly than the plotters realized. In effect, plotting limited the total number of targets a CIC might handle, whether or not there were enough aircraft or guns or (later) missiles to, theoretically, destroy all of those targets.

Successful interception depends, moreover, on the accuracy of the CIC, since the fighter pilot does not search randomly for targets. His efficiency depends upon how well the CIC fighter controller can vector him onto a target, so that he can 'acquire' and then attack it. This is as true for a radar-equipped all-weather fighter as it is for a day fighter guided by the pilot's eye. In effect the CIC bridges the gap between search and fire control; the latter function requires a very precise location of the target by the intercepting fighter. If the latter is using a radar, fire control precision demands the use of a very narrow pencil beam – which cannot efficiently (or rapidly) search large volumes of sky. Thus, the more accurate the CIC data – itself derived, however, from inherently imprecise wide-beam search (scanning) radars – the faster the transition to fighter fire control and the quicker the attack, when every minute of delay may bring a bomber ten miles closer

Ultimately the airborne radar platform and CIC functions were merged; an E-2 Hawkeye such as this one can control fighters directly through automated data links and, indeed, can replace the surface radars of a task force. The enormous 'rotodome' houses an APS-125 antenna with integral IFF, capable of detecting targets over land by means of an airborne moving-target indicator (AMTI). Sufficient heat is generated by the system electronics that a cooler is required, indicated by the air scoop just aft of the cockpit. *Grumman History Center*

to the task force. A similar equation holds for the pilot making a visual attack. He, too, cannot search a great volume of sky, although in his case the limit is more on the distance out to which he can see than on the angle through which he can look.

THE SATURATION PROBLEM

CIC saturation was a relatively minor problem through much of World War II. Attacks tended to be concentrated in time and space to achieve maximum effect, partly in view of the limited lethality per weapon, ie per airplane. Also, individual airplanes were too easily dealt with by shipboard weapons. In effect mass air raids were an attempt to saturate the fighters rather than the CIC, on the theory that the former would be unable to deal with targets appearing too rapidly: some large fraction would leak through. With jets the equation changed. Jet aircraft were not available in comparable numbers, but their diminished numbers were balanced by far more lethal weapons: air-to-surface stand-off missiles and nuclear bombs. A large number of jets attacking simultaneously on very different courses would saturate the ability of the CIC to assign and maintain tracks, and also the ability of the fighter controllers in CIC to calculate intercept courses. No matter how lethal the fighters, they would be unable to appear in time or in the appropriate numbers. It was sometimes argued that the bombers would have to fly together until some intermediate dispersal point was reached, so that saturation could be reduced by increasing radar and interceptor range and feeding fighters into the bomber stream, but even that required a high order of accuracy and fighter control.

The solution adopted was automation and, to some extent, the dispersal of fighters control to the fighter themselves. By the early 1950s both the US and Royal Navies were painfully aware of the saturation problem, and both looked towards some automation of the plot itself, so that it could store data more efficiently, and perhaps

even calculate target tracks. The automated plot could display its data, and ultimately it could transfer data to other ships and even aircraft via high-speed data links. In the Royal Navy of the mid-1950s this development was denoted the Comprehensive Display System, or CDS. Data entry was still manual: the radar operator still decided whether he had a valid target, but now he entered it into the system by means of a contact pressed against the surface of the radar display.

Even before it could bring CDS into the fleet, the Royal Navy introduced a new simplified concept of fighter control: 'broadcast control', in which a single 'broadcaster' provided all fighter pilots with a running commentary on the incoming raid, allowing them to compute intercept courses themselves. This system had the advantage of greatly increasing the rate at which fighters could engage, but on the other hand it required a means of distributing the available fighters over the incoming attackers, as otherwise all might concentrate on only a few of the targets. Broadcast control lent itself to automation, as a computer aboard the fighter could communicate directly with the carrier via a data link, if the radar data were automated in the first place. Broadcast control did require one entirely new piece of electronic gear aboard the carrier. In order to compute an intercept course to a bomber located relative to the carrier, the fighter needed some means of precisely locating *itself* relative to the carrier, both in distance and in bearing. That was TACAN (Tactical Air Navigation aid), the now-standard transponder beacon at carrier mastheads.

As computer technology advanced, it was natural to use the electronic plot for more than display purposes. In effect it converted the information on radar screens into numbers which could feed computers, and which could be exchanged with other ships and even with aircraft via high-speed digital data links, far more reliable than voice radio. Thus the US NTDS (Naval Tactical Data System) acts as a means of sharing tactical information throughout a task force: in effect every ship is able to use the output of the radars of the entire group, which greatly increases the probability that any given target will be detected. Automated information processing can easily extend to automated weapon assignment and then to an automated transition from search radar to fire control in, for example, a surface-to-air missile system. Thus what began in the

Royal Navy as CDS became ADA (Action Data Automation), and then ADAWS (Action Data Automated Weapon System).

The weakness of the entire system was the imprecision of the radar scope. Thus came about the logical conclusion of the automation process: the newest radars decide automatically that an echo is a real target, generally on the basis of how many echoes return from a given direction. The returning signal within the radar system carries, in theory, far more information than does the point of light on the scope face. For example, such subtleties of its form as doppler shift indicate target course and speed, and permit a much faster establishment of a target track. Such Automatic Detection and Tracking (ADT) radars are more urgently required by surface missile ships, whose weapon systems tolerate smaller margins of error than does the carrier/fighter system, but it seems likely that this technology will soon be extended to the carriers as well.

Effective search radar range is limited by, among other things, the altitude of the target: the lower the flier, the closer he can approach without being seen. Beginning in 1944, the US Navy tried two approaches to this problem, both of which have since become standard. One was to station destroyers equipped with extra radars, enlarged CICs and fighter control parties at a distance from the center of the task force. These radar picket ships would, in theory, detect approaching low fliers well before the carrier, and they would be able to vector CAP sections to deal with them. After World War II the United States converted additional picket destroyers, and the Royal Navy at one time planned to convert half of its fleet destroyers to pickets. Even after the end of this program, US task force escorts were fitted with picket radars, and were designed to control fighters.

The other way of extending the radar horizon is to raise the radar to a considerable altitude. The US Navy placed a large radar aboard a Grumman Avenger torpedo-bomber, with a data link which reproduced the radar picture on board on aircraft carrier. This Project 'Cadillac' was originally conceived as an extension of shipboard surface search radar, to see 'over the horizon'. However, as the Kamikaze threat became more pressing, it was reoriented towards the detection of low-flying aircraft. As an alternative, ex-Army B-17 Flying Fortresses were provided with a similar radar and with a miniature CIC. Neither part of Project 'Cadillac' became operational before the end of the war, but both were then very close to completion, and both were continued postwar. Avengers and later Skyraiders with large belly radomes housing the APS-20 radar became a standard feature of carrier air groups, and the Navy also produced a series of 'airborne CICs': first the converted Fortresses, then converted P2V Neptunes, and finally very long-endurance converted Constellations. The latter were also adopted by the US Air Force, to extend land-based radar coverage in a fashion analogous to that envisaged by the Navy. Generally, the airborne CIC differed from the single-engine AEW airplane in that it could control its own CAP section directly, whereas the smaller airplane fed directly into the carrier CIC and acted simply as an additional carrier search radar. On the other hand, the carrier could maintain its own AEW aircraft at sea, whereas the availability of an airborne CIC depended upon shore bases, and then upon the endurance of the airplane itself.

There was an additional problem: the same radar which gave the AEW airplane long-range surface and low-altitude radar coverage also provided the best possible means of detecting submarine snorkels and periscopes. Thus although the carriers of Task Force 77 off Korea included AEW Skyraiders in their air groups during the Korean War, these aircraft were used exclusively for anti-submarine patrol. On the other hand, a very successful test of converted B-17s (PB-1Ws) provided a considerable impetus for the land-based airborne CIC program. Moreover, with the development of much larger carriers and more powerful catapults, development of carrier-based airborne CICs began.

These twin-engine aircraft, first the E-1 Tracer based on the S-2 ASW aircraft, and then the current E-2 Hawkeye, mounted their large radars atop their fuselages, where they could achieve good high *and* low-altitude coverage. Signal processing techniques permit a degree of height-finding, so that the airborne CIC can direct fighters efficiently. Moreover, it can move out from the task force center in the direction of the threat, to permit CAP operation at longer range and, incidentally, to permit the carrier to protect herself to some degree by shutting down her own distinctive air search radars. The current E-2 is data-linked both to the interceptors and to the carrier, so that she is tied to the NTDS network. Her own computer system is designated ATDS (Airborne Tactical Data System).

The airborne CIC can be a useful adjunct to strike operations. It can, for example, observe a strike area, warning friendly aircraft of enemy fighters not yet visible to them, or directing them into efficient interception positions. For example, during the 1971 India-Pakistan War, the Indian Air Force was able to strike Pakistani airfields virtually at will, largely thanks to the efforts of a Soviet-supplied 'Moss' airborne CIC. US airborne CICs, including land-based Constellations, operated in a similar role in Vietnam; in addition, many of them operated as passive detectors of enemy radio and radar emissions, such as those characteristic of enemy air defenses. An Israeli E-2 controlled the F-15s which destroyed five Syrian MiG-21s over Lebanon in June 1979. It might be suggested that the presence of the airborne radar and controllers provided an important measure of superiority.

Given the cramped conditions of a carrier deck, any force multiplier is extremely valuable. The carrier can maintain only a few fighters on CAP at any one time, but their connection with a superior radar system, both ship- and airborne, and with an elaborate target assignment system, does provide them with net capabilities well beyond those of a few single aircraft.

However, the advantages associated with AEW or with an airborne CIC carry with them considerable costs. In either case the airplane is large and relatively underpowered, since it is optimized for long endurance at low speed. Generally it requires a catapult for take-off, although that catapult need not be quite as powerful as jet fighters require. Long endurance in itself requires a substantial fuel load and seems to rule out the use of a V/STOL or a helicopter, at least without some considerable improvement in each technology. Even a long-loiter V/STOL might be limited to the pure AEW role, in which case the simplicity (at least of data transmission) associated with the airborne CIC would be lost. Thus any navy which abandons carriers in favor of V/STOL may well lose any hope of a serious AEW capability just as advances in Soviet (and other) anti-ship weapons would seem to make longer-range AEW more vital.

The AEW/CIC aircraft imposes a considerable 'overhead' on any carrier. Typically, four aircraft are carried to ensure that one is airborne on station at all times; the multiplier is a measure of the complexity of the system and thus of the maintenance load it imposes. Such aircraft are considerably larger than other tactical types, and the smaller the carrier the greater the percentage reduction in striking power they impose. There are subtler considerations as well. For example, of all operational carrier air-

The Royal Navy adapted its Gannet ASW airplane for AEW, using the US APS-20 radar: this is a Gannet AEW3. Although the Gannet could be replaced by helicopters in the ASW role, no such replacement was possible in AEW, so that the demise of the large carrier in the Royal Navy also meant the demise of airborne early warning for the Fleet. The reason was the low endurance of helicopters; in 1980 there is neither helicopter nor V/STOL AEW clearly in sight, although the US Navy is striving for the latter. Without AEW, it would seem, there is also little hope of effective air defense for any task force, whatever the performance built into V/STOL fighters or shipborne missiles. *Royal Navy*

craft in current US service, the E-2 requires the greatest overhead clearance for maintenance (in its case, of the rotodome radar antenna). This in turn sets a requirement on carrier hangars: at the very least, the hangar must provide some space (a 'top hat', for example) of this height. The E-1, with a height of 16ft 10in, was barely compatible with the nominal 17ft 6in hangar clearance of US carriers built during World War II, whereas its successor requires a full 18ft 4in. That is one reason why the *Franklin D Roosevelt* carried E-1s during her last cruise, and also why she was not retained in reserve. All war-built carriers were considered limited by their hangar deck clearance, and the remaining *Essex*s would be less expensive to operate, either in a limited strike role or as helicopter carriers.

WEAPONS

Of the entire carrier/fighter air defense system, the only really visible element is the fighter itself, which generally combines fire control and the actual bomber-killing weapon. One major consequence of higher jet speed and performance was a general demand for radar in every fighter plus more lethal weapons. Early jet fighters had extremely large turning circles at high altitude; their pilots had, therefore, to begin passes long before an enemy bomber came into sight. Moreover, since the fighter would generally have to attack from a head-on position, the pilot's reaction time would be keyed not to his own airplane's speed but to the closing speed, the sum of the two speeds – 1000kts even for slow 500kt bomber and fighter aircraft. Even allowing one fighter per attacker, the fighter pilot would probably get only one firing pass, and a very short one at that.

By the mid-1950s Bureau of Aeronautics studies were showing that a salvo of unguided rockets would be far more effective than conventional cannon fire: many Navy fighters carried pods of 2.75in folding-fin high-velocity rockets. In principle, guidance would improve effectiveness even further, particularly since a fighter with long-range guided weapons would be able to cover a much larger volume of sky. This is a force multiplier issue; so is the ability of an interceptor to deal with several targets either simultaneously or in very rapid succession. Finally, the fighter may well not be able to operate entirely unopposed. It is more than a long-range missile platform, and there may be a trade-off between missile and aircraft performance.

The main stream of postwar US Navy long-range air-to-air missile development runs parallel to the trend in surface-to-air weapons. Thus the original Sparrow I, like Terrier and Talos, was a beam-rider. The single fire control radar in the fighter both tracked the target and generated a spinning beam along which Sparrow I flew. This system required the fighter to fly along a very limited path which in itself made it vulnerable. Moreover, the narrowness of the beam, necessary for effective fire control, required great stability of the fighter and very good pointing in the radar system. Similar beam-riding shipboard systems were considered unsatisfactory partly because of just this requirement for precision pointing from a moving platform, as well as poor low-altitude performance.

From the fighter designer's point of view, radar size and weight was also an important consideration. The diameter of a radar dish antenna determines the width of its beam: the wider the beam (the smaller the dish), the more power is required to achieve a given range. Very long range demands both a very wide dish (which adds considerable drag) and high power (which, at best, consumes considerable weight). For example, the F-4 Phantom was preferred over a competitor, the single-seat F8U-3 Crusader, partly because it could accommodate the largest existing airborne radar dish, the 28in APQ-72. The abortive F6D Missileer was limited to subsonic speeds partly in view of the drag associated with its 60in AWG-9 antenna – which also added considerable weight, given its requirement for a very high power level, in order to control missiles up to 50nm away, and to detect and track targets at perhaps

Given long-range radar contact and efficient IFF, the most effective fleet air defense weapon should be the longest-range missile, which in turn should require a large radar and a fighter capable of lifting it and the weapon. Here an F-14 Tomcat fires its Phoenix missile over the Pacific.

Long range means a very large air-to-air missile, as this catapult launch photograph shows. The F-14A can carry up to six Phoenixes, four under the body, two under the wing 'gloves'.

twice that range. To some extent both size and power could be reduced if signal processing was improved in sophistication, but that in turn required large weights of its own. The AWG-9 system was cut down, first to fit the F-111B and then, through a far more sophisticated electronic technology, to fit the F-14. Even so, it imposes considerable penalties. Although the Sparrow can be carried by a single-seat aircraft, the Navy prefers a specialized radar officer, and this demand for two seats, associated with a long-range weapon, further penalizes the designer.

These considerations would seem to apply to any missile system in which the fighter continues to guide its missile after launch. Sparrow I was succeeded by a semi-active homing Sparrow III, just as beam-riding Terrier gave way to semi-active versions of the same weapon, and to the smaller Tartar and Standard missiles; improved versions remain the standard US long-range (about 10nm) air-to-air missile. In this system the fighter-borne radar bathes the target in its radar beam; the missile homes on the reflected radiation. Semi-active homing places few demands on the fighter-borne radar, which can employ a more diffuse beam and therefore which may enjoy a somewhat lower standard of steadiness and pointing accuracy. The missile designer benefits from the increased intensity of the reflected radar beam as the missile approaches its target.

Even so, a semi-active weapon shares one vital defect with the beam-rider. At any one time, the fighter can engage only one target. There will never be very many fighters, and they will probably be operating close to the range at which enemy bombers can launch their weapons: time per target will be very limited. At Mach 4 it takes a Sparrow only about 15 seconds to cover 10nm, but the switch to another target is much slower: the pilot must make his turn, acquire the new target, lock-on, and then launch. By the late 1950s, with Sparrow III just beginning to enter fleet service, it was clear that the future threat would be saturation attacks. Every missile platform, ship or fighter, would have to be able to engage several targets at once, and those at longer range than had previously been accepted. This in turn required both a larger (and heavier) radar aboard the fighter and larger (and much heavier) fighter-borne missiles. The surface system became first Super Talos and then Typhon; it proved too massive, and was cancelled in 1963. However, that did not solve the saturation problem, and a new system, ASMS (Advanced Surface Missile System) was evolved to a similar requirement. It will soon become operational as Aegis.

The airborne requirement was, if anything, even more urgent, particularly given the small number of missiles per fighter. It was met by the AWG-9 weapon system, employing the Eagle missile, the predecessor of the current Phoenix. The radar tracks both the air-to-air missiles and their (multiple) targets, using 'track-while-scan' techniques. Each missile incorporates an autopilot which the weapon system sets as the missile is fired; the weapon system can also correct missile aim during flight, using a special data link. Only when the missile approaches its target is the latter illuminated, and that only very briefly. This sequence is common to Eagle/Phoenix and to Aegis. However, the airborne system also incorporates a short-range active radar on the missile proper, so that beyond a point the missile homes by itself. Presumably this feature reduces the load on the illuminating radar. Even so, the F-14 is limited in the area in which it can engage several targets simultaneously: all must be simultaneously in the field of vision of its big radar, and the F-14 pilot must keep them there at least until the missiles reach the point of turning on their own radar.*

In an ideal system the fighter would sight an enemy, lock-on the missile, then leave to seek an alternative target. The missile might incorporate an autopilot which the fighter could set to steer it toward a target no longer in view, and the load on the radar of the missile might thereby be reduced: lock-on would occur well after launch. Advantages for the fighter designer would include much reduced weight, since the fighter fire control radar would not have to be capable of precision tracking at very long range. Rather, some homing device in the missile itself would perform most of the precision guidance.

Infrared homing weapons such as Sidewinder provide some of this capability, but in most cases only at relatively short range. Moreover, since it homes on sources of heat, the infrared missile may be effective only in a tail chase. However, the long-range fleet interceptor may most often find itself approaching its target from ahead: getting into the tail-chase position may waste far too much time. This problem has been solved in part, so that advanced infrared missiles home on the skin heating of an airplane, due to its high speed, or on the glint of the sun off a cockpit canopy. However, these are subtle effects, not easily detected (or locked onto) at long range.

That leaves the radar-guided weapon, producing its own radar signals. It suffers from the small size of the missile, limited by factors such as aircraft size and undercarriage clearance, both of which are determined to a considerable extent by the design of the aircraft carrier herself. Missile

diameter in turn limits the size of the radar antenna in the nose of the weapon; for long range, the missile's radar requires the largest possible antenna in relation to its radar wavelength. however, very short wavelength radars have developed only very slowly. For example, they suffer from absorption in the atmosphere, eg by water vapor. Signal generators suffer from low efficiency, which in turn requires more electrical power (and more weight) in the missile proper. Thus the original Sparrow II 'fire-and-forget' radar-guided missile project had to be abandoned in favor of Sparrow III about 1956, and a projected radar-guided Sidewinder also proved unsuccessful. However, the 'fire-and-forget' weapon with a range quite comparable to that of Sparrow III (and at a similar all-up weight) seems a likely prospect for the early 1980s, at least in prototype form. The electronic miniaturization which makes such a weapon practical will probably also greatly shrink the size and weight of longer-range missiles such as Phoenix, and, in turn, may permit the ultimate replacement of heavy fighters such as the F-4 by far lighter machines, perhaps late versions of the F-18.

The advent of a 'fire-and-forget' radar missile of Sparrow performance would have a dramatic effect on the prospects of V/STOL carriers. V/STOL fighters are notoriously limited in weight, and therefore are poor prospects for heavy permanent radar installations. However, they can trade off range for temporary weapon weights, such as air-to-air missiles: for example, many US Harriers carry Sidewinder. An effective 'fire-and-forget' weapon would also change the character of a medium-weight fighter such as the F-18, permitting it to engage several targets almost simultaneously, albeit probably at far shorter ranges than the F-14. Moreover, the high maneuverability of the lighter airplane would allow it to engage widely spearated targets, without the limit of radar field of vision or of continuous observation of the target almost until the missile hits.

Any reduction of fighter size or weight or complexity is valuable aboard a carrier with, at best, limited maintenance space and limited aircraft capacity. Moreover, it can be argued, the more the interceptor function is placed aboard a specialized missile rather than aboard the fighter, the more flexible the airplane becomes, the more airplanes of the same type can be procured, the less the investment in specialized maintenance and specialized spare parts and, perhaps no less importantly, the longer the production run of the fighter and thus the lower its unit cost. There remains, of course, the issue of missile maintenance. However, with the widespread use of integrated circuits and long-life propellants, a properly stowed missile comes close to the ideal of the 'wooden round', usable as soon as it is uncrated.

All of this development is aimed at long-range fire, probably well beyond visual range. Indeed, given Soviet saturation tactics, one might say that there is a choice between long-range/multiple-target engagement and a massive increase both in fighter numbers and in fighter size, to loiter at greatly increased range. Every argument points to longer and longer range fighter-borne weapons — except for one: IFF. In Vietnam, US Phantoms equipped with what was then perhaps the longest range air-to-air missile in tactical service achieved an abysmal kill rate, not because of some inherent mechanical or electronic defect but because in a sky crowded with friendly and enemy aircraft it was too easy to shoot at the wrong target. IFF could not be relied upon, partly because it could too easily fall victim to battle damage. Thus pilots were forced almost to come alongside their targets before falling back to fire. Many concluded that in future the only worthwhile weapons would be those effective within visual range and,

*Unlike the US Navy, the Royal Navy (and the RAF) adopted an infrared homing system in which the missile optics are locked-on by the fighter's airborne intercept radar. This is a 'fire-and-forget' system, but it is limited by weather and almost certainly by the requirement that the missile be launched at the tail of its target, which it must overtake in a stern chase. These defects may explain the Royal Navy's requirement for a large continuous-wave (CW) radar in its version of the P1154, ie a radar associated with a semi-active homing weapon. The newest British air-to-air weapon, Skyflash, is a semi-active homer related to the Sparrow.

Not every carrier can, or should, accommodate the most powerful air defense aircraft. Many US ASW carriers were provided with detachments of A-4 Skyhawks operating as fighters rather than attack aircraft.

Here Skyhawks of ASW Fighter Squadron One (VSF-1), attached to an attack carrier (*Independence*), await launch, June 1968.

moreover, in a dogfight: guns and perhaps Sidewinders. It may be argued that in a task force engagement the *only* incoming aircraft will be enemies, but that is open to some question, given the continuous carrier operating cycle. As Soviet bomber range improves, too, the attackers may begin to come from unexpected directions, and thus identification based on bearing may cease to be valuable. The problem is severe, and it is by no means limited to carrier operations. For example, land-based tactical aircraft will probably suffer severe losses from friendly SAMs in any future European war.

Several countermeasures have been proposed. If the new generation of radars can extract detailed information from their returning signals, some of that information should characterize the radar target, whether or not it cooperates by responding to IFF interrogation. For example, the portion of the radar echo returned from the air intakes of an airplane should contain information about the shape of its engines, the rate at which it is turning over, even the

A great deal depends upon the character of the threat. If the enemy flies large numbers of bombers, each of which carries one or more supersonic missiles, then the only way to defeat him is to shoot down bombers, missiles, or both. However, far out to sea the Soviets are more likely to attack with missiles launched from well over the horizon by submarines and surface ships, guided by the search radar of a 'Bear-D' reconnaissance bomber, such as this one escorted by an F-4J of VF-41 from USS *Franklin D Roosevelt*, September 1973. In such circumstances even a very small detachment of fighters of very moderate performance may prove effective; that is the rationale for the Sea Harrier in the air defense mission.

number of blades in the first few stages of its compressor. As it becomes less expensive and more compact, it is tempting to apply these considerations to IFF, in order to preserve confidence in long-range weapons.

At present all of the weapons of the carrier/fighter system are concentrated in the fighters. The primary link to surface ships carrying anti-aircraft missiles is the ATDS/NTDS data link, and that does not suffice to carry fire-control quality data to the surface ships. However, it can be argued that it is far more economical for a surface ship to carry the massive weight of missile than for the fighter to loiter on a distant CAP. If in fact the fighter can make do with radar data from an E-2, perhaps investment in a larger airborne radar will make possible control of very long range sea-based missiles by the airborne radar platoform itself. Space and weight aboard large surface ships can be relatively inexpensive, particuarly if the ships require little in the way of fire control systems or radars – those will be concentrated aboard a 'super E-2'. From the carrier point of view, the 'overhead' represented by air defense fighters can be eliminated; a carrier of a given size can support more intense strikes, accompanied, perhaps, by more fighter escorts. Such a system does little to enhance the prospects for V/STOL, since the 'super E-2' is even more difficult to fit into a V/STOL package than is the E-2 itself, and any attempt to reduce requirements by eliminating the airborne data processing will introduce considerable data link problems. However, it is attractive, and it has been proposed several times in the past: the technique is usually called Forward Pass.

The massive combination of AEW/CIC aircraft and long range fleet fighters is designed primarily to defeat the bomber/missile threat built up by the Soviet Navy from the late 1950s on, a threat any carrier group approaching launch positions off Soviet targets (such as Murmansk or Petropavlovsk) would have to expect to encounter. However, from the mid-1960s onwards the Soviets mounted a quite different air threat, further out to sea, consisting of surface ships and submarines launching a long-range cruise missile, SSN-3 ('Shaddock'). The effective performance of such strike forces requires the assistance of targeting aircraft, since the target is well over their horizon; indeed, the emergence of the 'Bear-D' radar reconnaissance bomber is associated with the emergence of SSN-3-equipped attack groups. It follows that the destruction of the reconnaissance airplane will spoil the attack, and such action seems well within the capabilities of even existing V/STOL fighters such as the Sea Harrier. Indeed, faced with only the mid-ocean SSN-3 (or successor) threat, the combination of Sea Harrier and small carrier might be quite effective. However, the same logic does not hold for the bomber/missile combination, since the bombers fly high enough to acquire their own targets before firing.

Probably the chief flaw in the Sea Harrier defensive concept is that initial acquisition of the 'Bear-D' may be difficult without the assistance of an AEW aircraft, particularly in view of the limited loiter capability of the fighter. However, at present there is no AEW aircraft in prospect compatible with the *Invincible*. The Sea Harrier must then fall back on the assitance provided by land-based AEW types such as the Nimrod and the AWACS. Worse, if the *Invincible* is within range of the land-based AEW aircraft, it may also be within range of Soviet bombers. Moreover, with the introduction of the 'Backfire', that range is being considerably extended.

8. Carrier Survivability

Even if it is accepted that a carrier represents a great and effective concentration of naval power, there remains the issue of her ability to survive and, moreover, to survive as an operational unit, in wartime. At first blush she seems terribly vulnerable. The same arguments which dictate an immense flat deck also seem to imply that any break in the deck will end all air operations. Aircraft are either exposed on deck or secreted in a hangar well above the waterline. They are usually filled with fuel, and often surrounded by masses of explosives. Piston engines required large amounts of explosive avgas; JP-5 is more benign, but it still burns, and a flood of JP-5 liberated from shattered fuel tanks can still carry fire deep into a damaged ship. Below decks, the carrier must concentrate large numbers of bombs and rockets in a few magazines, perhaps even more capacious than those whose explosion destroyed several battleships.

Moreover, the carrier is a very large target, difficult, it would seem, to hide from hostile radars. She constantly emits characteristic signals, partly because her strength as a weapon is largely derived from her ability to control large numbers of aircraft at a great range. At the same time, she does not have the weight to spare for heavy armor, partly because any protection at all spread over her immense surface area must consume immense weight. An armored flight deck adds immense topweight, even for relatively thin protection. Classical torpedo defense systems would consume precious volume below decks, yet without them she would be vulnerable to underwater attack.

HISTORICAL CONSIDERATIONS

The threat the carrier faces is similar to that which faces all warships. Until 1945 it consisted of bomb, mine, torpedo and shellfire, the last particularly from heavy units which might catch the carrier under conditions in which she could not launch her aircraft, as in the case of HMS *Glorious* in June 1940. The bombs were predominantly dive-bombs of limited penetrating power; however, their threat increased to include high-altitude armor piercing bombs when the Germans succeeded in developing guided missiles (stand-off bombs such as the FX 1400 which sank the Italian battleship *Roma*). The important point about bombs was that they attacked almost vertically, striking either the flight deck or the water alongside, in which case they spattered the side of the carrier with fragments. Late in 1944 the Japanese introduced the Kamikaze, which generally struck the flight deck, but at a shallow angle, setting off either a flight deck fire or exploding in the hangar deck below. By the late 1950s there were also cruise missiles, which would strike the side of the carrier, penetrating at a shallow angle almost like long-range shellfire. Moreover, there is the threat of nuclear attack; although no ship can withstand a direct hit, it is easy to imagine misses, in which case the question is how close a miss the ship can tolerate.

The mass of explosives and fuels tends to complicate the effect of any particular type of damage. For example, in June 1944 the Japanese armored carrier *Taiho* was torpedoed by a US submarine. Her conventional torpedo protection system absorbed the damage, but the shock of the explosion dropped an elevator to the bottom of its well, where it pierced the crown of a gasoline tank. Vapor formed. The damage control officer chose to ventilate the enclosed hangar deck, using the ship's forced-draught fans, and the vapor collected in the hangar in what turned out to be a fatal concentration. It was ignited by a random spark, and the ship was lost. Other carriers were lost after the primary damage was repaired or at least limited, due to hangar deck gasoline fires – which could have been stopped, not by some drastic change in design, but by a combination of training and improved fire-fighting gear. As everywhere else in carrier development, such details have effects often quite as great as the design features more easily visible.

The basic design features intended to improve carrier survivability fall into two categories: dispersal/redundancy, and conventional protection. There is a trade-off between the two. For example, when the US *Essex* class was designed in 1940 the US Navy was well aware of the details of British armored flight deck carriers; in fact, the US Naval Attaché in London wrote that he favored the British type for a trans-Pacific campaign of the type the United States then contemplated. The *Essex* class, however, was not given an armored flight deck, on the theory that it would cost far too much in aircraft capacity and in endurance for both ship and aircraft. It was also argued that her aircraft operating features were sufficiently spread out to permit survival of a significant fraction in the event of damage: armor weight went into survival of the hull. Thus, with two catapults forward, an *Essex* could launch aircraft even were most of her flight deck to be holed. She could retrieve aircraft fore or aft, and indeed arresting gear wires almost covered her flight deck. Her three elevators were well dispersed along her length. Clearly she would be far less efficient if damaged, but she would not be put out of action – unless the initial damage ignited something else, for example the kind of fire which almost sank the carrier *Franklin*. That sort of damage seems not to have been envisaged in 1940.

British logic was quite different. Aircraft were considered the main battery of the carrier, but they were probably unable to defend her. Moreover, dive-bombers could be sure of hits even on a radically maneuvering ship. In 1935 the Air Ministry assured the Admiralty that for about a decade the heaviest bomb a dive-bomber would be able to lift would be a 500-pounder (semi-armor piercing), and it was quite practicable to design a carrier with a flight deck protected against it, and sides protected against cruiser (6in) fire. The floor of the hangar became the armored deck to protect machinery and magazines against plunging 6in fire, and, as compared to the earlier *Ark*

Often ship survival hinges on relatively detailed issues. For example, HMS *Ark Royal* succumbed to slow flooding, partly because no emergency diesel generators had been incorporated in her design and partly because, as in the case of the *Prince of Wales*, her shaft, distorted by the explosion, opened up part of her hull as it turned. All boiler power was lost as a system of ducts immediately over the fire rooms (and therefore quite low in the ship) flooded. This design was a necessary consequence of the two-hangar arrangement, in turn a consequence of standard British air operating procedure. *Conway Picture Library*

Before World War II it was generally assumed that carriers were totally vulnerable to air attack but that their high speed would generally protect them against submarines. Both assumptions proved only partly correct: the US fleet carrier *Wasp*, incidentally one of only two US fleet carriers entirely without underwater protection, was sunk by a Japanese submarine on 15 September 1942 near Guadalcanal. Thus the loss of the *Wasp* can be traced in part to the design sacrifices attendant on a limit on total US carrier tonnage written into the Washington Treaty.

Royal (protected against cruiser fire but with unprotected aircraft), it was necessary to sacrifice one of the two hangars, about half the air group. This was the *Illustrious* design.

The US argument was that no one could make so bald a prediction about the bomb of the future. Flight deck armor was so heavy that even a relatively small increase in bomb weight would exact an immense price. Even in 1935 the US Navy was dive-bombing with 1000-pounders, and aircraft development was so rapid that no one could be sure of any stopping point, particularly as carriers would probably have to confront land-based aircraft. Like the Royal Navy, the US Navy considered its standard cruiser threat the 6in gun. It provided a conventional side belt and armored deck low in the ship to protect magazines, machinery and gasoline. In addition, the *Essex* incorporated a relatively thin armored deck at the hangar level. It would protect the interior of the ship from non-armor piercing bombs. As for AP or semi-AP (SAP) weapons, hopefully the hangar deck would activate their time-delay

fuzes, causing them to burst above the main armored deck deep in the ship; it would protect the vitals from the resulting fragments. US constructors argued that any bomb *not* defeated by the 3in plating of the British flight deck would penetrate, and would not explode soon enough for the hangar deck armor to have any effect: it might well blast a magazine. Fortunately for HMS *Illustrious*, when she was penetrated by a German bomb, it burst within rather than under her hangar.

The US demand for an armored hangar deck *and* a protective deck deep in the ship meant that any US armored flight deck carrier would have to be extremely large. Indeed, studies for such a ship, begun in 1940, showed that the addition of ½in to the main protective deck, 1in to the hangar deck, and 1in to the flight deck would raise displacement from about 27,000 to 33,400 tons. The *Midway* design called, in the end, for far more. She was to be able to survive 8in shellfire, far more logically a US requirement than the previous 6in, given the Japanese preference for heavy cruisers, and she had a 3.5in flight deck, even heavier than that of a British armored carrier of prewar design. This, plus the other armor decks, drove up displacement. The *Midway*s were large, and therefore were to be given large air groups, but they were designed to displace 45,000 tons to accommodate protective weights, not aircraft. Even at that displacement they incorporated no side protection for their hangars. That must have been partly because the hangar deck did not occupy nearly the same position in US as in British thinking: protecting it was by no means protecting the air group.

The Kamikaze was the ideal weapon for the British armored flight deck to counter: it was very explosive, but could not penetrate any substantial thickness of armor. Thus a Kamikaze hitting a British flight deck would go off, perhaps blow aircraft off the deck, and perhaps start a minor fire. The carrier would return to action within a few hours. An *Essex* would find instead a large explosion on her hangar deck, elevators blown out and large fires. Among the differences might be the much larger *Essex* air group, but there would also be the sheer size of the Kamikaze and its own load of avgas: the standard armor-piercing bomb left a much cleaner hole as it penetrated the hangar deck, but a Kamikaze would be stopped by that armor, and would detonate there. Thus at the end of the war the concept of the armored flight deck was once again in favor in the United States, and the price it exacted was little understood.

All subsequent US carriers have armored flight decks, but that represents some naval architectural realities as well as concentration on protection. The immense ships of the *Forrestal* and later classes are so long that the flight deck must be the strength deck; there is insufficient hull depth for strength if the hangar deck is used instead. Only a relatively thick flight deck will provide sufficient strength. Indeed, the use of a single thick armored deck introduced a new problem. The designers of the *United States* (CVA58), the forerunner of the current generation of carriers, reasoned that a big break in the flight deck might not only interrupt flight operations, it might also break up the ship by destroying too much of her strength. They therefore split the original 3in flight deck into two layers, a 2in flight deck and a 1in gallery deck which would take the load of a low-speed run out of the battle area. The loss of some bomb protection had to be accepted: the combined decks were roughly equivalent to 2.5in. It says a great deal for the cost of deck armor that the ship could not take the weight of more armor, even at 65,000 tons. Of course, there was considerable internal armor much deeper in the ship, descended from the armored decks of traditional US designs.

CARRIER PROTECTION SINCE WORLD WAR II

With the end of World War II US carrier designers no longer considered shellfire an important threat. However, late in the war, near-missing bombs had caused considerable damage by their splinters. It became common, then, for carriers to exchange their heavy, concentrated belt armor for thin splinter protection spread along their sides, up to their hangar decks, which in postwar designs were themselves almost fully enclosed. In addition, the postwar carriers incorporate internal armor boxes enclosing

Probably the closest World War II equivalent to a modern anti-ship cruise missile was the Kamikaze, seen here in action against USS *Essex*, 25 November 1944. The Kamikaze combined a substantial explosive charge (in the form of a bomb) with gasoline (for fire effect) but, unlike an armor-piercing missile, it could not penetrate even relatively thin deck armor. Thus it could start massive fires on the flight and hangar decks of unarmored American carriers, but could not severely damage British-type armored flight decks. In the case illustrated, a hit near the forward elevator touched off fully armed aircraft on the flight deck, and the resulting series of explosions killed 15 men and wounded another 44. However, 30 minutes later the fire had been smothered – and the flight deck was operational. To some extent this result vindicated the US Navy's belief that a thin wooden flight deck could be repaired rapidly after battle damage whereas an armored deck might not be reparable outside a major base.

magazines, engine rooms and, as designed, avgas stowage. Although individual layers of armor are relatively thin, the totals are impressive, as a penetrating bomb or rocket has to penetrate several layers of armor. Side protection, for example, is generally reinforced by upward extensions of the bulkheads of the underwater side protection system. Moreover, much of the structure of the ship consists of steels similar to World War II STS, ie, to splinter protection or deck armor. One consequence of all of this is that it is difficult to calculate precisely the protection afforded any interior space in the carrier, for example to fill partiucularly weak spots or to reduce excessive thickness.

Cruise missiles pose a new threat. They approach the ship at a shallow angle, and will probably home either on her hull or on the sharp corner her island makes with the flight deck. A large-diameter shaped charge, which is the conventional warhead of most Soviet cruise missiles, can penetrate over its diameter in steel. It produces a long, hot jet of metal. In a ship as large as a carrier, there is a fair chance that the jet will pass through enough of the ship to dissipate without hitting anything vital. However, should it strike a magazine, the effect will probably be catastrophic. No ship can survive the detonation of that much explosive.

Two kinds of protection have been proposed. One would be more armor, perhaps an anti-shaped charge type similar in principle to the well-publicised Chobham tank armor. In theory it should be possible to break up the concentrated jet of hot metal produced by a shaped charge, perhaps by deflecting it through a series of baffles. Any such system must necessarily cost internal volume, but surely the sacrifice in ordnance capacity would be worth while. The alternative would be some kind of protection within the magazine, perhaps a very quick-acting fire suppression system, or a better means of isolating one

weapon from another. Again, this would consume volume, but it might be easier to develop. It would probably require a considerable reduction in the weight of ammunition the carrier can accommodate, but then again it can be argued that with 'smart' bombs the carrier can afford precisely this sort of sacrifice.

Magazine protection is important because a magazine hit is almost the only way of sinking a modern carrier, at least at one shot. Most kinds of attack will damage her, but at least not fatally. Bombs can smash part of her flight deck, but a modern US carrier can still launch aircraft, using one of two widely separated sets of catapults. It is true that she cannot easily recover them if her arresting gear is destroyed, but one might also argue that there is little joy in preventing the perpetrators of a successful strike from landing back aboard their carrier. Flight or even hangar deck fires may burn her out, but they are far from certain to, and the survival of the *Forrestal* and *Enterprise* after spectacular fires, which set off numerous bombs and other weapons on their flight decks, suggests that fire-fighting techniques are quite effective. Nor is it clear whether the ships might have resumed some limited air operations after the fires were put out. They did not in practice, but then again it was not urgent that they did so. Again, both ships required extensive refits after their damage, but that is not to say that desperate captains might not have launched strikes, leaving much of the operation in the hands of the pilots of undamaged aircraft.

Other forms of attack may be even less profitable. Of all modern warships, only a carrier has the hull volume to accommodate a substantial side protective system, a sandwich of full and empty spaces designed to absorb the explosion of several torpedoes. Even the damage from a penetrating hit will probably be limited by the internal bulkheads of the armored box; like her World War II forebears, a modern large carrier has her machinery arranged on the 'unit' system and therefore can operate on a fraction of it. Such an arrangement does present problems, particularly in the size and length of uptakes, but they are generally accepted. There are, to be sure, caveats. Steam catapults are great consumers of boiler steam, and one might suspect a disproportionate loss of speed if a carrier

The Japanese light carrier *Katsuragi*, shown here lying at Kure in October 1945, was used to repatriate Japanese from overseas after the war. Her flight deck was buckled by a bomb which penetrated it and then exploded in the closed hangar; the result was considered an object lesson in the virtues of the standard US open hangar. One elevator (which is just visible alongside) was blown out; the other was noticeably buckled. *USN by courtesy of A D Baker III*

had to operate her catapults just after she had lost a quarter of her power. In the new nuclear carriers, there are only two separate plants, each with its own reactor, so that conceivably a single hit can cut boiler power in half.

Her magazine is the only point target within a carrier the destruction of which would be fatal. However, there are area weapons which may be well suited to attack on a ship offering a few vulnerable targets distributed over a substantial area. One is shock. A weapon exploding under the keel of a carrier may, if it is powerful enough, blow her in half. More probably it will transmit a shock wave into the carrier, breaking up machinery foundations and throwing elevators and flight deck out of alignment. Catapults might be particularly susceptible to this kind of attack, since they require rather precise alignment over their considerable lengths. Under-bottom attack is not new, having caused the near-loss of the British cruiser *Belfast* in December 1939. At that time it was imposed by bottom mines, which were unlimited in weight but which were generally limited to shallow water. However, since 1945 many torpedoes with under-bottom warheads have been devised, and they would probably be used against carriers in any major future war.

There is no defense against under-bottom explosion comparable to a standard side protective system: since none of the force of the explosion is vented to the atmosphere, much more energy is transmitted into the bottom of the ship. Moreover, there is not enough depth in the bottom of a ship to fit even a shallow conventional system. In a smaller ship these facts would make defense hopeless. However, a carrier is so large that she can afford to have her bottom broken over a limited area, as long as some fraction of her vital spaces remain undamaged. It can be argued that if the bubble of the underwater explosion is permitted to smash in part of the carrier's bottom, then it loses the area shock effect it has if it merely bounces off the bottom.

Shock is also a common effect of near-misses, and indeed it and whipping due to nearby explosions may be the most significant effects of such attacks. Much of the mechanism of the carrier, as we have noted, depends for its operation on precise alignment maintained over considerable dimensions. Electronic equipment may be vulnerable to shock damage, and severe shock may burst pipes and so permit flooding by the large volumes of liquids the carrier must accommodate. Modern US carriers are designed to withstand a level of underwater shock damage, and are tested against live explosives, just as are lesser ships. At this level shock protection includes the details of machinery mountings and attempts to isolate equipment and piping from the ship structure proper, to reduce the extent to which a shock is transmitted through the ship.

There are also area weapons dispensing bomblets over a ship. Thus far there are no known anti-ship missiles designed for this kind of attack, but it is certainly within the capabilities of US naval aircraft, and it would be unwise to put such weapons beyond Soviet capability. A bomblet attack up the axis of the flight deck would certainly start major fires – if the aircraft making it can approach that closely, or if a cruise missile can be designed to release its bomblets from above the carrier, flying the appropriate course.

PASSIVE DEFENSE AND AREA EFFECTS
Nuclear and chemical weapons also have area effects. An operating carrier requires a very large deck crew, and that crew is difficult to protect from gas or fall-out. The US Navy position is that generally either is restricted in area, so that a ship moving at high speed is exposed only rather briefly; during exposure the crew can be buttoned up, and the ship washed down. Against such a hope, many chemical agents are quite persistent and are difficult to remove from metal surfaces; they kill by contact with exposed skin, and only a short exposure by the ship herself may suffice. For some years the United States official position has been that chemical warfare is unlikely either on land or sea; on the other hand the Soviets are great exponents of chemical attack, perhaps as a less devastating equivalent of nuclear attack, at least on land. It would not be surprising if this interest were to extend to naval warfare. US experiments in design specifically to counter chemical or biological weapons (STOPS) foundered on the twin rocks of official disbelief in the reality of the threat and severe operating problems, with the ship totally sealed and all exposed crewmen in protective garb.

A nuclear weapon also produces a shock wave through the air, as well as a pulse of intense heat and other radiation, including an electromagnetic pulse (EMP). The size of the carrier makes it relatively easy for her designer to incorporate extra strengthening against the air pulse and the heat; indeed, his problem may be to balance the two so that excessive weight is not devoted to one without commensurate protection against the other. Presumably nothing can prevent the air wave from clearing the flight deck of aircraft, but the strength of the flight deck can protect aircraft in the hangar. Radar antennas are likely to be far more vulnerable than the rest of the structure of the carrier, although perhaps the new generation of phased arrays can be hardened. Once more, there is an alternative. If the carrier has some of her airborne early warning aircraft stowed at the time of attack, they may survive to provide rudimentary airborne radar coverage afterwards.

EMP, an intense pulse of electromagnetic waves stretching across the radio spectrum, is a particular problem for a ship as dependent upon electronics as is a carrier. A bomb exploded within the atmosphere produces an EMP, but only over a relatively short distance. However, a large bomb exploded just above most of the atmosphere produces EMP over a continent-sized area. The pulse might well put out of action not merely the carrier's radars and radios but also her internal telephone system (at least for a time) and perhaps her computers as well. Despite considerable test effort, EMP effects are not well understood, partly because they are applied to extremely complex systems. One would suspect that the heavy steel of the flight deck would tend to shield aircraft in the hangar, although those on the flight deck itself might well be disabled. However, because aircraft are much simpler than a ship and can be tested as single units, they can also be designed to resist EMP effects. A ship dependent upon her aircraft, then, might conceivably be in a better position to resist EMP strikes than a surface ship dependent on shipboard systems.

SURVIVAL PROSPECTS
In summary, one might say that a modern heavy carrier is certainly not invulnerable, but on the other hand she can withstand considerable damage, in some cases merely by virtue of her size and the fact that vital systems can be distributed over a considerable area within her. Unless she is subject to a direct nuclear hit, multiple hits are required to sink her, and possibly even to disable her – with the single caveat that a lucky hit in a magazine will be fatal. On the other hand, large as it is, a magazine occupies only a relatively small fraction of the length of the carrier, and therefore the probability that it will be hit is low. All or most of it is below the waterline, and the typical cruise missile trajectory is almost horizontal. Many of the most important targets for the missile are either on the flight deck or deep in the hull, but most radar homing

A modern carrier is perhaps best described as a volcano waiting to erupt. However, with good damage control that volcano can be controlled, and the ship can survive the equivalent of numerous severe hits. This is the nuclear carrier *Enterprise* (January 1969), following a series of fires and explosions which completely wrecked the after part of her flight deck. All aircraft abaft her island were burned out; in some cases the only recognizable part is the engine. However, note that aircraft and, perhaps as importantly, catapults and elevators forward of the island were not damaged. Given the total destruction of the arresting gear area, *Enterprise* would have been able to launch a strike but not to recover one. However, also given the large repair force aboard ship, some arresting gear might well have been rigged by the time the strike returned.

devices will go either for the center of the side of the hull, or for a corner reflector such as the edge of the island. A hit on the island would destroy many vital command spaces, including 'pri-fly', but the carrier can survive at a lower level of efficiency, particularly if she can operate her E-2s or their equivalent.

Perhaps most importantly for the attacker, he must make many hits to expect to succeed. He has to locate her in the first place: the Soviets generally exploit the copious radiation (radar and radio) which a carrier force emits, and which includes signals quite specific to the carrier (air search radars and presumably CCA radars). Such techniques can of course be exploited by the carrier task force, and they invite decoying and deception. Once the carrier force has been located approximately, Soviet practice is to conform and refine target position by means of reconnaissance aircraft and ships. In peacetime a 'tattletale' ship is generally assigned to the task force. Its function is to report the position of the carrier within the force, a func-

tion of great importance if missiles are not to be wasted on the carrier's escorts. In addition, as the tattletale leaves the carrier task force (so as to avoid attracting and thus wasting incoming missiles), it can fire its own short-range weapons over its stern at the carrier; that tactic explains the Soviet practice of mounting short-range ('Styx') anti-ship weapons pointed *aft* aboard destroyers suitable for the tattletale role. It seems noteworthy that the tattletale is suited only to peacetime and to the outbreak of war, and it is not clear how the essential intelligence mission might be accomplished in wartime, with the carrier's aircraft sinking any tattletale coming within visual distance.

Again, Soviet practice is then to combine air-, ship- and submarine-launched cruise missile attacks, generally coordinated as well as possible to saturate the task force defenses. The latter would include CAP fighters controlled by E-2s, and then escorts with surface-to-air missiles. Finally the carrier herself has short-range point-defense missiles and Phalanx Gatling guns. Moreover, the entire task force employs countermeasures: first to confuse the attackers as to which ship is the appropriate target (given some means of neutralizing the tattletale) and then to jam or deflect missiles which survive active defenses. For example, the carrier can fire packets of chaff. Her escorts can activate repeaters which make them similar to the carrier, as far as enemy radar is concerned; and of course the carrier task group commander is not so foolish as to operate his ship in the center of the formation at all times.

In theory, then, it is possible to raise quite considerably the scale of attack needed to inflict a few hits on a carrier, and if several carriers are concentrated together they may have some fair chance of surviving even in the Norwegian Sea. One end of the survival issue is the extent to which the active and countermeasures defenses can reduce the number of missiles leaking through, so that the scale required for a successful attack comes to exceed what the Soviets will be willing to expend. A side issue here is that the primary Soviet anti-carrier force, the land-based naval air force, is by no means an unlimited resource. Its elite crews must be difficult to replace, and the production level of large bombers such as the 'Backfire' must also be quite limited, when compared to possible wartime losses. Thus a campaign resulting in severe losses to the Soviet naval air force might well have the effect of permitting much freer carrier operations around the European coast in a sustained war.

The other end of the scale is what the carrier can sustain, and that is the province of the designer, and of his attempts to disperse vital functions through the ship. On balance past experience suggests that he has done quite well. However, there is one great proviso. Most of the carriers lost in World War II sank not because of some gross lapse in protective design, but because of some relatively small problem: an inept damage control officer who did not understand gasoline vapor, inefficient fire fighting gear, even missing watertight doors in the case of the immense Japanese *Shinano*. Modern US carrier practice has been tested by several disastrous fires, but no one has any idea of what severe shock damage or cruise missile hits in a carrier's hull will do, in practice rather than in a computer. We can only hope that we have been more careful than the pre-1939 experts, and that our training has been more realistic and our attention to detail more complete.

9.The Future of the Aircraft Carrier

The fate of the carrier is far from settled. On the one hand, its enormous cost and supposed vulnerability make it a natural target for budget-cutters in a time of very rapid inflation. On the other, the reasoning which saved the British carrier force after the 1957 Defence White Paper remains valid: there are many areas of the world, vital to the West, prone to crisis, yet far from Western bases. No matter how friendly the neighboring states, the free use of their own bases cannot be guaranteed. A carrier is soveriegn territory: its presence therefore ensures a certain independence of action.

As for vulnerability, any warship is vulnerable, but a carrier, properly handled, should be more survivable than most. The effect of the proliferation of anti-ship missiles is not so much to eliminate the carrier as an effective weapon as to raise its minimum cost. Torpedoes and torpedo-boats had a similar effect on battleship design at the turn of the last century: the capital ship remained viable, but the cost of sea power greatly increased. At that time many countries which had previously been able to maintain high-seas navies were forced back into the coast defense role. Similarly, the rising cost of maintaining effective carrier forces, ie effective sea power projection forces, has pushed several navies back into very limited regional roles. In the British case, for example, the demise of the carrier force was linked to abandonment of a British role 'east of Suez.' In the Soviet case, the construction of a new generation of carriers in the mid- and late-1980s may well presage a global role for the Soviet fleet, which previously has concentrated on denying the seaward approaches of the Soviet Union to Western naval forces.

As Third World states come to possess more and more sophisticated weapons, and, indeed, as the level of expertise needed to operate them falls with increasing automation, the level of threat faced by warships operating off the coasts of these states rises. Where previously there was a sharp distinction between 'high threat' areas such as the seaward approaches to the Soviet Union and the 'low threat' Third World, the latter is now a 'medium threat' area. Thus even a navy not intended to attack Soviet targets must buy more expensive and more sophisticated forces if it is to retain its ability to influence events in the Third World. Even the open ocean, previously very 'low threat' indeed, at least as regards air defense, is now at least 'medium threat,' given the reach of such Soviet bombers as the 'Backfire'.

Thus the small carrier, which for many navies was a relatively inexpensive way to support some air capability at sea, is increasingly unsatisfactory. This trend pushed Canada and the Netherlands out of conventional carrier operations in the early 1960s, when increased carrier size was little more than a matter of supporting better ASW aircraft to counter better Soviet submarines. At that time the Canadians felt that they would have to go from an ex-British light carrier, HMCS *Bonaventure*, to an ex-American *Essex* about three times the size. Instead they

Several navies first learned to operate carriers by purchasing British light fleet carriers which became surplus after 1945; others took over ships which had been laid up incomplete. The Royal Canadian Navy, for example, operated the light carrier *Bonaventure* until the mid-1960s, retiring her in favor of land-based patrol aircraft. A tentative project to acquire a rebuilt *Essex* proved abortive, and there was a considerable uproar over the decision to give up a ship not even a decade old, after an expensive modernization. Here she appears in happier days, newly completed, arriving at Belfast, 12 April 1957. In service, her air group consisted of US Grumman S2Fs and McDonnell Banshees; two of each are lined up on her flight deck. *Royal Canadian Navy*

abandoned open-ocean ASW support of convoys, and bought land-based patrol aircraft. The Royal Navy experienced the same pressures a few years later. Where a 22,000-ton carrier such as HMS *Hermes* was quite satisfactory in the mid-1950s, a decade later even the much larger *Ark Royal* was no more than marginal, given the growth in aircraft to match a mounting air threat. The minimum satisfactory carrier of the 1970s and 1980s, CVA-01, was just too large and too expensive, at least in the politicians' eyes.

THE FUTURE OF THE AIRCRAFT CARRIER 149

HMCS *Magnificent* shows the original configuration of the *Majestic* class light fleet carriers, with the usual heavy wartime battery of light automatic weapons. These and the earlier *Colossus* class were originally to have had 4in guns as well, but (as in the US light fleet carriers) they were given up in favor of the smaller weapons. *MoD(N)*

The British light fleet carrier *Majestic* was completed in 1955 as the Australian *Melbourne*, shown here in 1979 with her long steam catapult, Dutch-type radar, and 5½° angled deck. In 1980 she operates about 17 aircraft, including Skyhawks (A-4G) and Sea King and Wessex helicop-ters, all three of which are shown. Despite modernization in 1969 and large refits in 1971, 1972–73, and 1978–79, *Melbourne* will soon require replacement, and the Royal Australian Navy is currently considering a variety of V/STOL carriers. *Royal Australian Navy*

However, with the end of the British carrier force also came the end of the active British role 'east of Suez,' and that had costs of its own. But in 1966 they were only potential costs, and not nearly so well defined as the immense cost of four or five new 50,000-ton carriers. This incident was only one example of a far more general problem. In peacetime a carrier is a means, perhaps often the only means, of asserting national power in a remote area. The consequences of a failure to assert that power are at best difficult to calculate; moreover, the need to be able to influence events at a particular time in a particular place is not likely to be foreseen at the time, perhaps ten years earlier, when a government decides to build a carrier capable of that mission. History is a guide, but Western governments have a habit of imagining that somehow it will not be repeated, particularly when large sums of money are involved.

Thus since World War II successive US administrations have vowed again and again to eliminate this expensive and apparently vulnerable weapon system, only to dis-cover that carriers are virtually the only quick-response weapon in the US inventory – short of a strike by a ballistic missile. For example, the Truman administration cancelled the immense carrier *United States* in 1949, but fourteen months later found that carriers in the Far East were the only viable means of projecting US air power into Korea, as the North Koreans overran most of the air bases on the Peninsula. In 1964, with the role of the carrier again in question, carriers were the only means of attacking North Vietnam after the Tonkin Gulf incident. In 1980 they are the principal form of US power in the Persian Gulf, where previously the USA had been able to rely on airfields held by a friendly Shah. Other local powers may grant the United States limited base rights in time, but the era of the vast US worldwide base structure seems over – as the British discovered at the time of Suez in 1956. In this respect the failure of US allies to provide base and transit rights at the time of the October 1973 Middle East War must have been sobering.

French carrier aviation was revived postwar with the transfer of the British light fleet carrier *Colossus*, name ship of the class, which became the *Arromanches*. Here she lies at Portsmouth, 6 November 1948, with ex-US Dauntless dive-bombers and ex-British Seafire fighters on deck. *Conway Picture Library*

The Brazilian and Argentine navies entered the carrier age by buying former British Light Fleets; in the 1980s they will be potential customers for new V/STOL ships. Here the Brazilian *Minas Gerais* (formerly HMS *Vengeance*) shows seven S2F Trackers on deck. She was rebuilt in Rotterdam in 1960, with a steam catapult, an 8.5° angled deck, mirror landing equipment, new radars (including the US SPS-8B prominent atop her bridge) and new elevators. *Ministério da Marinha, Rio de Janeiro*

THE CASE FOR THE SUPER-CARRIER

The large carrier generally suffers in budget battles because it represents a single, apparently indivisible, cost. Most other military weapon systems have large costs, but they are spread over a large number of units, so that the high total system cost can be spread over a number of years. Moreover, program costs can be reduced by cuts in the total number of units procured: the Army may want 8000 tanks, but the Administration may choose instead to buy 6000. It is rather more difficult to buy three-quarters of a single carrier. It is also easier to believe that the 6000 tanks will suffice, since the gap is between some theoretical level of required force and some affordable level. In the case of the carrier, comparisons between a smaller affordable ship and a somewhat more expensive ship are embarrassingly easy, as the US debate over the austere carrier (CVV) showed.

In effect, the V/STOL offers a way around this problem, since it reduces the minimum size of ship which can support some aircraft at sea. That is not to say that it reduces the cost of supporting some more substantial level of sea-based air power, or the cost of achieving some level of effectiveness, such as some level of probability that a given Soviet bomber strike will not destroy a convoy, or that some tonnage of bombs can be delivered against a given target, or even, given PGMs, that some particular target system can be destroyed. The most vital achievement of the V/STOL, from the point of view of the peacetime naval analyst, is that it permits the purchase of sea-based air power to be stretched over an extended period of time, just as purchases of land-based aircraft or tanks can be stretched out. In each case, the total cost of the system, or the net cost of a given capability, is of little moment: what matters is the visible cost in each year's budget.

This is not a terrible rational approach to budgeting, and in some important ways a small V/STOL carrier may not be a particularly rational approach to the requirements of an oceanic navy. Perhaps the principal contribution that Robert S McNamara made to US defense policy was his insistence that alternative programs be compared on the basis of total program costs to achieve net levels of capability. On this basis the larger carrier usually wins out; the only major exception is that when a very low level of capability is acceptable, the larger carrier brings far more than is needed, and so costs far more than is necessary. In consequence a force composed of smaller numbers of larger carriers cannot cover as many eventualities as can a more numerous force of smaller, individually far less capable, ships: one carrier cannot be everywhere at once. However, as the threat rises even in the open ocean, the minimum

Compared to the Royal Navy, the United States Navy was quite sparing in selling or transferring its wartime carriers. Two light fleet carriers served in the French Navy, and in 1967 USS *Cabot*, which had been rebuilt for ASW service in the early 1950s, was transferred to Spain as the *Dédalo*. She was the first carrier in the world to operate the Harrier (AV-8A; Matador in Spanish service) on a regular basis, as in this recent photograph. *Spanish Navy*

required of any particular naval force grows, and the smaller carrier becomes less cost-effective in a net sense.

Generally, a larger carrier costs less per aircraft embarked, and it can fly larger airplanes which themselves can both dominate larger areas of sea. Moreover, they may represent a lower cost per unit of ordnance delivered, or per unit of defensive capability. The former is to some extent subject to the qualification that a larger airplane may be more vulnerable in the face of heavy SAM fire; on the other hand, it can carry more electronic countermeasures – and more armor – than can a smaller airplane, without losing all of its ability to carry payload. As for defensive power, the requirement to support a combination of airborne early warning aircraft and Phoenix-armed F-14s sets a very high lower limit on the size of any carrier which must face heavy air attacks. The only alternative is to transfer the self-defense weapons to surface ships, but then the cost of the carrier task group as a whole rises beyond what it would be if those weapons were shared between the carrier and her consorts.

Although its high unit cost is undeniable, the 'super-carrier' is arguably the most satisfactory method of projecting sea power, since it combines functions which, if deployed amongst smaller, more numerous units, would be, collectively, either more expensive or less potent – or both. The modern 'super-carrier' is typified by the USS *Nimitz* (seen here in the Solent off Portsmouth, England, 25 September 1980). Note the A-6 and the A-7 on the lowered deck-edge elevator. *Richard L Ward*

The efficiency of a large carrier is in part a consequence of the way the volumes which comprise her hull scale as her displacement is raised or lowered. Both her shaft horsepower (and, therefore, the weight and volume of her machinery) and her radar-reflecting cross-section are proportional, crudely, to the two-thirds power of the displacement, so that, for example, engines take up a smaller proportion of the internal volume of a larger carrier, leaving larger fractions of that volume available for aviation ordnance and aviation fuel, ie for air group endurance. To some extent horsepower determines the infrared signature of the carrier. Thus both radar cross-section and infrared detectability rise more slowly than displacement, ie more slowly than some important carrier operating capacities. In an angled-deck carrier, the capacity for aircraft themselves depends to some extent on hangar and flight deck areas, ie also, it would seem, on the two-thirds power of the displacement. However, these numbers actually depend upon the length of the carrier, and a larger carrier can be proportionately longer than a smaller one, hence can carry more aircraft per ton. Similarly, each airplane can be supported for more sorties, as the larger hull accommodates more fuel and more ordnance – and more spare parts – per ton. These points are apart from the 'overhead' inherent in carrier design, which all carriers larger and smaller must share: special radars, the volume of underwater protection (the depth of which is determined by the charge it must defeat, not the size of the ship) and some defensive weapons. In a conventional carrier there are also, of course, catapults and arresting gear, which take their share of available weight and volume and whose size depends not on that of the carrier but rather on that of her aircraft.

Survivability considerations, too, favor a larger ship. She can accommodate more armor, and her structure itself is massive enough to afford some considerable protection even if it is not designed specifically for that purpose. Conventional weapons can be characterized by the areas or lengths over which the damage they do extends, and normally a ship can absorb damage over a fixed proportion of her length. The larger the ship, the greater that length in absolute terms and hence the greater the number of hits she should be able to survive; moreover, if the hits are randomly distributed, the vitals of the larger carrier should represent a smaller proportion of her length and so should be less susceptible to destruction. Thus it can be argued that, for a given level of capability well beyond the capacity of any small carrier, the equivalent force of large carriers will be less expensive to operate, harder to locate (at least as far as infrared and radar signatures are concerned) and also harder to sink. As for passive electronic detection, if every carrier requires roughly the same complement of radios and radars, then there is little or no distinction to be drawn between large and small carriers, and in fact a more numerous force of smaller carriers will be easier to detect at a greater range.

A direct hit by a nuclear weapon will, of course, sink any ship. However, the larger the ship, the better it can be hardened and consequently the better it can withstand the effects of a near-miss; an alternative formulation would be the better it can withstand a given level of failure of defenses.

In the early 1950s the US Marines sought to expand the potential role of the carrier by introducing the concept of vertical envelopment. Nuclear weapons appeared to make the great concentrations of shipping common in World War II amphibious assaults impossible, but concentration of force at the objective was still a prerequisite for success. The Marine concept called for helicopters to move in troops and light equipment from widely separated ships, while more conventional landing ships ultimately brought heavy equipment such as tanks up to the beach. The *Guadalcanal*, shown here in May 1978, was one of seven specially built helicopter carriers, which were supplemented for a time by refitted *Essex*s. Prominent in this view are a Sea Sparrow missile launcher forward of her twin 3in/50, ECM arrays outboard of her island, a large SPN-6 approach control radar (outboard) and her (black-painted) SPS-40 air search radar antenna. The aircraft on deck are CH-53 Sea Stallions and CH-46 Sea Knights.

THE FUTURE OF THE AIRCRAFT CARRIER 153

It must, however, be admitted that a carrier task force consisting of a single carrier surrounded by escorts is not entirely satisfactory. It is less costly than a pair of carriers, but on the other hand no single ship is inherently immune from damage, or even from mechanical failure. A pair of carriers appears, then, to be the minimum investment to achieve a given level of sea-based air power; and it pays to make them as powerful as possible, not merely because in war more is generally far better, but also because it is more economical, to buy a given level of air power in halves rather than in quarters or sixths.

V/STOL AND THE 'HARRIER CARRIER'
On balance, then, as in the case of the battleship, every technical point favors a continuing increase in the size and unit cost of the carrier. Moreover, there is as yet no alternative capital ship in sight: to abandon the big carrier is to abandon an important range of naval capabilities. On the other hand, when the carrier replaced the battleship as the principal type of warship, no major capabilities were given up, and quite important ones were gained. However, unlike the history of the battleship, the recent history of the carrier shows just the opposite trend, away from unit size and capability. In some ways the rush to V/STOL carriers is reminiscent of the attempt on the part of some navies to build smaller, less expensive battleships or semi-battleships in the period between the World Wars, when the growing threat to such ships should instead have forced up unit size.

Thus, except in the United States, the favored Western carrier is a small ship capable of supporting perhaps ten or twenty V/STOLS or helicopters on a displacement of up to 20,000 tons; even in the United States there is intense pressure for the abandonment of the large conventional carrier in favor of large numbers of V/STOL ships. The one attempt at a compromise, the austere carrier which was to have been the prototype for a new generation of large V/STOL carriers, failed precisely because the costs of reductions in size were so obvious in its design. However, the failure of the CVV only focussed attention on the claimed virtues of a much smaller dedicated V/STOL ship, the VSS (V/STOL Support Ship).

V/STOL operation buys a level of simplicity absent from carrier flying since the 1930s. Take-off is either vertical or out of short roll, and no catapult is required. Nor is there any arresting gear. Perhaps more significantly, there is no longer any need for a very precise approach: the pilot has a far larger target at which to aim, can come in from any bearing, and lands vertically: several aircraft can, then, land simultaneously. There need be no mirror landing aid, no complex array of approach radars beyond general air control and some means of bringing the airplane to the

Although the US Marines conceived the vertical envelopment tactic, it was first used in battle by the Royal Navy, at Suez in 1956. Several British carriers were converted for the 'commando' role, the latest being HMS *Hermes*, at one time the most sophisticated of the light fleet carriers. This is her half-sister *Bulwark*, photographed in March 1979. One advantage of the British shift from fixed-wing to helicopter ASW aircraft was that such carriers could perform a dual amphibious and ASW role, depending upon which aircraft they carried. This flexibility is characteristic of all carriers. The helicopters shown here are Westland Sea Kings and Wessexes. *Royal Navy*

To many, the V/STOL fighter is the key to an inexpensive carrier. The US Marine Corps bought large numbers of AV-8A Harriers, and several were tested aboard the helicopter assault ship *Guam* in 1972. Here one lifts off just forward of the island, showing its two 30mm cannon in detachable pods as well as a pair of fuel tanks. Harriers were also tested aboard the full-deck carrier *Franklin D Roosevelt* several years later.

carrier. It is also possible to envisage simultaneous take-offs, although in that case there is a considerable cost in payload, since short rather than vertical take-off adds greatly to the load a V/STOL can lift. Such operation has considerable benefit even for a large carrier since at least part of her air group can operate independent of the catapult and arresting gear cycles. If the carrier is damaged, that same fraction of the air group can operate as long as a fraction of the carrier deck remains intact: V/STOLs may even be able to fly from the elevators.

In a sense a carrier operating V/STOLs is reminiscent of a carrier of the early 1930s. Her aircraft operating capac-

The most advanced V/STOL combat aircraft currently flying is the McDonnell Douglas/British Aerospace AV-8B. Closely related to the Harrier, it differs from that aircraft principally in having a new, larger wing, redesigned jet intakes, and lift-improvement strakes below the fuselage, adding up to great advances in payload capability and range. This is the second YAV-8B, September 1979. *McDonnell Douglas*

ity is determined primarily by the number of deck spots available, given the space required for take-off runs into the wind. Just as there was an issue in the 1930s of just what determined carrier operating capacity, there is a similar issue for a V/STOL carrier. Helicopters take up more space on deck than in a hangar, because there must be clearance for their rotors, so that additions of flight deck parking space buy relatively little for a mixed helicopter–V/STOL ship. However, V/STOLs awaiting their chance to run down the flight deck can be quite tightly packed, as long as they are protected from the jet blast of earlier take-offs. It appears, for example, that the quoted air group of HMS *Invincible* is based on her hangar rather than on her flight deck, and therefore may be unrealistically low. In effect she employs a parallel flight deck reminiscent of that designed for CVA-01, but with its functions reversed: she has no catapults, and her 'angled' deck is for take-offs, not landings. The use of the parallel deck design should maximize parking space.

A great deal depends upon the details of the V/STOL aircraft itself. At present there are two types in service, the Sea Harrier with its single lift/cruise engine and four swivelling nozzles, and the Soviet Yak-36 ('Forger') which employs a pair of small lift engines forward and a lift/cruise engine aft with swivelling nozzles for vectored thrust. In principle the Yak-36 can be better optimized for a narrowly defined mission, since neither its lift nor its cruise engine need be designed for a very wide range of operation. On the other hand, the simpler system of the Sea Harrier is inherently quite flexible: for example, it is well adapted to the use of vectored thrust in maneuvering. One severe difficulty the 'Forger' faces is the inherently slow response of its engines. For example, in a STOL take-off the lift engine thrust must be continuously balanced against the lift provided by the wing; if the lift engines are on full throttle at the beginning of the roll while the cruise engine is at full cruise power (to gain maximum runway acceleration), the airplane may flip over on its back, yet without considerable lift thrust it will not be capable of STOL operation. The great variety of hazards inherent in the 'Forger's triple-engine layout requires a high degree of automation, even for conven-

tional VTOL operation, whereas the Harrier is capable of nearly fully manual operation. It is arguable, too, that the 'Forger' is subject to uncontrollable pitching with any of the three engines out, and therefore gains nothing in reliability from its multi-engine configuration.

In practice, 'Forger' rarely if ever employs a STOL take-off; rather, it carries out a stereotyped vertical take-off followed by a 1½-minute transition to conventional (wing-borne) flight. For a Sea Harrier the transition to fully conventional flight is typically accomplished in far less than a minute, thanks presumably to the greater simplicity of the vectored-thrust system. This time difference alone might be of great signifcance in any high-intensity V/STOL or VTOL operation, given the need for each aircraft to be well clear of the ones preceding and following it.

Another important issue is room for growth, particularly growth in payload. The fully-VTOL airplane can achieve improvements in lift only by increasing its engine thrust; to some minor extent aerodynamic devices which trap the jet efflux or which maintain the air cushion under the airplane can also help. Any significant improvement in payload would have to come from some comparable improvement in cruising fuel economy, so that payload might be traded off against fuel for a fixed range. The STOL airplane, on the other hand, can benefit from aerodynamic devices which increase the lift of its wing at low airspeeds. For example, the US AV-8B version of the Harrier was designed to achieve the improved performance planned for a re-engined aircraft (the abortive AV-16A), solely by the use of aerodynamic devices. These include a supercritical wing, specialized Lift Improvement Devices, and a better engine inlet which in itself increases engine thrust. The result is better than a doubling of range or payload compared to the original AV-8A, with no change in the original engine, to the point where the

The *Guam* tests were an attempt to evaluate a new austere carrier (Sea Control Ship) concept. Here an AV-8A lifts while two others occupy the forward end of the flight deck. A modified version of the LPH has been offered to the Australian Navy as a replacement for the ageing *Melbourne*; one of its important features is the ability to operate V/STOL fighter and attack aircraft as well as helicopters.

AV-8B is considered comparable to the conventional F/A-18 in range and payload, though not, of course, in speed.

Given the very limited payload a V/STOL can lift vertically, a principal issue in V/STOL carrier design is the improvement of this payload through a deck run. For example, a Harrier can roughly double its load of fuel plus ordnance by means of a rolling take-off. In another formulation, the Harrier gains about 6lb of payload for every foot that it rolls, up to about 1000ft for maximum advantage, and about 66lb for every knot of wind over deck. Deck run can be traded against WOD at about 11ft per knot. Although these figures show that a flat-deck launch can be valuable (and that 30kts of WOD is equivalent to a third of the optimum flat-deck run), it is possible to do even better. The shorter the run, the more aircraft can be parked on deck or, equivalently, the less the impact of the aircraft on a carrier.

A 'ski-jump' is the equivalent of a considerably lengthened deck. The concept was introduced by a Royal Navy engineering officer, Lt Cdr D R Taylor, in 1973; however, a similar device was employed at least once in the more distant past, when HMS *Furious* used a ramp at the fore end of her short flight deck to launch heavily-laden Barracudas against the *Tirpitz* in August 1944. Basically, an airplane forced to run up an incline gains some upward velocity simply because part of its velocity is in the upward direction. At the time of launch, the airplane is already moving fast enough for its wings to lift a substantial fraction of its total weight, as would be the case in a conventional take-off. In effect its trajectory after leaving the ramp is partly ballistic, but lift is increasing throughout, so that at some point along the trajectory the airplane flies fully supported. The steepness of the ramp is limited by the speed with which an aircraft leaving it can pick up enough velocity for conventional flight. Further, it can be argued that only a V/STOL can successfully utilize the ski-jump because only the V/STOL is fully controllable at low speeds near the point of stalling.

The ski-jump permits a very small ship to operate V/STOL aircraft such as the Harrier at the limits of their lifting potential, and thus appears to permit a vast shrinkage in carrier size. In fact the number of such aircraft a small 'Harrier carrier' can support is limited by factors such as ordnance stowage and fuel capacity, not to mention a capacity for spares.

Indeed, perhaps the true significance of the Harrier is that it makes possible the quick conversion of fast merchant ships to primitive carriers in an emergency: all that is needed, at a bare minimum, is a length of flat deck and some fuel and ordnance stowage. The result is not too impressive, but in some very low-threat cases it may be enough. Certainly it may be enough to support ASW operations, particularly if the ship is sufficiently capacious to take aboard some self-contained data processing equipment with which the output of a field of sonobuoys sown by Harriers can be interpreted. Certainly, too, no emergency conversion has nearly the capability per ton of a specially-designed carrier. On the other hand, in a period of very tight money, no navy can support in peacetime the force it may require in war.

The counterargument is generally that war will come with so little warning that clever mobilization arrangements will be to no avail. Ships in particular will offer few opportunities for rapid increases in numbers, given the lengthy lead times for construction and for crew training. However, in a world of rough nuclear parity, it appears increasingly that war will come only as the culmination of a series of crises and, moreover, that it may be both less destructive and considerably more drawn out than appeared in, say, 1960. In this context arrangements for rapid fleet expansion over a period of a year or two are once more of great interest, as indeed they were before World War II.

At that time carriers were clearly of great value, yet their number was severely restricted by treaty. Moreover, it appeared that full fleet carriers would take so long to build that even a massive program undertaken at the outbreak of war would be far too late. As early as 1923 the US Navy therefore began to plan for the emergency conversion of selected liners. This program had only a low priority, partly because existing US passenger ships were too slow to make attractive emergency carriers. However, as faster ships began to enter service plans were elaborated, and some long lead-time components, such as elevators, were actually ordered in 1935. In 1938 the then Maritime Commission actually designed a liner with features permitting rapid conversion into a carrier in wartime, and in fact the Japanese built (and converted) two dual-purpose liners of their own. In each case the hope was that the converted ship might be usable in fleet operations, and all the features of a conventional fleet carrier were incorporated.

No conversion could be nearly as satisfactory as a carrier

The Sea Control Ship was designed for minimum unit cost, and some of its critics contended that that meant minimum capability as well. A modified version, with a ski-jump, is to be built for the Spanish Navy. Among other things, austerity was taken to mean a close-in battery limited to two Vulcan-Phalanx; no sonar; no catapult; no deck-edge elevator; and no protection. Radar was limited to air search and carrier-controlled approach (SPN-35, in the big radome), and the only elevator was right aft.

The great defect of the LPH was that it was unusable in bad weather. Moreover, it always had to operate in company with ships capable of transporting over-the-beach craft. About 1965 the Marines proposed a combination assault ship which would have both a flight deck and a well for large landing craft. That became the 40,000-ton LHA, the first of which, *Tarawa*, is shown here on sea trials, January 1976. These ships are so close to the *Essex* in size that they are sometimes proposed as the basis for a new generation of austere carriers. They are steam powered and may, therefore, be suitable for modification to take a steam catapult; compared to older carriers their principal deficiencies are low speed and, probably, a lack of armor protection.

built as such from the keel up, and the US Navy abandoned its plans when a major new construction program of fleet carriers was authorized in 1940. It was argued, moreover, that large passenger ships were too valuable as transports to be laid up for reconstruction. Japan had a far smaller shipbuilding industry, and therefore found conversion far more attractive, and even went to the length of installing new machinery to give the rebuilt ships sufficient speed to operate with her main fleet.

In more modern language, each of these ships was intended to operate in a 'high-threat' or at least a 'medium threat' environment, and the cost of such capability was an elaborate conversion. However, much of the naval war of 1939–45 was fought in a 'low threat' environment in which any seaborne air capability was quite valuable. Unit cost was far less important than the speed with which minimal capability could be attained, and in this context the design of escort carriers was a test of just how little a minimal capability might entail. At the lowest end of the scale was a simple flat deck with arresting gear and fuel stowage: a MAC-ship, a converted merchant ship retaining her carrying capacity. Her aircraft rode the deck in all weather. The next step up was the escort carrier, with a hangar, however crude, and elevators, and generally a catapult as well. It had no protection, and it might be characterized as a remarkably inefficient use of tonnage (for example, a substantial portion of the displacement of an escort carrier was expended for ballast), but it did provide that minimal capacity in the shortest possible time, using existing hulls, or holls already in mass production for other purposes.

In a modern context, minimal capability may still be useful for ASW, particularly if the attack carriers can neutralize Soviet long-range bombers and surface ships. Although there is no mass-production merchant ship program, there are very large numbers of existing ships, many of them quite large and fast by World War II standards. V/STOL does offer a simplicity of conversion which is quite attractive, and this possibility is being actively explored. For example, the US Navy has an 'Arapaho' program for a containerized V/STOL system to be placed aboard a large container ship; 'Arapaho' includes a prefabricated runway. Of course this is a very inefficient way to use a large, fast hull, but the system can be emplaced (or removed) very rapidly, and since the hull already exists it represents no great cost for what may be a valuable potential.

STO-SHIPS

Perhaps the greatest defect of V/STOL for mobilization is that the base production rate of such specialized aircraft in peacetime is very low, and thus production would probably expand relatively slowly in an emergency. It would, therefore, be extremely valuable to be able to adapt existing conventional aircraft to some type of emergency carrier operation. To some extent this possibility seems to be implied by the characteristics of modern fighters and attack aircraft.

In the Fall of 1978 Rear-Admiral George Jessen of the US Naval Air Systems Command proposed an inexpensive conventional carrier in which a combination of wind-over-deck and a modest ski-jump would replace the catapult. He believed that major economies might be realized by the use of gas turbines (ie by the elimination of the

Carriers are far too expensive in peacetime for sufficient numbers to be available in war. In World War II the Admiralty went to an extreme to obtain air .capable ships for convoy protection, essentially decking over bulk carriers (oilers and grain carriers), which continued to fly the Red Ensign. This idea finds a modern counterpart in schemes such as the containerized 'Arapaho'. *Empire MacAlpine* is shown. *Conway Picture Library*

steam catapult) and merchant ship construction standards and, moreover, by abandoning the objective of very intensive air operations, ie by giving up the simultaneous landing and take-off requirement. A single long deck could be used for both, with retractable arresting gear well down its length. Take-offs would be conventional deck runs, as in carriers of the pre-jet era.

Compared to the true V/STOL, a conventional airplane generally enjoys considerable advantages in high speed performance and in endurance. Perhaps most importantly, by using an airplane already in volume production, a STO mobilization program cuts its lead times. In peacetime, a 'low threat' STO-carrier building program would have

It is likely that the Soviets will deploy their first full-deck carrier later this decade; thus their *Kiev* class semi-carriers probably represent a dead-end. Shown here is *Minsk*, being passed by HMS *Hermes*. *MoD(N)*

important political benefits. It would share aircraft types with conventional large-deck high-performance carriers and thus would benefit from reduced cost per airplane at sea. Advocates of high-capability carriers would not see it as a political threat, since it would be clear that some large hull would be required to support a useful naval air force; the choice would be between more and less capable ships of roughly the same size.

Perhaps most significantly, a large, fast STO-ship can support land-based aircraft. They have impressive thrust-to-weight ratios not because of any need for short take-offs but rather because of the need for high performance in air-to-air combat; but those ratios in turn translate into short deck rolls. It has been estimated that at a WOD of 60kts (30kts of ambient wind, 30kts of ship speed, both of which are plausible figures) deck roll is cut by 89 per cent. A variable-geometry airplane such as a Tornado might benefit even more, given the excellent low-speed characteristics associated with its swing-wing. Moreover, more and more land-based aircraft now incorporate arresting gear for short-runway operation. Thus the penalty associated with naval aircraft design is now almost non-existent, at least for high-performance aircraft. Further, the STO-carrier can gain some effective additional deck length by the use of a modest ski-jump, far less steep, of course, than that suited to a true jump-jet.

The gain due to a modest ramp can be quite significant. For example, with 20kts of wind-over-deck, computer estimates suggest that a 67,000lb F-14 can take off in under 700ft using a 6° ramp. The same ramp cuts the take-off distance of the F-18 (35,215lb) to about 550ft, and even the E-2C can take off under its own power in about 400ft. Only the S-3A cannot take off within carrier deck length: it must either be modified or make use of a low-energy catapult. In each case take-off performance is calculated on the basis of the airplane sinking up to 10ft after it leaves the ramp. Other computer calculations suggest

Is this the shape of the future? HMS *Invincible*, which began life as a 'through-deck cruiser' but is now acknowledged a carrier, is shown as completed, in March 1979. She has a twin Sea Dart launcher blocking part of what might have been her flight deck forward, and, although she will operate Sea Harrier V/STOL fighters, she will not be able to accommodate the extreme ski-jump which would give them optimum load-carrying capacity. Although her original design called for the installation of ship-to-ship Exocets, these were deleted in view of the far greater capabilities of her Sea Harriers. The immense size of her island is due in part to the demands of her gas turbines for air intakes and uptakes, and she is the first twin-funnelled British carrier since the *Eagle* of World War I origin. *Royal Navy*

that an 8°, 100ft ramp reduces the deck roll of an F-14 by as much as 70 per cent, with similar effects on F-18 performance. Thus the F-18, which takes off at 35,215lb in 950ft, is estimated to take off in 350ft with a 6° ramp (both figures assume 20kts WOD).

All of these estimates made Admiral Jessen's STOL ship proposal quite attractive, and funding has been forthcoming for full-scale tests. As of July 1980, a feasibility test with a fixed-angle 3° ramp at a land site was scheduled to begin on 10 August 1980; a variable-angle ramp was to be placed in service in December, and tests were to continue through March 1981. Aircraft types to be tested were to include the T-2, F-4, and later the E-2C and the F-18, and a sea-based test was scheduled tentatively for May 1982. The ultimate objective was a 'light carrier' of roughly one-third the cost and one-third the capability of a full attack carrier, with a displacement of about 40,000 tons.

As envisaged in mid-1980, such a ship might support an air group consisting of four E-2C AEW aircraft, eight S-3As, two helicopters (LAMPS III), and fourteen F/A-18s in an ASW mode; five EA-6Bs, twelve A-6s, six F/A-18s and three E-2Cs, plus the two helicopters, in a strike mode; four E-2Cs, nine F-14s, twelve F/A-18s and the two helicopters in an air defense mode; or fourteen CH-53s, sixteen AV-8Bs, and the two ASW helicopters in a Marine assault mode. Current proposals envisage a deck take-off

For some years the French Navy has projected the construction of a nuclear-powered helicopter carrier, originally designated PH75. Studies of a ship similar in concept to the US LHA began in 1970, on the basis of a twin-shaft frigate (*Tourville*) powerplant, a full-length flight deck, and four 100mm automatic cannon. A typical version displaced 22,000 tons, was capable of 27kts, and had a capacity of 600 troops, their vehicles, four landing craft in a well deck, and 26 helicopters (18 Lynx and 8 Super Frelon heavy troop-carriers). It could perform ASW duty but, probably more importantly, was well suited to the French national policy of continuing military support for former colonies, particularly in Africa. In 1972 the French government decided to include four 'air capable ships' in its long-range 'Plan Bleu'. Since it could not afford to buy new conventional carriers, all would have to be helicopter or V/STOL ships and there was no French V/STOL comparable to the British Harrier. A 65,000shp nuclear plant (28kts) was selected for the new ship, which ultimately was designed to displace 16,400 tons in trial condition. The French explained their choice of this rather expensive powerplant in terms of high cruising speed for relative immunity to submarine attack, great range at high speed for air operations, and the release of scarce hull volume for aviation fuel, so that the ship could actually be reduced in size relative to a conventionally-powered helicopter carrier. It was claimed, too, that the

cost of construction would be no more than 10 per cent above that of a conventional ship, although an American might dispute that. Indeed, it appears that the cost of the carrier has repeatedly delayed its commencement: PH75 indicated the year of authorization, but in 1980, however, it appeared that at the earliest the ship might be laid down at Brest for completion in 1990. Reportedly the same design, in conventionally powered form, was offered to the Spanish Navy as an alternative to the US Sea Control Ship. Official French policy calls for two ships, one to operate in home waters and the other in the Indian Ocean, as *Foch* and *Clemenceau* do at present. The designation was altered to PA (Aeronefs) 75, to reflect hopes of including V/STOL combat aircraft. However, the official air group continues to consist of 25 Lynx and 10 Super Frelon or 13 Puma helicopters, all of which would be accommodated on the hangar deck. Defensive armament is to consist of two Crotale point defense missile launchers and two automatic 100mm cannon, and, since all French escorts are likely to be conventionally powered, PA75 is to accommodate 1250 tons of fuel oil for them. It was announced in September 1980 that two new nuclear-powered 32,000-ton carriers are to be laid down, to replace *Foch* and *Clemenceau* in the early 1990s; these, apparently, are additional to the PH75s. *French Navy*

run of less than 800ft (without any catapults) and a landing run of less than 650ft, with provision for arresting gear. All of these figures, which refer to some of a great variety of tentative designs, both official and unofficial, are illustrative rather than indicative of the final form of the proposed light carrier.

The STO-ship is by no means a substitute for a full carrier; however, it seems superior to the purely V/STOL ship in that it can support the full variety of naval aircraft including, almost certainly, Airborne Early Warning types. Its capacity is quite limited, and it cannot support high-tempo operations. In cost it lies somewhere between the true V/STOL ship and the full carrier, since it must support more landing-approach radar and it must accommodate arresting gear. Some types of aircraft do require catapult launch, but a much less powerful device than presently fitted would be adequate; thus the STO-ship, like the V/STOL carrier, can employ gas turbine propulsion with its attendant personnel savings.

Thus the STO-ship is an attractive supplement to more conventional concepts. If seaborne aircraft do indeed retain great value, if control of the sea is still the most

valuable Western asset, they and not the specialized V/STOL and helicopter carriers may be the mobilization carriers of the future. In a world of increasing Western dependence upon resources in Third World countries increasingly subject to anarchy or to attack by the Soviets and their proxies, it seems likely that the day of the carrier is far from over. There must be some way of maintaining a carrier capability beyond that of the US Navy, and STO may be the appropriate route.

If indeed NATO urgently requires an ability to sustain sea power far beyond the range of its bases, and at the same time no individual NATO power other than the United States can maintain attack carriers, then perhaps it is time to consider a carrier force maintained by the Alliance as a whole. It is not that a single carrier is beyond the means of any one state, but rather that a useful capability demands several carriers. Perhaps the British and West German initiatives to assist the United States in the Indian Ocean presage the ultimate creation of a NATO fleet to which all of the states of the Alliance might contribute ships – including carriers. Their absence may prove a particularly expensive economy.

Appendix 1: Carrier Data

These tables include all of the carriers built as such from the keel up between the end of World War I and the end of World War II; most conversions have been omitted. Data are generally presented in the form used by the navy which designed the ship, to avoid confusion arising out of conversion to and from metric units. Thus British and US data are in Imperial units, except that aviation fuel capacities of US ships are in US gallons (about 1.2 of which equal an Imperial gallon of the Royal Navy). Japanese data are in metric units, except for standard displacements, which by Treaty had to be in long tons. In addition, the Japanese Navy designed in terms of 'trial displacement', roughly with two-thirds loads; the weight breakdowns for Japanese carriers are taken from trial displacement data. In the British tables, the two postwar classes (*Eagle* and *Albion*) are each listed with two aviation fuel capacities: one for gasoline (petrol), the other for aviation diesel fuel, for jets. In the Japanese tables, the numbers of aircraft are given in the form of operational aircraft and then spares. All navies carried spare aircraft (in the US Navy the norm was 25 per cent in 1941) but only the Japanese systematically listed their numbers. Generally they were stowed disassembled.

The weight breakdowns have been arranged to facilitate comparisons between navies, although individual practices make exact comparison impossible. The basis used is the Royal Navy system, in which the hull weight includes hull fittings, and equipment includes outfit, as well as personnel weights and stores. The aeronautical weight includes specialized equipment, aircraft, and aircraft fuel and lubricating oil. The US Navy was unique in counting deck protection under the sum of hull weights, so that the sharp decline in armor weights in later classes is due to a change in priorities, in which the emphasis shifted from side protection to heavy decks. Given the immense area of carrier decks, even an inch or two on them would outweigh the thick belts formerly standard. The British carrier designs of 1944, with their very heavy decks, give a better idea of the cost of armor intended to keep bombs out. It appears that both the British and the Japanese differed from the Americans in including bombs and other aviation ordnance in their aeronautical weights, and the treatment of the weight of elevators and catapults may also have been different.

The sum of all the weights listed should be, but generally is not, the standard displacement of the carrier. Generally standard displacement was calculated, not on the basis of full load capacities of, for example, aircraft and ship ammunition, but on the basis of fractional loads. In a few cases consumables were omitted entirely; for example in the 1920s the carrier *Lexington* was credited with a standard displacement from which aviation fuel had been eliminated. In addition much of her deck and underwater protection was omitted, on Treaty grounds.

GREAT BRITAIN

Each of the three major carrier-operating navies began with a pair of converted capital ships. In the Royal Navy the first modern carriers were the *Courageous* and *Glorious*, the earlier types being considered obsolescent as early as the mid-1920s. The 1931 study listed next was intended as the basis for a British negotiating position in naval arms limitation talks, and as such represented the Admiralty's concept of an ideal carrier. Both it and the *Courageous* were provided with double-decked hangars, which were necessary if sixty aircraft were to be accommodated

under cover. The alternative single-hangar ship with a deck park would have been significantly smaller, but that concept was not taken up at the time. Possibly the most important consequence of the 1931 study was that it provided an estimate of the minimum acceptable displacement, which found expression both in limits on the *Ark Royal* design (at a time when the treaties allowed up to 27,000 tons) and in the British position at the time of the London Treaty of 1936, which combined a new limit of 23,000 tons (as in the *Illustrious*) with the elimination of any limit on the total size of the force. Thus the designers of the *Illustrious* could afford to trade aircraft capacity for survivability, since the fleet could be provided with sufficient strike aircraft by building more carriers.

HMS *Illustrious* in effect symbolized the Admiralty position of the late 1930s: the carrier was essential to fleet operations, but as a strike rather than a fighter-defense platform. Moreover, dive-bombing at last presented a serious threat to the flight deck itself, and not merely to aircraft parked in the open atop it; they had been vulnerable to strafing attack. In 1937, however, Admiralty objectives shifted. At first the new ships were merely to have greater speed, but quite soon a Staff paper showed a strong preference for a larger air group, 48 rather than 36 aircraft. The result was the *Implacable* class, which reintroduced the double hangar to British practice. The London Treaty remained in force, so any great increase in displacement was impossible. Weight compensation was obtained by a reduction in the side armor of the hangar, given the probability that any shell entering the hangar would have to pass through at least one deck or the ship's side. In this design the concept of the carrier as a mother ship for floatplanes remained important, the height of the lower hangar being fixed for a time at 16ft to allow a Swordfish to be fitted with floats. By 1939 policy had been changed and the lower hangar reduced to the 14ft of the upper one, a figure intended to save weight. At this time it was expected that the upper hangar would accommodate 33 aircraft, the lower one 15. Meanwhile the last of the *Illustrious* class, *Indomitable,* was redesigned to incorporate an additional hangar, weight compensation coming from a reduction in hangar side armor. Some space in the upper hangar was lost, nominal capacity falling to 30 aircraft (with 16 below).

When the reconstruction of British carriers was discussed in the early 1950s, the original *Illustrious* class had the important advantage of greater hangar depth, to accommodate jets; in addition, they were more amenable to the installation of deck-edge elevators. Plans to reconstruct HMS *Implacable,* for example, called for the elimination of one of the two hangar decks and the installation of a new gallery deck, to bring hangar clear height to the required figure of 17ft 6in.

The last British fleet carriers, of the *Ark Royal* class (1942: HMS *Eagle* is listed here), began as improved *Implacables*, with deeper hangars, better deck protection, and an increase in aircraft stowage and in the size of flight deck and forward elevator. Increased stowage would be attained by stowing aircraft four rather than three abreast, and in 1940 it appeared that the repeat *Implacable* would displace about 23,900 tons. When no new carrier was ordered in the Spring of 1941 (under the 1940 Supplementary Programme, as had been planned) a more thoroughgoing effort was made; some of the changes were based on lessons learnt from the loss of the 1934 *Ark Royal*. Ultimately a combination of 4in flight deck protection and a double hangar was adopted. The hangar height of 17ft 6in was based on a requirement to operate US aircraft designed with this limitation in mind. The data listed in the table refer to the postwar redesign of the ship, representing a further enlargement over the original 1942 concept. For example, the original approved design was 790ft long overall, displaced 31,600 tons (standard), and accommodated 115,000 gallons of avgas; she was armed with sixteen 4.5in guns, and eight 8-barrelled pompoms. Endurance at 24kts was, however, 6000nm, with 7000 tons of fuel.

In 1943 work began on yet another carrier design, which was ultimately ordered as the *Malta* class. The first sketch designs called for armored hangars, and Design C was tentatively approved in mid-1944. However, by that time British observers of US practice were becoming impressed with the greater strike potential of the US open-hangar type. Aircraft still in the hangar could be warmed up, and the entire air group flown off in one operation. Moreover, the open-hangar carrier could accommodate deck-edge elevators. On this basis Design X was adopted in August 1944. However, it was a very large ship and doubts were expressed as to docking; Design X1 was an attempt to pare 50ft from its length. In both cases great attention was paid to vulnerability to bomb attack, and very thick armored decks were specified. It was believed that flight deck armor would be incompatible with deck-edge elevators and an open hangar, but by 1944 the Admiralty had full details of the US *Midway* class which did combine these features – hence the final design, with light flight deck armor and an open single hangar. Three ships were planned, but they were cancelled in 1945.

The other major line of British wartime carrier evolution was the light carrier. The *Unicorn* was not intended as a light fleet carrier, but she makes an interesting starting point, as she was of about the same size and indeed was sometimes operated as a full carrier. The *Colossus* class began in 1941 as an inexpensive fighter support ship; merchant ship practice was to prevail below the hangar deck (except in regard to main propelling machinery, which was half a cruiser set) in order to speed production. However, there appears to have been no intention for postwar reconversion to merchant use, as has sometimes been reported. In 1942 the design was enlarged to accommodate RAF fighters; it was sometimes referred to as a 'Combined Operations Carrier.' The design was frozen early in 1942 when the first three were ordered; later changes were attempts to simplify it, and to increase air capability by extending the flight deck. The latter required elimination of the originally planned pair of twin 4in AA guns, and the carrier's battery was restricted to light automatic weapons. This was in considerable contrast to earlier British practice. Of the sixteen ships planned, two became maintenance ships and six were modified to become the *Majestic* class.

The 1943 Programme included another eight light fleet carriers, initially modified *Colossus* types. However, given their completion dates of 1946 and later, and the feeling that the original light fleet carriers would be entirely obsolete within a few years (because of the rate of aircraft development), the design was recast to provide ships compatible with the new *Ark Royals*. The original draft staff requirements included four twin 4.5inch guns, and consideration was to be given to provide deck protection over machinery, magazines, and avgas stowage. The result was far larger than the original light fleet design, and was in effect an unarmored fleet carrier. There was always some question as to the wisdom of expending great resources on second-rate ships, but approval for construction was finally obtained in 1944 and eight units ordered, four of which were cancelled at the end of the war. The others were completed to a modified design, three of them to the one given in the tables.

UNITED STATES

American carrier development, as reflected in these tables, was relatively straightforward until after 1945. The driving force was generally air capability as determined by the size of the flight deck, which until the advent of the *Midways* was considered inherently vulnerable and, indeed, not worth armoring. Deck armor was reserved for hull protection, partly on the theory that a light flight deck could generally be repaired relatively easily after bomb damage. The other factor was the sequence of naval treaties. The Washington Treaty led to the conversion of the *Lexington* and *Saratoga*, which were relatively inefficient in terms of tonnage expended per aircraft carried, given their non-carrier origins. Once carriers were designed from the keel up, the motive was the maximum number of aircraft in the carrier force as a whole, given the dual constraints of the Treaty (ie, the limit on total carrier tonnage, which favored many small carriers) and of the need to operate large strike aircraft (a 10,000lb bomber, the prospective Martin T3M, was extensively cited in discussions prior to the *Ranger* design decision). Thus the *Ranger* was conceived as the smallest carrier which could efficiently operate the heavy bomber. Well before her completion she was herself considered inadequate, largely on the basis of experience with the *Langley*, and interest shifted to larger carriers of the *Yorktown* (CV5) class, represented here by the *Hornet* (CV8). They formed the basis for the very sucessful *Essex* class of World War II.

This progression towards larger ships was interrupted by the *Wasp*, a consequence of the Washington Treaty limit on total carrier tonnage. Weight-saving measures in her design included the (temporary) sacrifice of belt armor: backing for future installation was, however, provided, in the expectation that the armor itself would be installed in wartime. Relatively low speed was also accepted, but it was clear from the beginning that *Wasp* was no more than an expedient. Thus when the Treaty was revised in 1936 to remove the total tonnage limitation, attention returned to the larger carrier design, and the *Hornet* was built as a duplicate *Yorktown* to save time. Meanwhile interest turned to a somewhat larger, improved, design, which became the *Essex*.

The motivation for that development was initially a desire for a larger flight deck and for more defensive armament. Thus the cut-outs in the flight deck for the four starboard 5in guns were eliminated, and these weapons (plus four more) were mounted in gunhouses near the island. Later in the design process additional armor was provided at the hangar deck level. However, there was no serious interest in flight deck or hangar protection, given the sacrifice such weights would have entailed.

Interest in protected flight decks was revived in 1940, as the US Navy became aware of the character of the British *Illustrious* class. By then the *Essex* design was too far along to alter in any substantial way; however, a series of sketch designs for ships with *Essex* characteristics but with armored flight decks was begun. Unlike the Royal Navy, the US Navy chose to maintain at least the aviation characteristics of the earlier ship, accepting considerable hull growth to balance off the great weight of the armored deck. Ultimately the large *Midways* resulted. The weight breakdown provided is somewhat deceptive in that the US Navy did not include deck protection among its armor weights; the great armor weight of the *Midways*, then, reflects only their length and the decision to protect them against 8in rather than 6in shellfire, as had previously been the case. Moreover, their increased size in no way reflected a choice to pass to a generation of larger carrier aircraft. Increased beam balanced off the very heavy flight deck, and increased length was necessary to maintain an appropriate high-speed hull form, as well as to accommodate more powerful machinery to maintain speed. Given the larger hull, it was of course possible to provide more aviation fuel and somewhat larger catapults, but the new aircraft ordered in wartime were nonetheless designed to operate from all US fleet carriers.

Indeed, the *Midways* were not considered entirely satisfactory. Design C-2 was a 1946 effort to incorporate war experience in a new fleet carrier, a successor to the *Essex*. This series, which began in the Spring of 1945, ended only with the decision to pass instead to carriers capable of accommodating strategic bombers, a decision to which the present *Forrestal* class and its successors can be traced. These latter were the first ships, apart from the original *Ranger*, in which the requirement to operate a specific type of airplane was a major determining design factor.

Thus the very large *United States* was designed, above all, to operate a new 100,000lb long-range nuclear bomber. There would not be many such aircraft and they would fly relatively few sorties – hence the limited load of aviation ordnance reflected in the weight of armament. Almost the only armor was deck armor, which explains the small weight of protection as compared to the growth in hull weight. The *United States* was cancelled in 1949, a victim of interservice rivalry, but her principal features were revived in the *Forrestal* designed in 1950–51. However, the new carrier was designed as much for tactical operations as for strategic, and therefore she required a much larger aviation fuel load (750,000 gallons of avgas which could, however, be blended with an equal amount of fuel carried in ship-fuel tanks) and also a greater load of ordnance (often reported as about 1650 tons of conventional weapons and 200 of nuclear). All of this had to be accommodated on a displacement of less than 60,000 tons, a limit imposed by Congressional champions of a new carrier. Sacrifices in the new design, which is not described in detail in these tables, included much of the gun battery originally planned for the *United States*. Moreover, the *Forrestal* was designed to accommodate only a 70,000lb bomber, which became the A3D Skywarrior.

The wartime emergency led to the design of two other carrier types, the light fleet carrier (CVL) and the escort carrier (CVE). The former began as an attempt to enlarge the carrier force by the quick conversion of light cruiser hulls already under construction. It was not entirely satisfactory, but it did have the virtue of early availability. The *Saipan* class was an attempt to design a better CVL on the basis of a much-modified heavy cruiser hull. The weights listed for *Saipan* was based on an estimate of weights for the ship under construction, and a much earlier estimate of loads, and are therefore approximate.

Finally there were the CVEs. Many were merchant ship conversions, but the two classes listed were designed as carriers. The *Casablancas* were built on a mass production basis, fifty being completed in about a year. The *Commencement Bay* class, the only type considered sufficient for postwar operation, was based on an earlier oiler conversion and was, in effect, a slow CVL. In each case water ballast consumed a large fraction of the total displacement, although in the *Commencement Bay* it appears that some ballast tankage could be used to carry oil, for example for fueling escorts. New CVEs were proposed postwar, but construction was deferred, given the very large number of existing ships of wartime construction.

JAPAN

Japanese development roughly paralleled that of the United States, one important difference being that the Japanese equated aircraft capacity with hangar, rather than flight deck, size. Thus, as in the other major carrier navies, the Japanese began with a pair of converted capital ships and then, in the *Ryujo*, sought a minimum carrier within the treaty limits. Also as in the United States case, the minimum was not satisfactory. *Ryujo* had to be reconstructed to improve her stability; among other things two out of her six twin 5in mounts were removed, and she was blistered. By this time two more carriers, *Soryu* and *Hiryu*, had been ordered. They were intended to operate as a pair, and were, therefore, to have their islands on opposite sides, *Hiryu*'s to port. This combination duplicated that presented by *Akagi* and *Kaga* which, when reconstructed at about this time, also had their islands on opposite sides, *Akagi*'s to port. Both *Hiryu* and *Soryu* had cruiser machinery in cruiser-form hulls; however, *Hiryu* was ultimately completed to a considerably enlarged design, much of the increase in tonnage being absorbed by additional side protection. One peculiarity of the design was that both ships had their uptakes trunked on the starboard side, so that *Soryu* was vulnerable to smoke interference, whereas in her half-sister the funnels in effect balanced off the weight of her small island, and discharged away from it.

The two *Shokaku*s can be considered as enlarged *Hiryu*s with additional protection and with larger hangars; they were the Japanese equivalents of the *Essex* class. When large numbers of additional carriers were required in wartime, the *Hiryu* design was again adapted, to become the *Unryu* class. *Katsuragi*, described here, was one of three ships completed. She and an incomplete sister, *Aso*, were fitted with pairs of 52,000shp destroyer machinery; the others had the standard 152,000shp cruiser installation. Eleven more units contemplated in the 1942 program were never laid down.

The end of the main line of Japanese carrier development is represented by the *Taiho*, being sacrificed for additional flight deck protection. 'Project 5021' was a modified *Taiho* ordered under the 1942 program and represents Japanese carrier thinking in mid-war. *Taiho* differed from all other Japanese carriers built as such from the keel up in incorporating an uptake into her island proper; one can speculate that the concentration of uptakes simplified their protection. The other major Japanese wartime fleet carrier, *Shinano*, was converted on the slip from the third *Yamato* class battleship, and indeed retained the latter's central armored citadel – in fact, the avgas tanks at the ends of the ship were not included in this protected section. *Shinano* was intended more as a spare flight deck for use in battle than as a full fleet carrier, and so had a relatively small air group.

From the mid-1930s onwards the Japanese Navy constructed auxiliaries suitable for ultimate conversion to fleet carriers: fast submarine tenders (which became *Ryuho*, *Zuiho* and *Shoho*) and fast seaplane tenders (*Chitose* and *Chiyoda*). They are not listed here as they were not originally built as carriers and indeed except for *Zuiho* were converted after alternative service. All were flush-decked, and the former submarine tenders had only a single hangar. The former seaplane tenders did have two hangars, but both were only half-length. As for machinery, the diesels of the submarine tenders were replaced by destroyer turbines (52,000shp). In addition, the Japanese Navy subsidized merchant ship construction as a mobilization base, converting two liners into the fleet carriers *Hiyo* and *Junyo*, with destroyer boilers but retaining their original turbines. Unlike the former auxiliaries, they did have double hangars, but overhead clearance in the lower hangar was restricted to about 10ft, and it could accommodate only fighters. Other conversions, not listed here, corresponded to the Allied escort carriers and suffered from similar limitations.

Name	No	Launch date	No in class	Airplane capacity					Flight deck (ft–in/m)	Hangar height (ft–in/m)
				Fighter	Torpedo	Dive	Attack	Other		
GREAT BRITAIN										
Courageous	–	5.2.16	2	–	24[1]	–		–	500 × 84–6	
Study (1931)	–	–	–	60[2]					606 × 84–6	
Ark Royal	–	13.4.37	1	12	48	–		–	797 × 96	16–0/16–0
Illustrious	–	5.4.39	3	12	18	–		–	740 × 95–9	16–0
Indomitable	–	26.3.40	1	40[3]	15[3]	–		–	751–3 × 69	14–0/16–0
Unicorn	–	20.11.41	1	27	–	–		–	640 × 80	16.1/16.1
Implacable	–	10.12.42	2	59[4]	21[4]	–		–	760 × 88–6	14–0/14–0
Colossus	–	30.9.43	16[5]	34	18	–		–	690 × 75	17–6
Design C (1944)	–	–	–	72	36	–		–	950 × 135	17–6/17–6
Design X (Aug 1944)	–	–	–	60	30	–		–	938 × 136	17–6
Design X1 (Oct 1944)	–	–	–	40	40	–		–	888 × 121–9	17–6
Eagle	–	19.3.46	4[6]	39[7]	36[7]	–		–	797–6 × 112	17–6/17–6
Malta	–	–	3[8]	40	40	–		–	909 × 136	17–6
Albion	–	6.5.47	8[9]	16	16	–		–	732 × 90[10]	17–6

[1]Capacity 48. [2]Total. [3]1943 figure. [4]1945 figure. [5]15 completed. [6]2 completed. [7]1950 figure. [8]None completed. [9]4 completed. [10]Mean figures.

Name	No	Launch date	No in class	Fighter	Torpedo	Dive	Attack	Other	Flight deck (ft–in/m)	Hangar height (ft–in/m)
UNITED STATES										
Saratoga	CV3	7.4.25	2	18[1]	–	40[1]		5[1]	893 × 84	20–0
Ranger	CV4	25.2.33	1	36	–	36		4	709 × 86	18–11
Wasp	CV7	4.4.39	1	27[2]	12[2]	37[2]		–	727 × 93	17–2
Hornet	CV8	14.12.40	3	18	36	37		5	802 × 86	17–3
Essex	CV9	31.7.42	24	36	18	37		–	862 × 96	17–6
Independence	CVL22	22.8.42	9	36	12	–		–	544 × 73	17–6
Casablanca	CVE55	5.4.43	50	9	9	9		–		17–6
Commencement Bay	CVE105	9.5.44	35[3]	18	15	–		–		17–6
Midway	CVA41	20.3.45	3	73	–	64		–	932 × 113	17–6
Saipan	CVL48	8.7.45	2	36	12	–		–		17–6
Design C-2 (Nov 1945)	–	–	–	35	–	18		–	870 × 111	17–6
United States	CVB58	–	–	54	–	12/18		–	1090 × 190	25–0
Saratoga	CVA60	8.10.55	4	28[4]	–	–	48[4]	10[4]		
Kitty Hawk	CVA63	31.5.60	3	24[5]	–	–	54[5]	9[5]	1062–6 × 249	
Enterprise	CVAN65	24.9.60	1	24[5]	–	–	66[5]	9[5]	1102 × 257	
John F Kennedy	CVA67	27.5.67	1	24[7]	–	–	35[7]	15[7]		25–0
Nimitz	CVN68	31.5.72	4	24	–	–	34	31	1040 ×256	25–6
CVV Project	–	–	–	c60					912 × 256–6	24–6

[1]1936 figure. [2]1942 figure. [3]19 completed. [4]1960 figure. [5]1963 figure. [6]As built; unofficial. [7]Vietnam War figure. [8]Estimated figures.

| Avgas (gal) | Avord (tons) | Machinery | | | Oil fuel (tons) | Displacement (tons) | | |
		Power (shp)	Speed (kts)	Radius (nm/at kts)		Light	Standard	Full load
37,000		90,000	30.5	5860/16	3900		22,500	
		120,000	32.5	6650/16	3900		23,400	
100,000		102,000	31.0	4300/12	4443		22,000	27,700
51,000		111,000	30.0	14,000/10	4854		23,207	28,619
70,000		111,000	30.0	13,000/10	4517		23,080	28,216
36,500		40,000	24.0	7000/13.5	3000		14,950	
96,000		148,000	32.0	11,300/14	4693		23,460	28,968
80,000		40,000	25.0	8500/20	3190		13,109	18,040
195,000		190,000	33.5	6000/24	8600		47,740	59,230
190,000		220,000	34.5	6000/24	8800		48,400	
190,000		200,000	32.5	6000/24	7600		46,890	56,800
103,000/279,000		152,000	30.5	5000/24	6510		36,970	45,720
		200,000	32.0		6000		46,900	56,800
160,470/184,640		76,000	28.5	6000/20	4133		22,471	27,015
137,000		180,000	33.25	10,500/15	3600		36,220	40,898
157,000		53,500	29.0	10,000/15	2350		13,800	17,577
159,000		70,000	29.5	12,000/15	2403		14,700	18,450
178,000		120,000	32.5	12,000/15	4360		19,875	25,484
240,000		150,000	32.7	20,000/15	6330		27,208	34,881
122,000		100,000	31.6	11,000/15	2633		10,662	14,751
100,000		9000	19.0	10,200/15	2228		8188	10,902
150,000		16,000	19.0		1789		18,908	21,397
365,000		212,000	33.0	15,000/15	10,032		47,387	59,901
143,000		120,000	32.5	10,000/15	2400		14,500	17,800
500,000		212,000	33.2	11,600/20			40,590	54,790
500,000		280,000	33.0	12,000/20	11,505		66,850	78,500
1,400,000	1800	280,000	33.0	12,000/20			60,000	78,000
1,900,000		280,000	30.0+	12,000/20			60,100	78,250
2,720,000	2520	280,000	30.0+	c400,000/20[6]	Nuclear		75,700	89,600
1,950,000	2150	280,000	32.0	12,000/20			61,000	80,800
2,800,000	2570	280,000	c33.0	1,000,000/20[8]	Nuclear	72,700	81,600	93,400
1,320,000	1191	140,000	28.0					62,427

	Dimensions (ft–in/m)					Armor (in/mm)				
	Length oa	Length wl	Beam ext	Beam wl	Draft (full load)	Belt	Hangar side	Flight deck	Hangar deck	Armor deck
GREAT BRITAIN										
Courageous	786–0[11]		90–0		27–6	3.0	–	–	–	1.0–2.0
Study (1931)	815–0[11]	770–0	92–0		26–6	3.5	–	–	–	1.25–2.4
Ark Royal	800–0[11]	685–0	112–0	94–9	27–4	4.5	–	–	–	2.5–3.5
Illustrious	740–0[11]	673–0	106–9		28–2	4.5	4.5	3.0	2.5, 3.0	–
Indomitable	753–11[11]	673–0	116–3		27–9	4.5	1.5	3.0	2.5, 3.0	–
Unicorn	640–0[11]	545–0		90–0	22–4	2.5–3.0[14]	–	2.0	–	2.0
Implacable	766–2[11]	690–0	141–5		26–8	4.5	1.5	3.0	1.5, 2.5	–
Colossus	695–0[11]	630–0	112–6	80–0	23–5	–	–	–	–	–
Design C (1944)	950–0[11]	870–0		115–4	34–0	3.0	2.0	4.0	5.0	4.0
Design X (Aug 1944)	947–0[11]	870–0	136–0	115–3¼	34–7	3.0	–	–	6.0	–
Design X1 (Oct 1944)	900–0[11]	820–0	136–0	115–5	34–7	4.0	–	–	6.0	–
Eagle	803–9[11]	720–0	135–0	112–9	32–10	4.5	1.5	4.0	–	4.0
Malta	916–0½[11]	820–0	136–0	115–7½	34–6	4.0–3.0	–	1.0	4.0–3.0	4.0–3.0
Albion	736–0[11]	650–0	120–6	90–0	27–2½	1.0[15]	–	–	–	1.0, 2.0

[11]Length between perpendiculars. [12]Total. [13]Included in hull figure. [14]Over magazine. [15]Internal.

	Length oa	Length wl	Beam ext	Beam wl	Draft (full load)	Belt	Hangar side	Flight deck	Hangar deck	Armor deck
UNITED STATES										
Saratoga	880–0	850–0	130–0	105–5	33–4	7.0–5.0	–	–	–	2.0
Ranger	769–0	730–0	109–6	80–0	22–5	–	–	–	–	–
Wasp	720–2	690–0	100–0	80–6	22–6	–	–	–	–	1.25
Hornet	809–6	770–0	114–0	83–3	26–0	4.0	–	–	–	1.5
Essex	855–10	820–0	147–6	93–0	27–6	4.0	–	–	2.5	1.5
Independence	622–6	600–0	109–2	71–6	24–3	5.0[10]	–	–	–	2.0
Casablanca	512–3	490–0	108–1	65–2	20–9	–	–	–	–	–
Commencement Bay	557–1	525–0	105–2	75–0	27–11	–	–	–	–	–
Midway	968–0	900–0	136–0	113–0	34–6	7.6/7.0	–	3.5	2.0	2.0
Saipan	683–7	664–0	108–0	76–8	27–0[12]	4.0	–	–	–	2.5
Design C-2 (Nov 1945)		890–0		107–0	31–9	4.0	–	3.0	1.5	1.5
United States	1090–0	1030–0	190–0	130–0	34–6	1.5–3.0	1.5	2.0+1.0[13]	1.5	1.5
Saratoga	1039–0	990–0	252–0	129–6	37–0					
Kitty Hawk	1062–6	990–0	249–0	129–0	35–11					
Enterprise	1123–0	1040–0	257–0	133–0	35–9					
John F Kennedy	1047–6	990–0	252–0	130–0	36–6					
Nimitz	1092–0	1040–0	252–0	134–0	37–0					
CVV Project	923–0		256–6	126–6	34–0					

[9]1942 figure. [10]BHDS. [11]Total. [12]Max. [13]GD. [14]Added 1967. [15]1978 figure.

Armament	Complement		Weights (tons)							
	Ship	Air Group	Hull	Equipment	Armor	Machinery	Armament	Aeronautics	Margin	Total
16–4.7in AA, 16–2pdr (2×8)	839[12]		17,035	1020	[13]	3040	665	740		22,500
16–5.1in DP, 16–2pdr (2×8)			16,910	1110	[13]	3440	930	1010		23,400
16–4.5in (8×2), 48–2pdr (6×8), 32 MG (8×4)	858	742	13,651	1382	2854	2468	1042	1629		22,000
16–4.5in (8×2), 48–2pdr (6×8), 50–20mm (14×1, 18×2)	842	434	12,724	1264	4941	2464	997	1186		23,576
16–4.5in (8×2), 48–2pdr (6×8)	865	527	12,969	1328	4299	2471	997			23,080
8–4in DP (4×2), 16–2pdr (4×4)	981[12]		10,090	770	950	1390	500	1250	–	14,950
16–4.5in (8×2), 52–2pdr (6×8, 1×4)	840	550	13,235	1428	3645	3128	1074			23,460
24–2pdr (6×4), 64–20mm (11×4, 10×2)	854	222	9240	1440	–	1180	215	1240	300	13,190
16–4.5in (8×2), 54–40mm (9×6)	3300[12]		25,180	2380	10,610	4370	1440		470	47,740
16–4.5in (8×2), 48–40mm (8×6)	3300[12]		27,505	2520	8506	4515	1380	3500	475	48,400
16–4.5in (8×2), 42–40mm (7×6)			25,900	2445	8620	4225	1330	3900	470	46,890
16–4.5in (8×2), 64–40mm (8×6, 2×2, 12×1)	1562	1177	20,680	2510	6320	3560	1390			36,970
16–4.5in (8×2), 55–40mm (8×6, 7×1)	3535[12]									
32–40mm (2×6, 8×2, 4×1)	1028	362	14,916	1583	–	2109	358	2352		22,471
8–8in (4×2), 12–5in (12×1)	1940[9]	851[9]	24,007	1626	1437	7375	1508	688	–	36,641
8–5in (8×1)	1369[9]	779[9]	10,274	936	48	1604	595	556	–	14,013
8–5in (8×1), 16–1.1in (4×4), 24–0.5in	1388	779	10,364	992	205	2020	738	987	–	15,306
8–5in (8×1), 16–1.1in (4×4), 24–0.5in	1366[9]	851[9]	14,576	1155	907	2833	835	896	–	21,202
12–5in (4×2, 4×1), 32–40mm (8×4), 46–20mm (46×1)	1531	851	18,521	2547	997	3333	2356	1238	–	28,992
24–40mm (2×4, 8×2), 22–20mm (22×1)	1019	333	7461	1098	254	1958	691	554	143	12,159
1–5in, 8–40mm (4×2), 12–20mm (12×1)	860									
2–5in (2×1), 36–40mm (3×4, 12×2), 20–20mm (20×1)	1066									
18–5in (18×1), 84–40mm (21×4), 68–20mm (34×2)	4104[11]		30,170	3177	3423	5562	4536	5990	500	53,358
40–40mm (5×4, 10×2), 32–20mm (16×2)	1821		8663	1155	705	1650	566	718	150	13,607
26–3in (13×2), 16–40mm (4×4), 40–20mm (20×2)	3216[11]									
8–5in (8×1), 12–3in (6×2)	4127[11]		50,009	4342	1214	6450	3784	2999	1650	70,448
16 Sea Sparrow (2×8)[14]	2865	2400								
4 Terrier (2×2)	2900	2500								
16 Sea Sparrow (2×8)[14]	3061[15]	2627[15]								
24 Sea Sparrow (3×8)	2900	2500								
24 Sea Sparrow (3×8)										
?None										

	No	Launch date	No in class	Fighter	Torpedo	Dive	Attack	Other	Flight deck (ft–in/m)	Hangar height (ft–in/m)
JAPAN										
Kaga	–	17.11.21	1	60[1]					171.2 × 30.5	
Kaga (as rebuilt 1934–35)	–	–	1	24/6	36/9	12/3		–	248.6 × 30.5	
Akagi	–	22.4.25	1	60[1]					190.2 × 30.5	
Akagi (as rebuilt 1935–38)	–	–	1	19/5	35/16	12/4		–	249.2 × 30.5	
Ryujo	–	2.4.31	1	24/8	–	12/4		–	156.5 × 23.0	
Hiryu	–	16.11.35	1	12/4	9/3	27/9		9[5]	216.9 × 27.0	
Soryu	–	23.12.35	1	9/3	18/6	18/6		8/3[5]	216.9 × 26.0	
Shokaku	–	1.6.39	2	18/2	27/5	27/5		–	242.2 × 29.0	
Project 5021 (1942)	–	–	5	27	18	–		6[5]	261.5 × 30.0	
Taiho	–	7.4.43	1	24	24	–		4[5]	256.0 × 28.0	5.0/5.0
Katsuragi	–	19.1.44	6[6]	12	27	–		18[5]	214.5 × 27.0	4.6/4.2
Shinano	–	8.10.44	1	18/2	18/2	–		6/1[5]	256.0 × 40.0	

[1]Total. [2]Plus 1700 tons coal. [3]Trial. [4]Plus 2100 tons coal. [5]Scouts. [6]3 completed.

	No	Launch date	No in class	Fighter	Torpedo	Dive	Attack	Other	Flight deck (ft–in/m)	Hangar height (ft–in/m)
FRANCE										
Béarn	–	15.4.20	1	20[1]			5[1]	–	180.0 × 27.0	
Joffre	–	[2]	2	15			25	–	200.0 × 28.0	5.9/4.9
PA28 Project (1947)	–	–	–	5			22	–	200.0 × 30.0	
Clemenceau	–	21.12.57	2	40[3]					257.0 × 47.0	
PA58 Project	–	–	–						280.0 × 58.0	
GERMANY										
Graf Zeppelin	–	8.12.38	2	12			30	–	240.0 × 27.0	
ITALY										
Aquila	–	–	–	36[3]					211.6 × 25.72	

[1]1939 figure. [2]Construction halted 1940. [3]Total. [4]JP-5. [5]Avgas. [6]Legend displacement 28,090 tons.

| Avgas (gal) | Avord (tons) | Machinery | | | | Displacement (tons) | | |
		Power (shp)	Speed (kts)	Radius (nm/at kts)	Oil fuel (tons)	Light	Standard	Full load
c225,000		91,000	27.5	8000/14	3600[2]		26,900	33,693[3]
		127,400	28.3	10,000/16	8208		38,200	42,541[3]
		131,200	31.4	8000/14	3900[4]		26,900	34,364[3]
		133,000	31.2	8200/16	5775		36,500	41,300[3]
47,000		65,000	29.0	10,000/14	2943		8000	10,150[3]
98,000		153,000	34.6	7670/18	3750		17,300	20,165[3]
96,000		152,000	34.5	7680/18	3400		15,900	18,800[3]
187,000		160,000	34.0	9700/18	5000		25,675	29,800[3]
		160,000	33.3	10,000/18			30,360	35,300[3]
176,000		160,000	33.1	10,000/18	5700		29,300	34,200[3]
53,500		104,000	32.7	8000/18	3671		17,150	20,899[3]
171,000		150,000	27.0	10,000/18	8904		62,000	68,059[3]
26,000		40,000	21.0	6000/10	2100		22,100	25,000
		120,000	33.0	7000/20			18,000	20,000
150,000		105,000	32.0				15,700	20,000
317,000[4]/105,000[5]		126,000	32.0	7500/18	3700		22,000	32,800
		200,000	33.0				35,000	45,500
54,000–72,000		200,000	34.0	8000/19	6740		24,500[1]	31,367[6]
72,000		140,000	29.0	4150/18	2800			27,800

	Dimensions (ft–in/m)						Armor (in/mm)			
	Length oa	Length wl	Beam ext	Beam wl	Draft (full load)	Belt	Hangar side	Flight deck	Hangar deck	Armor deck
JAPAN										
Kaga		230.0	29.6		7.93[7]					
Kaga (as rebuilt 1934–35)	247.7	240.3		32.5	9.5[7]					
Akagi		249.0	29.0		8.07[7]					
Akagi (as rebuilt 1935–38)	260.7	250.4		31.3	8.7[7]					
Ryujo	180.0	175.4	20.3		5.56[7]					
Hiryu	227.4	222.0	22.32		7.74[7]	90–150	–	–	–	25, 55
Soryu	227.5	222.0	21.3		7.62[7]	55	–	–	–	25, 55
Shokaku	257.5	250.0		26.0	8.9[7]	165	–	–	–	157
Project 5021 (1942)	264.5	257.0		28.0	9.64[7]					
Taiho	260.6	253.0	33.6	27.7	10.15[7]	165–70	–	75	–	115
Katsuragi	227.35	223.0	26.8	22.0	7.8[7]	90–150	–	–	–	22, 55
Shinano	266.0	256.0		36.3	10.3[7]	205	–	75	190	–

[7]Trial. [8]Total.

FRANCE										
Béarn	182.6	170.6	31.0	27.1	8.6	83	–	24	24	28/70
Joffre	236.0	228.0	35.0	25.0	6.6	105				40/70[7]
PA28 Project (1947)	230.0	215.0	36.0	25.4	6.5					
Clemenceau	265.0	238.0	51.2	31.7	8.6					
PA58 Project	286.0	262.0	58.0	34.0						
GERMANY										
Graf Zeppelin	262.5	250.0		31.5	8.5	100[10]	–	20	–	40
ITALY										
Aquila	231.4	207.3	30.1	29.0	7.4	–	–	–	–	60–80

[7]Over magazine. [8]Including fuel. [9]Including aeronautics. [10]Max. [11]Included in hull figure.

| Armament | Complement | | Weights (tons) | | | | | | | |
	Ship	Air Group	Hull	Equipment	Armor	Machinery	Armament	Aeronautics	Margin	Total
10–8in, 12–4.7in AA	1340[8]									
10–8in, 16–5in (8×2), 22–25mm (11×2)	2016[8]									
10–8in, 12–4.7in AA										
6–8in, 12–4.7in AA, 28–25mm (14×2)	2000[8]									
12–5in (6×2), 24 MG	600		5301	1125	783	1856	384	427	–	9876
12–5in (6×2), 31–25mm	1100		9785	1294	1720	3159	541	906	–	17,405
12–5in (6×2), 28–25mm	1100		8783	1164	1341	3163	578	919	–	15,948
16–5in (8×2), 36–25mm (12×3)	1660[8]		14,160	1071	5153	3599	802	1390	–	25,679
16–3.9in DP (8×2), 66–25mm (22×3)	1800									
12–3.9in DP (8×2), 51–25mm (17×3)	1747		13,705	1151	8795	3766	676	799	186	29,300
12–5in (6×2), 51–25mm (16×3, 3×1)	1500		9214	1652	2729	2965	710	849	158	18,277
16–5in (8×2), 145–25mm (35×3, 40×1)	2400		37,052	1531	24,244	1106	1454	474	–	65,861

Armament	Ship	Air Group	Hull	Equipment	Armor	Machinery	Armament	Aeronautics	Margin	Total
8–155mm, 6–75mm, 8–37mm, 96 MG (12×8), 4–550mm TT	875									
16–130mm (4×4), 8–37mm (4×2), 24–13.2mm (6×4)	1251									
16–100mm (8×2), 16–57mm (8×2)	c1800									
8–100mm			13,000	5200	2100	6800[8]	4200[9]			31,300
8–100mm, 4 Masurca (2×2)										
16–150mm (8×2), 12–105mm AA (6×2), 22–37mm (11×2), 7–20mm (7×1)	1760		17,800	1400	[11]	4700	1600	600	–	
8–135mm, 12–65mm, 132–20mm (22×6)	1175	245	13,300	3650	3200	2375	390	–	–	22,875

Appendix 2: Carrier Aircraft Data

Aircraft	Year	Engine	Powerplant — Rating (hp/lb thrust)			Fuel capacity (gal)
			Normal	Take-off	Dash	
GREAT BRITAIN **Fighter Aircraft**						
Sopwith 2F1 Camel	1918	1 × Clerget	130			37
Fairey Flycatcher I	1928	1 × Jaguar IV	400			
Hawker Osprey III	1932	1 × Kestrel IIMS	630			90
Hawker Nimrod IIS	1934	1 × Kestrel IIS	477			64[1]
Blackburn Skua	1938	1 × Perseus XII	620	830	905[2]	163
Gloster Sea Gladiator	1939	1 × Mercury VIIA	720[3]	725		70
Fairey Fulmar II	1941	1 × Merlin 30	1260[5]			155
Hawker Sea Hurricane	1941	1 × Merlin III	1030[7]			97
Supermarine Seafire LIIC	1942	1 × Merlin 46	1415[8]			85
Fairey Firefly I	1943	1 × Griffon II		1735[10]		192
De Havilland Sea Hornet[11]	1945	2 × Merlin 130		2080[12]		347
Fairey Firefly FR4	1947	1 × Griffon 74	2245[13]	2750		201
Hawker Sea Fury FB11	1947	1 × Centaurus 18	1845	2480	2550[2]	200
Supermarine Seafire 47	1948	1 × Griffon 88		1935	2350[15]	152
Supermarine Attacker F1	1951	1 × Nene 3	5100			310
Hawker Sea Hawk FGA6	1953	1 × Nene 103	5400			395[16]
De Havilland Sea Venom FAW22	1954	1 × Ghost 105	5300			
Supermarine Scimitar F1	1958	2 × Avon 202	11,250			
Saunders Roe SR177[19]	1958	1 × Gyron Junior DGJ-1 plus 1 × Spectre 5A	14,000+ 10,000			580+ 111[17]
De Havilland Sea Vixen FAW2	1959	2 × Avon 208	11,230			
McDonnell Phantom FG1	1966	2 × Spey 201	12,250		20,515	
BAe Sea Harrier FRS1	1979	1 × Pegasus 104	21,500			660

[1]Plus 1–16gal auxiliary. [2]Military rating. [3]840hp at 14,600ft. [4]At 30kts WOD. [5]Rating at 7250ft. [6]At 20kts WOD. [7]840hp at 16,250ft. [8]Rating at [15]Military rating at 1250ft. [16]Plus 2–100gal drop tanks. [17]Plus 599.8gal HTP. [18]Max. [19]Project.

Aircraft speeds quoted in the following tables are in knots, *not* miles per hour, corresponding to official British and Japanese practice, and to US Navy practice after 1945; one knot equals 1.15 statute miles per hour. Similarly, all distances have been converted to nautical miles. Altitudes are in feet, except for Japanese entries for which the original metric figures have been retained. Up to three figures for engine power are given: normal, or rated, or cruise power; take-off power, which often corresponds to military power; and a maximum (dash) figure. For a jet engine the latter corresponds either to water-injection power (which is noted) or to afterburning power. For a piston engine it is water-injection or combat rating; if no third figure is given the take-off rating is also the maximum power rating. Figures for dash performance refer to this maximum rating, which in an afterburning jet can make a dramatic difference in overall performance. Generally, dash or military power performance figures have been computed on the basis of a combat weight which may be considerably less than take-off weight, and on the basis of a combat configuration in which drop tanks have been jettisoned. Range, on the other hand, is calculated on the basis of the listed take-off condition. Range and combat radius definitions varied so considerably from navy to navy that these figures are far from strictly compatible, but they do give an indication of effective operating distances. In the case of US attack aircraft, the maximum range is a scouting range in which bombs were not carried.

From a carrier compatibility point of view, take-off weight determines the requirement for strength in the flight deck and the elevators. An airplane generally lands at 3 or 3.5g, which means that the deck must withstand an impact of about 3 to 3.5 times the landing weight, and must support a dead load of the take-off weight. Where no landing weight is given, the landing stall speed corresponds to take-off weight less fuel weight. In jets, landing weight generally includes some fuel; in a few cases, such as that of the AJ-1 Savage, it does not include bombs. Aircraft fuel

Carrier compatibility										
Dimensions						Take-off				Landing
Span (full) (ft–in/m)	Span (folded) (ft–in/m)	Length (ft–in/m)	Height (folded) (ft–in/m)	Wing area (sq ft/m²)	Weight (lb)	Stall speed (kts)	Roll @ 0kts WOD	Roll @ 25kts WOD	Weight (lb)	Stall speed (kts)
26–11	–	18–6	9–1	221	1482					
29–0	–	23–0	12–0	288	3028					48.0
37–0	15–7	29–4	10–5	339	4950					
33–7	–	26–7	9–10	301	4059					
46–2	16–2	35–7	14–2	312	8230					
32–3	–	27–5	10–7	323	5020	50.4		195[4]	4495	47.8
46.0		40.2	11.6	377	10,350		420[6]	260[4]	8650	
40.0	–	31.4	10.5	258	7015		400[6]	270[4]	6100	
32–7		30–0	13–0	232	7006			225[9]		
44.5	13.5	37.0	12.3	328	12,131	71.0	490[6]	330[4]	10,290	62.0
45.0	27.5	36.8	13.0	361	15,682	80.0	350[6]	160[4]	12,570	68.0
41.0	16–0	37–8	15–6	330	13,500					
38–5		34–8	15–11	280	12,350		1150	500[14]		
36–11		34–4	12–9	244	10,700			378[14]		
36–11	30–11	37–6	9–11	226	11,500					
39–0	13–4	39–8	8–8	278	16,200	105.0				
42–10		36–8	8–6	280	15,400					
51–0	22–3	55–7	15–3		40,000					
30–3		50–6	14–4	327	25,786					
51–0	22–3	55–7	15–0	648	41,575					
38–5		57–7	16–1	520	56,000				38,000[18]	
25–3	–	47–7	12–2					500[9]		

14,000ft. [9]At 30kts WOD, with 45gal tank. [10]1495hp supercharged. [11]Spec N.5/44 (day version). [12]1890hp supercharged. [13]At 9250ft. [14]WOD 27kts.

load (in gallons, or Imperial gallons for British aircraft) determines the number of sorties the carrier can support without refueling, given the fuel capacity listed in the carrier data tables in Appendix 1. Deck roll is the distance required to lift off, with wind-over-deck either zero or at 25kts. In a non-catapult ship it would determine how far aft the deck spot would have to start. The great deck rolls required of most jets explain the modern need for catapults. The combination of stall speed at take-off weight and take-off weight itself is a measure of the rising requirements set on the catapults, just as the combination of landing stall speed (power on) and weight is a measure of the increasing requirement for energy absorption in arresting gear. In both cases the energy requirement is proportional to the weight and to the *square* of the speed. Wind-over-deck is thus extremely valuable. For example, a 30kt wind cuts the energy requirement of an airplane with a 100kt stall speed by 51 per cent.

For jet aircraft, CAP loiter time is time on station about 150nm from the carrier, which is only a fraction of the total (mission) time the jet fighter is airborne. It is a measure of the extent to which a limited number of aircraft can maintain continuous Combat Air Patrol assignments; like the definition of combat radius, it is hedged about by a variety of requirements for reserve fuel load, and in effect is a means of comparing different aircraft rather than an absolute measure of capability. CAP loiter was not employed to measure the performance of propeller fighters largely because their CAP stations were generally quite close to their carriers.

Finally, in range and radius data, the number following the slash is the average speed, eg 440/221 should be read as 440nm at an average of 221kts; in dimension data a slash in the span (full) column separates upper and lower mainplane figures.

| | | Range | | | | Climb | | | | | Low altitude | |
	Max (nm)	At (kts)	With tanks (no–gal)	CAP loiter (hrs)	Mission time (hrs) or combat radius (nm)	To 5000ft (min)	To 10,000ft (min)	To 20,000ft (min)	To 30,000ft (min)	Initial rate (sea level) (ft/m per min)	Speed (kts)	At (ft/m)
GREAT BRITAIN												
Fighter Aircraft												
Sopwith 2F1 Camel						11.7	23.7[19]					
Fairey Flycatcher I						8.0	18.8[19]			1090	117	SL
Hawker Osprey III						7.7						
Hawker Nimrod IIS						6.1						
Blackburn Skua							43.0			740	177	SL
Gloster Sea Gladiator	361	191	83[23]			4.7	9.1				182.6	SL
Fairey Fulmar II												
Hawker Sea Hurricane	957	181	90[23]				10.0					
Supermarine Seafire LIIC	600	190	1–45			5.0[24]	8.0			4380[25]	275	SL
Fairey Firefly I	1186	188	2–50			9.6[24]				1930[26]		
De Havilland Sea Hornet	1678	231	2–100				6.4			3400[27]		
Fairey Firefly FR4	930	198	2–90			7.2	15.5				275	SL
Hawker Sea Fury FB11	904		2–90			5.7	10.8			4320		
Supermarine Seafire 47	817		1–90, 2–22.5				4.9			4800[25]	307	SL
Supermarine Attacker F1	1035	309	1–270				6.6			6350	513	SL
Hawker Sea Hawk FGA6							5.8[30]	12.0[31]		4720[32]	450[33]	SL
De Havilland Sea Venom FAW22										5750	500.9	SL
Supermarine Scimitar F1	1300		2–150, 2–250 or 4–150							20,000	560	SL
Saunders Roe SR177							1.45	3.1[37]				
De Havilland Sea Vixen FAW2			2–150		1.5			8.5[38]			600	SL
McDonnell Phantom FG1		2500[39]								32,000	M1.2	1000
BAe Sea Harrier FRS1			208[23]								640	SL

[19]To 15,000ft. [20]Endurance (hrs). [21]Endurance (hrs) at 114kts. [22]Endurance (hrs) at 125–143kts. [23]Max capacity of tanks. [24]To 15,000ft. [25]Combat [33]521kts clean. [34]460kts clean. [35]40,000ft clean. [36]DLI only. [37]To 60,000ft. [38]To 40,000ft. [39]Max ferry. [40]Additional load. [41]High altitude intercept.

High altitude				Dash		Service ceiling (ft/m)	Guns	Armament — Load	
Speed (kts)	At (ft/m)	Range/at (nm/kts)	Combat radius (nm)	Speed (kts)	At (ft/m)			Bomb load for given performance	Alternative loads
		3.0[20]					2–0.303	–	Up to 2–50lb bombs
114	10,000	1.8[21]				20,600	2–0.303	–	4–20lb bombs
146	5000					23,500	2–0.303	–	2–112lb or 8–20lb bombs
170	12,000					26,900	2–0.303	–	4–20lb bombs
196	6700	4.5[22]				19,100	5–0.303	1–500lb	
220	14,600	278/187				32,200	4–0.303	–	–
231.3	9600	691/152				23,900	8–0.303	–	–
267.8	18,000	482.6/180.9				32,700	4–20mm	–	2–250lb bombs
295	6000	440/192	140			24,000	2–20mm, 2–0.303	–	Up to 1500lb total
257.4	3500	671.3/187.8		277.4	17,000	29,700	4–20mm	–	2–500lb bombs, 8 RP
370.4	6000	1000/231.3		400	18,750	37,500	4–20mm	–	2–1000lb bombs or 8 RP
300	12,500	506/203				29,290	4–20mm	–	2–1000 or 500lb bombs, 8 RP
400	18,000	609				35,800	4–20mm	–	2–1000 or 500lb bombs, 12–3in or 5in AR
377	24,250		217[28]			43,100	4–20mm	–	2–1000 or 500lb bombs or 4 AR
468	30,000	513/309				45,000	4–20mm	–	2–1000lb bombs or 8 AR[29]
456[34]	10,000[35]		250			44,500	4–20mm	2–500lb	10 AR
482.6	30,000	1.7[20]				40,000	4–20mm	–	Bombs or 8–60lb AR
550	35,000		250			50,000	4–30mm	–	Up to 2000lb on each of 4 pylons; Bullpup, Sidewinder or tactical nuclear bombs for ground attack
			160	M2.35	60,000	85,000	–	2 Red Top	
556	10,000					48,000	–	4 Firestreak, 28–2in AR	2–1000lb or 4–500lb bombs or 12–3in (4×2) or 96–2in (4×24) AR
			500	M2.1	40,000			4 Sparrow	4 Sidewinder or up to 10,000lb of ordnance[40]
		400[41]					2–30mm	2 Sidewinder; 5000lb total stores	4 hard points. 2000lb inboard, 650 outboard; Harpoon, Martel

condition. [26]2260ft per min combat. [27]5400ft per min combat. [28]Max fuel. [29]Attacker FB1. [30]4.0 mins clean. [31]8.0 mins clean. [32]5700ft per min clean.

Aircraft	Year	Engine	Powerplant Rating (hp/lb thrust) Normal	Take-off	Dash	Fuel capacity (gal)
Attack Aircraft						
Sopwith Cuckoo	1918	1 × Arab	200			
Blackburn Dart	1923	1 × Lion IIB	465			78.5
Blackburn Ripon IIA	1929	1 × Lion X	570			155
Blackburn Baffin	1934	1 × Pegasus IM3	565			120
Blackburn Shark II	1935	1 × Pegasus III	800			171
Fairey Albacore	1940	1 × Taurus XII		1085	1130[1]	193
Fairey Swordfish II	1943	1 × Pegasus 30	750[2]			143
Fairey Barracuda II	1943	1 × Merlin 32	1640[5]			226
Blackburn Firebrand TF4	1945	1 × Centaurus IX	1975	2520	2225[1]	168
Fairey Spearfish[6]	1946	1 × Centaurus 175M	2525[11]			388
Short Sturgeon	1946	2 × Merlin 140S	1660		2050[1]	
De Havilland Sea Mosquito TR33	1946	2 × Merlin 25	1640			405
Westland Wyvern S4	1953	1 × Python 3	3670[8]			511
Blackburn Buccaneer S2	1963	2 × Spey 101	11,100			1560[9]
Anti-Submarine and Airborne Early Warning Aircraft						
Fairey Gannet AS1	1954	1 × Double Mamba 112	3875			
Fairey Gannet AEW3	1960	1 × Double Mamba 112	3875			
Spotter-Reconnaissance Aircraft						
Avro Bison	1923	1 × Lion II	480			93
Blackburn Blackburn I	1923	1 × Lion IIB	450			90
Fairey IIIF Mk IIIM	1928	1 × Lion XIA	570			
Fairey Seal	1933	1 × Panther IIA	525			
Airspeed AS39 Fleet Shadower	1939	4 × Niagara V	130			170

[1]Military rating. [2]Rating at 4750ft. [3]At 20kts WOD. [4]At 30kts WOD. [5]Rating at 1750ft. [6]Spec O.5/43. [7]At 27kts WOD. [8]Plus 1180lb thrust. [9]Plus 425gal

Aircraft	Year	Engine	Normal	Take-off	Dash	Fuel capacity (gal)
UNITED STATES						
Fighter Aircraft						
Boeing FB-5	1926	1 × Packard 2A-1500		520		
Boeing F2B-1	1927	1 × R-1340B	450			100
Curtiss F6C-3 Hawk	1927	1 × Curtiss D-12	400			100
Boeing F3B-1	1928	1 × R-1340B	450[1]			110
Vought O2U-4 Corsair	1929	1 × R-1340-88	450[1]			110
Grumman FF-2	1931	1 × R-1820-78	700[1]			140
Boeing F4B-4	1932	1 × R-1340-16	550			55[2]
Vought SU-4 Corsair	1933	1 × R-1690-40	600[1]			130
Grumman F2F-1	1933	1 × R-1535-72	650[1]	700		110
Grumman F3F-1	1935	1 × R-1535-84	650	700		110

	Carrier compatibility									
Dimensions						Take-off				Landing
Span (full) (ft–in/m)	Span (folded) (ft–in/m)	Length (ft–in/m)	Height (folded) (ft–in/m)	Wing area (sq ft/m²)	Weight (lb)	Stall speed (kts)	Roll @ 0kts WOD (ft/m)	Roll @ 25kts WOD (ft/m)	Weight (lb)	Stall speed (kts)
46–9	–	28–6	10–8	566						
45–6	17–6	35–5	12–11	654	6400	38.0				
44–10/45–7	17–10	36–9	12–10	683	7405					
44–10/45–7	17–10	38–4	12–10	683	7610					
46–0/36–0	15–0	35–3	12–1	489	8050					
50–0	17–9	39–10	12–6	607	11,186					
45.5	17.3	36.3	12.4		9250	64.0	540[3]	345[4]	8120	54.0
49.2	17.75	39.9	12.3	414	14,103	71.0	805[3]	600[4]	12,321	65.0
51–4	16–10	38–9	13–3	383	15,671					
60.0	20.0	45.0	17.0	530	22,137	75.0	670[3]	470[4]	19,101	67.0
60–0	20–0	44–7	14–5				825	350[7]		
54–2	27–3	42–3	13–6	450	21,000					
44–0	20–0	42–0	18–2	355	21,200					
44–0	19–11	63–5[10]	16–8	515	46–56,000					
54–4	19–11	43–0	13–9	483	19,600					
54–4	19–11	44–0	16–10	483	25,000					
46–0	–	36–0	13–6	620	5800					
45–7	17–6	36–2	12–6	650	5960					
45–9	14–3	34–0	12–9	443	5874					
45–9		33–8	12–9	444	6000					
53–4	18–0	40–0	10–5	460	6935	28.7				

in bomb bay doors. [10]51ft 10in folded.

32–0	–	23–10	9–5	241	3249					
30–1/24–3	–	22–11	10–2	243	2874	52.1			2574	47.8
31–6/26–0	–	22–10	10–8	252	1963	52.5	344	102	2663	
33–0/26–6	–	24–9	10–1	275	2950	48.0	272	72	2650	46.0
36–0/34–6	–	25–1	11–0	319	1885	52.1	434	132	3335	47.6
34–6/31–6	–	24–6	11–1	310	4826	56.4	585	202	3986	51.3
30–0/26–4	–	20–4	9–9	227.5	3178	54.3	430	139	2807	51.7
36–0	–	27–5	11–5	337	4778	53.0	345	108	4118	49.3
28–6/26–0	–	21–5	10–6	230	3787	57.0	360	126	3127	51.7
32–0/29–6	–	23–5	10–6	260.6	4148	57.0	522	183	3488	52.4

	Performance											
	Range					Climb					Low altitude	
	Max (nm)	At (kts)	With tanks (no-gal)	CAP loiter (hrs)	Mission time (hrs) or combat radius (nm)	To 5000ft (min)	To 10,000ft (min)	To 20,000ft (min)	To 30,000ft (min)	Initial rate (sea level) (ft/m per min)	Speed (kts)	At (ft/m)
Attack Aircraft												
Sopwith Cuckoo							31.0					
Blackburn Dart										600	93	3000
Blackburn Ripon IIA	927									610	110	SL
Blackburn Baffin										480	109	SL
Blackburn Shark II			1–150							990	122	SL
Fairey Albacore	900	100	1–120			8.0[12]						
Fairey Swordfish II	896	91	93[13]			10.0				565		
Fairey Barracuda II	1000	145	1–116			6.0				850[14]	198.3	1750
Blackburn Firebrand TF4										2200	278	SL
Fairey Spearfish	1652	187	1–275[15]				10.8			1720[16]		
Short Sturgeon	1391		1–170							2330[17]		
De Havilland Sea Mosquito TR33										1870	323	5500
Westland Wyvern S4										2350	333	SL
Blackburn Buccaneer											560	200
Anti-Submarine and Airborne Early Warning Aircraft												
Fairey Gannet AS1										2000	270	5000
Fairey Gannet AEW3										2000	217	5000
Spotter-Reconnaissance Aircraft												
Avro Bison							24.0			600	96	SL
Blackburn Blackburn I										690	106	3000
Fairey IIIF Mk IIIM						5.56					118	SL
Fairey Seal						5.34					120	SL
Airspeed AS39 Fleet Shadower							8.0			865		

[11]Endurance (hrs) at 87kts. [12]To 6000ft. [13]Max capacity of tanks. [14]1350ft per min combat. [15]Bomb bay. [16]1720ft per min combat. [17]4120ft per min dash

	Max (nm)	At (kts)	With tanks (no-gal)	CAP loiter (hrs)	Mission time (hrs) or combat radius (nm)	To 5000ft (min)	To 10,000ft (min)	To 20,000ft (min)	To 30,000ft (min)	Initial rate (sea level) (ft/m per min)	Speed (kts)	At (ft/m)
UNITED STATES												
Fighter Aircraft												
Boeing FB-5										2100	152	SL
Boeing F2B-1	612					3.0	7.0	27.8		1890	137.7	SL
Curtiss F6C-3 Hawk	570					3.5	8.5	40.0			133.6	SL
Boeing F3B-1	687		1–50			3.1	7.6[22]	33.0			136	SL
Vought O2U-4 Corsair						4.7		23.0[23]			119.8	SL
Grumman FF-2						2.9		11.9[23]			179.8	4000
Boeing F4B-4	654.8					2.3		8.7[23]				SL
Vought SU-4 Corsair						4.4		22.0[33]			148	SL
Grumman F2F-1						2.0		7.6[23]				
Grumman F3F-1						2.9	5.1	13.7		1900	187	SL

APPENDICES 179

High altitude Speed (kts)	At (ft/m)	Range/at (nm/kts)	Combat radius (nm)	Dash Speed (kts)	At (ft/m)	Service ceiling (ft/m)	Guns	Bomb load for given performance	Alternative loads
						12,100	–	1 torpedo	–
87.0	10,000	223				12,700	–	1 torpedo	–
103	5000	709				10,000	1–0.303	1 torpedo	6–230lb or 3–520lb bombs
118	10,000	4.5[11]				15,000	2–0.303	1 torpedo	1–2000lb or 3–530lb or 6–230/250lb bombs
132	6500	623/103				14,600	2–0.303	1 torpedo	1500lb of bombs
150	5000	550/130	180			20,700	2–0.303	1 torpedo	4–500lb or 6–250lb or 12–100lb bombs or 4 Mk VII or 6 Mk XI depth charges
121	4750	450/91.3				12,400	1–0.303	1 torpedo	3–500lb or 6–250lb bombs or 8 RP or 1 mine or 4–250lb depth charges
		596/150				18,200	2–0.303	1 torpedo	3–500lb or 6–250lb bombs or 4–450lb depth charges
297	13,000	648/223				28,500	4–20mm	1 torpedo	–
247.8	5000	876/187				26,700	4–0.50	1 torpedo	1–1000 or 1600 or 2000lb or 4–500lb bombs
343	24,000	900	374		19,000	35,700	2–0.50	–	8 AR and 2–1000lb bombs[18]
337	13,500	809/209				30,000	4–20mm	1 torpedo, 8 AR	1–2000lb or 4–500lb bombs
330	10,000					28,000	4–20mm	1 torpedo	3–1000lb bombs or 16 AR
		2000				–	–	–	1–1000lb or 2–500/540lb bombs[15]; 3–1000 or 500lb bombs[19] or 1 Martel or rocket pod on each of 4 pylons – up to 16,000lb total
		576				25,000	–	2 homing torpedoes, 16–60lb AR, 2–1000lb bombs	4–1000lb bombs
		609				25,000	–	2 homing torpedoes, 16–60lb AR, 2–1000lb bombs	4–1000lb bombs
		296/78				14,000	2–0.303	–	–
98	10,000	4.5[20]				12,950	2–0.303	–	–
						20,000	2–0.303	–	–
		4.5[21]				17,000	2–0.303	–	Up to 500lb of bombs
110	5000	6.0[22]				14,700	–	–	–

(max boost). [18]Internal. [19]Ejector rack. [20]Endurance (hrs) at 90kts. [21]Endurance (hrs). [22]Endurance (hrs) at 98.3kts.

High altitude Speed (kts)	At (ft/m)	Range/at (nm/kts)	Combat radius (nm)	Dash Speed (kts)	At (ft/m)	Service ceiling (ft/m)	Guns	Bomb load for given performance	Alternative loads
		365/130				22,000	1–0.30, 1–0.50	–	–
134.8	5000	275.6				21,500	1–0.30, 1–0.50	–	–
133	5000	305				20,300	2–0.30	–	–
123	15,000	327				20,900	1–0.30, 1–0.50	–	2–116lb bombs
103.5	15,000	549				17,900	3–0.30	–	–
160.9	15,000	673				21,100	2–0.30[24]	–	2–100lb bombs
147.8	15,000	331.3				26,900	2–0.30	–	2–116lb bombs
133	15,000	592				18,700	3–0.30	–	–
200.9	7500	817.4				27,500	2–0.30	–	–
200.9	7500	793				28,500	1–0.30, 1–0.50	–	2–100lb bombs

Aircraft	Year	Engine	Normal	Take-off	Dash	Fuel capacity (gal)
Brewster F2A-3 Buffalo	1941	1 × R-1820-40	1000[3]	1200		240
Grumman F4F-4 Wildcat	1941	1 × R-1830-86	1100	1200		144
Grumman F6F-5 Hellcat	1944	1 × R-2800-10W	1675	1000	2135[4]	250[5]
Vought F4U-4 Corsair	1944	1 × R-2800-18W	1700	2100		234
Grumman F8F-1 Bearcat	1944	1 × R-2800-34W	1700	2100	2750[3]	185[5]
Boeing XF8B-1	1944	1 × R-4300-10	2500[1]	3000		384
McDonnell FH-1 Phantom	1945	2 × J30-WE-20	1285	1560		375[7]
Grumman F7F-3 Tigercat	1945	2 × R-2800-34W	1700	2100	2380[8]	455[9]
McDonnell F2H-2 Banshee	1948	2 × J34-WE-34	2650[1]	3250		877[10]
Grumman F9F-5 Panther	1949	1 × J48-P-6A	5000[1]	6250	7000[11]	763[12]
Douglas F3D-2 Skyknight	1951	2 × J34-WE-36	3000[1]	3400	3400	1350
Douglas F4D-1 Skyray	1951	1 × J57-P-8B	8700[1]		16,000[13]	1240[14]
Grumman F9F-6 Cougar	1951	1 × J48-P-8	5600[1]	7250	7000[11]	919
Vought F7U-3 Cutlass	1951	2 × J46-WE-8B	3620[1]	4020	5725	1320
Grumman F11F-1 Tiger	1954	1 × J65-W-18	6470[1]	7450	10,500	1023
North American FJ-4B Fury	1954	1 × J65-W-16A	6780[1]	7700		840
McDonnell F3H-2M Demon	1956	1 × J71-A-2B	8700[1]	10,000	14,400	1500
LTV F-8C Crusader	1958	1 × J57-P-16	9150[1]	10,700	16,900	1273
McDonnell F-4J Phantom	1966	2 × J79-GE-10	11,110[1]	11,970	17,659	1998
General Dynamics F-111B	1966	2 × TF30-P-1A	8500[1]	10,750	18,500	3383[16]
Grumman F-14A Tomcat	1970	2 × TF30-P-412A	12,350[1]		20,900	2380[20]
McDonnell Douglas AV-8B	1977	1 × Pegasus 11	21,180[1,11]			
McDonnell Douglas F-18A Hornet	1979	2 × GE F404-GE-400	10,600[1]		16,500	1700

[1]Cruise rating. [2]Plus 50gal auxiliary. [3]Sea level. [4]Military rating. [5]Plus 1–150gal tank. [6]Power off. [7]Plus 1–190gal tank. [8]To 15,000ft. [9]Plus 1–300gal [17]Swept. [18]61–9 folded. [19]Minimum WOD for catapult = 10.6kts. [20]Plus 2–280gal tanks. [21]STOL.

Attack Aircraft

Aircraft	Year	Engine	Normal	Take-off	Dash	Fuel capacity (gal)
Martin T3M-2	1926	1 × Packard 3A-2500	710			300
Martin T4M-1	1927	1 × R-1690-24	525			200
Great Lakes TG-2	1928	1 × R-1820-82	575[1]			220
Martin BM-1	1930	1 × R-1690-44	625			104[2]
Curtiss O2C-1 Helldiver	1931	1 × R-1340-4	450[1]			120
Great Lakes BG-1	1933	1 × R-1535-82	700	750		165[2]
Curtiss BF2C-1	1933	1 × R-1820-04	700	730		110[3]

| Carrier compatibility | | | | | | | | | | |
| Dimensions | | | | | | Take-off | | | | Landing |
Span (full) (ft–in/m)	Span (folded) (ft–in/m)	Length (ft–in/m)	Height (folded) (ft–in/m)	Wing area (sq ft/m²)	Weight (lb)	Stall speed (kts)	Roll @ 0kts WOD (ft/m)	Roll @ 25kts WOD (ft/m)	Weight (lb)	Stall speed (kts)
35–0	–	26–4	12–0	209	6321	70.2	508	230	5661	66.4
38–0	14–4	29–0	10–0	260	7975	70.6	640	278		66.7
42–10	16–2	33–7	12–6	334	13,797	79.2[6]	799	384		72.2
41–0	17–1	33–8	16–4	314	13,597	81.0[6]	790	377		66.9
35–6	23–9½	27–8	13–0	244	10,674	67.9	544	250		67.9
54–0	29–5	43–3	15–10	489	17,508	71.6	639	415		66.6
40–9	16–3	38–9	17–2	274	11,292	83.0	1520	785		72.2
51–6	32–4	45–5¼	17–0	455	21,720	79.2	701	495		74.2
44–10	–	40–2	16–0	294	19,602	100.8	2150	1300		100.8
38–0	23–9	38–10	18–9	250	17,766	114.2	2257	1435	12,819	94.0
50–0	26–10	45–5	16–6	400	24,614	97.1[6]	2080	1270	17,799	80.6
33–6	25–1⅞	45–5¼	12–11⅞	557	27,116	120.0[6]	3295	2300	18,982	100.0
34–6	14–2	40–11	15–10	300	18,450	111.0[6]	2100	1360	14,046	93.0
39–9	22–4	44–3	14–10	535	28,173	119.0[6]	2500	1650	21,593	96.0
31–8	27–4	44–10	13–3	250	21,035	124.5[6]	4260	3100	15,275	103.0
39–1	27–6	36–4	13–11	339	26,893	142.3[6]	6700	5050	16,419	106.2
35–4	25–3	59–0	14–7	519	34,641	117.0[6]	2330[15]	1550[15]	25,001	93.0
35–8	22–6	54–3	15–9	375	37,938	137.5[6]	5720	4130	19,560	110.4
38–4	27–6	56–3	15–8	530	46,838	138.0[6]	2490[15]	1230[15]	35,498	120.0
70–0	33–11[17]	66–10[18]	16–8	550	77,566	114.3[6]	[19]	[19]	56,980	99.6
64–2	38–2	61–10	16–0	565	70,700					
30–4	–	44–3	11–8	360	29,750[21]					
37–6		56–0	15–4	400	33,600					

tank. [10]Plus 400gal in tip tanks. [11]Wet. [12]Plus 240gal in tip tanks. [13]10,200 military rating. [14]Including drop tank. [15]Max. [16]Plus 2–450gal tanks.

56–7/56–7	–	42–6	15–11	883	9505	47.9			8683	
53–0/53–0	–	37–8	16–0	656	7387	49.3	674	185	6765	47.2
53–0/53–0	–	35–0	15–0	656	8377	52.5	687	211	7777	50.6
41–0/40–0	–	28–5	12–4	436	6181	53.7	592	189	5557	55.1
32–0/32–0	–	25–8	10–11	308	4141	53.8	465	149	3421	48.9
36–0/33–9	–	28–9	11–0	384	6297	58.1	591	214	5667	50.8
31–6/26–6	–	23–0	10–10	262	5086	63.5	828	331	4426	59.1

	Range Max (nm)	Range At (kts)	Range With tanks (no-gal)	CAP loiter (hrs)	Mission time (hrs) or combat radius (nm)	Climb To 5000ft (min)	Climb To 10,000ft (min)	Climb To 20,000ft (min)	Climb To 30,000ft (min)	Climb Initial rate (sea level) (ft/m per min)	Low altitude Speed (kts)	Low altitude At (ft/m)
Brewster F2A-3 Buffalo	1330	143	1–53			4.4	9.2			2290	247	SL
Grumman F4F-4 Wildcat	1109	133	2–58			5.6	12.4			3650[25]	238.3	SL
Grumman F6F-5 Hellcat	1339	148.7	1–150		375	5.2	11.2[26]			2980	276[27]	SL
Vought F4U-4 Corsair	1300	180	2–150		525	4.2	8.8			4770[25]	325	SL
Grumman F8F-1 Bearcat	1810	207	1–150, 2–100[28]		679	3.3	7.4			3230[13,29]	366	SL
Boeing XF8B-1	2417	149	1–270[31], 2–150[32]		850	3.8	8.1			2800[27]	296[27]	SL
McDonnell FH-1 Phantom	790	267	1–295[33]		320		15.5[34]			4800[35]	410[35]	SL
Grumman F7F-3 Tigercat	1365	193	1–300		360	2.3	5.4			4530	318	SL
McDonnell F2H-2 Banshee							6.7	12.1		7140[35]	474	SL
Grumman F9F-5 Panther	1130	418					4.8	8.7		5090	500	SL
Douglas F3D-2 Skyknight	1195	395	2–150		520		9.9	20.9		2970	420	SL
Douglas F4D-1 Skyray	1000	448		0.7	1.7		5.1	10.5		5400	495	SL
Grumman F9F-6 Cougar	810	470					4.0	6.8		5600	530	SL
Vought F7U-3 Cutlass	770	450	2–150		245		6.9	13.9		3770[30]	450	SL
Grumman F11F-1 Tiger	1146[40]	466	2–150	0.6[41]	1.6[42]		4.7	8.1		5130[43]	570	SL
North American FJ-4B Fury	995[45]	470		2.6	3.7		8.5	16.2		5100	547	SL
McDonnell F3H-2M Demon	1295	M0.74	[46]	0.74	2.13		6.98	15.75		4425[47]	M0.78	SL
LTV F-8C Crusader	1295	495		0.68	1.63		4.2	6.8		5200[48]	583[49]	SL
McDonnell F-4J Phantom	1521	496	1–600, 2–370	0.79[30]	1.47		0.62[51]	1.1[51]		41,250[51]	760[51]	SL
General Dynamics F-111B				1.52	2.37		1.2[51]	2.2[51]		17,900[51]	678[51,52]	SL
Grumman F-14A Tomcat	1740[53]			1.5							790[25]	SL
McDonnell Douglas AV-8B	2460[53]		4–300								585 (M0.85)	SL
McDonnell Douglas F-18A Hornet											795	SL

[22]15.0min to 15,000ft. [23]To 15,000ft. [24]1 flexible. [25]Dash. [26]7.9 min at combat rating, no drop tank. [27]Military rating. [28]Underwing. [29]5610 military [39]11,150 dash. [40]2.11 hrs. [41]1.08 with tank. [42]1.85 with tank. [43]16,300 dash. [44]Endurance (hrs). [45]1.7hrs. [46]Tanks in lieu of 2 Sparrows. [47]12,030 max.

Attack Aircraft

	Range Max (nm)	Range At (kts)	Range With tanks (no-gal)	CAP loiter (hrs)	Mission time (hrs) or combat radius (nm)	Climb To 5000ft (min)	Climb To 10,000ft (min)	Climb To 20,000ft (min)	Climb To 30,000ft (min)	Climb Initial rate (sea level) (ft/m per min)	Low altitude Speed (kts)	Low altitude At (ft/m)
Martin T3M-2						16.8					95.1	SL
Martin T4M-1	589.6					14.1					99.1	SL
Great Lakes TG-2	623.5					10.1					111.1	SL
Martin BM-1	610.4		1–60			7.3	36.2[12]					SL
Curtiss O2C-1 Helldiver						5.5	32.0[12]				127.9	SL
Great Lakes BG-1	1082.6	99.1	1–60			6.1	12.3	21.5		820	148.7	SL
Curtiss BF2C-1	916.5		1–50			3.1	11.0					SL

| High altitude | | | Combat radius (nm) | Dash | | Service ceiling (ft/m) | Guns | Armament Load | |
Speed (kts)	At (ft/m)	Range/at (nm/kts)		Speed (kts)	At (ft/m)			Bomb load for given performance	Alternative loads
258.3	4500	839				33,200	4–0.50	–	2–100lb bombs
278.3	18,800	722/140	91	247	SL	34,000	6–0.50	–	2–100lb bombs
308	23,900	950	340	330	23,400	35,100	4–0.50, 2–20mm	–	2–1000lb bombs or 1 torpedo
347	31,400	1005/185	315/178	393	20,500	38,400	6–0.50	–	2–500 or 1000lb bombs or 2–11.75in AR plus 8 HVAR
339	19,600	1230/217	216/203	372	18,800	34,700	4–20mm	–	1–1600lb bomb or 11.75in AR[30]; 2–1000lb or 11.75in AR or 4.5in HVAR[28]
347	26,400		170	357.4	26,900	35,300	6–0.50	–	1–2000lb or 2–1600 or 1000lb or 4–500lb or 1 or 2 torpedoes[31]; 2–2000 or 1600 or 1000 or 500lb bombs[28]
324[34]	20,000		245/245	421	15,000		4–0.50	–	–
346	23,100			378	22,200	40,700[27]	4–0.50, 4–20mm	–	1–2000 or 1600lb bomb or torpedo or 11.75in AR plus 2–1000 or 500lb bombs or 11.75in AR or 8–5in HVAR
475	10,000	715/400		517	SL	41,000	4–20mm	–	–
503	5000	420/418		525[36]	SL	42,800	4–20mm	–	6 AR or 2–1000lb or 6–500lb or 8–250lb bombs
426	15,000			460[37]	10,000	36,700	4–20mm	–	2–500 or 1000 or 2000lb bombs or 2–11.75in AR
529	15,000			623[38]	SL	37,600	–	4 Sidewinder, 2–300gal tanks	4–20mm or 4–2.75in pack (7 or 19 pack)
513	35,000		255/470	568	SL	44,500	4–20mm	–	–
473	18,000		160/450	589	SL	36,100	4–20mm	–	32–2.75in AR, 2 bombs up to 3500lb, or 1 Mk 7, 8 or 12 nuclear weapon
588	18,000	1.57[44]	310	654	SL	41,900	4–20mm	–	4 Sidewinder or 2–150gal tanks and 2 Sidewinder
502	20,000		780/442	552	10,000	40,200	–	1 Mk 28 bomb with 1–200gal, 2–150gal tanks	6 Sidewinder or HVAR or rocket packs or 500lb bombs or 5 Bullpup or 2–1000 or 2000lb bombs or 1 Mk 7, 12 or 28 nuclear weapon
M0.85	25,000	2.09[44]	302	M0.95	30,000	32,450	4–20mm	4 Sparrow or 2–141gal tanks	4 Sidewinder
		1.65[44]	320/495	960	35,000	41,700	4–20mm	32–2.75in FFAR	2 Sidewinder
601	25,000	981/480	351/489	1250	36,059	39,750	–	4 Sparrow	1 nuclear weapon or 24–500 or 750lb or 11–1000lb bombs or (total) 6 Sparrow or 4 Sidewinder or gun pods or rocket packs
		1830/416	475/420	1260	40,000	32,100	–	6 Phoenix, no tanks	Gun pod, Sidewinder, Shrike, 8 stores stations with 3000lb each (2 internal)
550[54]				1360	49,000	56,000	1–20mm	6 Phoenix	Sparrow, Sidewinder, up to 14,500lb stores
M0.91			601				2–30mm	7–500lb[55]	
1035			350[56]				1–20mm	2 Sparrow, 2 Sidewinder	

rating. [30]In lieu of drop tank. [31]Bomb bay. [32]Drop tanks. [33]No 190gal tank. [34]Cruise rating. [35]Take-off rating. [36]At 15,359lb. [37]At 21,374lb. [38]No tanks. [48]25,400 dash. [49]653 dash. [50]1.5 with 600gal tank. [51]Max. [52]568 normal. [53]Ferry. [54]With afterburner. [55]Hi-lo-hi. [56]CAP.

| High altitude | | | Combat radius (nm) | Dash | | Service ceiling (ft/m) | Guns | Armament Load | |
Speed (kts)	At (ft/m)	Range/at (nm/kts)		Speed (kts)	At (ft/m)			Bomb load for given performance	Alternative loads
93	5000					7900	1–0.30	1 torpedo	–
95.7	5000	315.7				10,150	1–0.30	1 torpedo	–
106.9	5000	293				11,600	2–0.30	1 torpedo	1–1000lb or 3–500lb
98.3	15,000	360.9				14,900	2–0.30	1–1000lb	1–500lb bomb
101.7	15,000	626				16,300	3–0.30	1–500lb	2–116lb bombs
151.3	15,000	504.3				19,100	1–0.30 or 1–0.50	1–1000lb	4–100lb or 1–500lb bombs
174.8	15,000	608.7				22,700	2–0.30	1–500lb	4–116lb bombs

Aircraft	Year	Engine	Powerplant Rating (hp/lb thrust)			Fuel capacity (gal)
			Normal	Take-off	Dash	
Douglas TBD-1 Devastator	1935	1 × R-1830-64	850	900		
Vought SBU-2	1936	1 × R-1535-98	700	750		145
Curtiss SBC-4 Helldiver	1938	1 × R-1820-34	850	950		135
Vought SB2U-3 Vindicator	1940	1 × R-1535-02	750	825		216
Brewster SB2A-1 Buccaneer	1941	1 × R-2600-8	1500[1]	1700		334
Douglas SBD-5 Dauntless	1942	1 × R-1820-60	1000	1200		254
Grumman TBM-3 Avenger	1944	1 × R-2600-20	1600	1800	1750[4]	335
Martin AM-1 Mauler	1944	1 × R-4360-4W	2500	3000		960[5]
Grumman XTB2F-1	1944[7]	2 × R-2800-22	1700[1]	2100		960
Curtiss SB2C-5 Helldiver	1945	1 × R-2600-20	1600[1]	1900	1750[4]	355
Douglas AD-1 Skyraider	1945	1 × R-3350-24W	2100[1]	2500	2950[4]	515[5]
Douglas XTB2D-1[8]	1945	1 × R-4360-8	2500	3000		774
North American AJ-1 Savage	1948	2 × R-2800-44W plus 1 × J33-A-10		1800+3900	2300+4600	1217[9]
Douglas AD-4 Skyraider	1949	1 × R-3550-26WA	2300	2700		380
Douglas A-3B Skywarrior	1955	2 × J57-P-10	9000[1]	10,500		4338
North American A-5A Vigilante	1958	2 × J79-GE-8	10,300[1]	10,900	17,000	2215
Douglas A-4C Skyhawk	1959	1 × J65-W-16A	6780[1]	7000		800
LTV A-7B Corsair	1968	1 × TF30-P-8	9600[1]	12,200		1500
Grumman A-6E Intruder	1970	2 × J52-P8-A/8	8200[1]	9300		2344[1]

Anti-Submarine and Airborne Early Warning Aircraft

Aircraft	Year	Engine	Normal	Take-off	Dash	Fuel capacity (gal)
Grumman AF-2S Guardian	1945	1 × R-2800-48W	1900[1]	2300		420
Grumman AF-2W Guardian	1945	1 × R-2800-48W	1900[1]	2300		420
Douglas AD-5W Skyraider	1951	1 × R-3350-26W	2300[1]	2700		380[5]
Grumman E-1B Tracer	1957	2 × R-1820-82A	1275[1]	1525	1425	753
Grumman S-2D Tracker	1959	2 × R-1820-82A	1275[1]	1525	1425	728
Grumman E-2C Hawkeye	1971	2 × T56-A-8/8A	3730[1]	4050		1824
Lockheed S-3A Viking	1971	2 × TF34-GE-2	17,130[1]			1933

[1]Cruise rating. [2]60gal auxiliary. [3]50gal auxiliary. [4]Military rating. [5]Plus 2–150gal tanks. [6]Power off. [7]Project. [8]Estimated figures. [9]Plus 2–300gal drop

	Carrier compatibility									
Dimensions						Take-off				Landing
Span (full) (ft–in/m)	Span (folded) (ft–in/m)	Length (ft–in/m)	Height (folded) (ft–in/m)	Wing area (sq ft/m²)	Weight (lb)	Stall speed (kts)	Roll @ 0kts WOD (ft/m)	Roll @ 25kts WOD (ft/m)	Weight (lb)	Stall speed (kts)
50–0	25–9	35–0	11–0	422	9800	59.4	820	330		
33–3/31–2	–	27–9	12–0	327	5620	57.3	604	224	5020	54.2
34–0/32–0	–	28–2	12–7	317	6624	60.6	648	260		
41–11	16–0	34–0	16–4	305	8373	66.6	1045	463		64.0
47–0	21–8	38–11	15–9	379	13,321	70.0	903	425	12,103	65.9
41–6	–	32–6	12–3	325	10,403	69.4	1225	570		64.0
54–2	19–0	41–0	13–9	490	16,761	67.7	1106	455		63.4
50–1	23–8	41–3	16–2	496	24,145	89.0	1045	520	19,285	85.0[6]
74–0	33–6	51–0	17–0	777	35,720	79.7	1032	518		73.0
49–9	22–7	36–9	16–10	422	16,287	77.8	1243	584	13,357	66.2[6]
50–0	24–0	37–8	16–11	400	18,029	81.0	958	455	15,739	76.0[6]
70–0	36–0	46–0	17–0	605	28,478	69.7	755	548		82.0
75–0[10]	49–4	64–1	17–4[10]	836	49,952	103.0[6]	1300	720	34,071	72.4
50–0	23–11	39–3	16–8	400	21,483	89.0[6]	1390	740	13,828	68.2
72–5	49–2	74–7	16–7	779	72,000	132.0[6]	4460	1940	42,916	99.0
53–0	42–0	76–6	14–6	700	55,132	134.5	2700	1800	35,963	106.0
27–6	–	40–1	15–0	260	17,837	118.0[6]	2900	2200	11,446	90.4
38–7	23–8	46–1	16–1	375	37,027	141.8[6]			19,420	100.3
53–0	25–4	54–9	16–3	530	54,393	124.0[6]	3990	3020	19,783	83.0
60–0	26–2	43–5	16–7	549	20,298	76.9[6]	925	545	16,862	65.1
60–0	26–2	43–5	16–7	549	19,637	76.8[6]	989	518	17,368	67.2
50–0	23–11	40–1	16–7	400	19,587	83.9[6]	980	470	15,566	69.1
72–4	30–3	45–4	16–10	506	26,594	84.0[6]	1960	1380		
72–7	27–4	43–6	16–8	496	29,217	85.0[6]	1940	1100	25,285	70.0
80–7	29–4	56–4	16–6	700	50,920	91.5[6]	1590	2285	39,756	71.0
68–8	29–6	53–4	15–3	598	43,449	100.0	2040	1310	31,409	80.0

tanks and 1–500gal bomb bay tank. [10]With tanks. [11]Plus 4–300gal tanks.

| | Performance | | | | | | | | | | | |
| | Range | | | | | Climb | | | | | Low altitude | |
	Max (nm)	At (kts)	With tanks (no–gal)	CAP loiter (hrs)	Mission time (hrs) or combat radius (nm)	To 5000ft (min)	To 10,000ft (min)	To 20,000ft (min)	To 30,000ft (min)	Initial rate (sea level) (ft/m per min)	Speed (kts)	At (ft/m)
Douglas TBD-1 Devastator						14.2				720	167	SL
Vought SBU-2	739.1	106.0				8.7	23.0			1180	149.6	SL
Curtiss SBC-4 Helldiver	950.4	110.4	1–45			6.2	15.7			1710	186	SL
Vought SB2U-3 Vindicator	2130	138.3			204	13.2					180	SL
Brewster SB2A-1 Buccaneer	1478[14]	153	425[15]			7.0	18.4			1510	241.7	SL
Douglas SBD-5 Dauntless	1360.9	121.7				7.4	19.1			1700	192.2	SL
Grumman TBM-3 Avenger	2200	125[14]	1–275[16], 2–100[13]			10.7	30.0			1170	219.1	SL
Martin AM-1 Mauler						7.0	18.6			1550[17]	283[18]	SL
Grumman XTB2F-1	2322	133	2–300[13]		715	7.7	18.9			1710[19]	261[19]	SL
Curtiss SB2C-5 Helldiver						8.8	22.4[20]			1320[21]	232[18]	SL
Douglas AD-1 Skyraider						6.0	14.4			2050[22]	311[18]	SL
Douglas XTB2D-1			1–300			10.0	25.4			1040	243.5	SL
North American AJ-1 Savage	2660	233[23]	2–300[24]				12.0[23]	26.0[23]		2900[23]	310	SL
Douglas AD-4 Skyraider						7.5	22.0			1540	232	SL
Douglas A-3B Skywarrior							4.9	8.7		5100[25]	558	SL
North American A-5A Vigilante	2270	487	2–400[27]				3.2	6.2		8000[28]	700	SL
Douglas A-4C Skyhawk							3.4	6.1		7200	562	SL
LTV A-7B Corsair	2770	462	2–300[15]				7.7			4040[31]	528	SL
Grumman A-6E Intruder	2866	415	5–300[15]				5.1	9.9		5280[32]	523	SL
Anti-Submarine and Airborne Early Warning Aircraft												
Grumman AF-2S Guardian	1315	145	2–150			7.3	22.0[12]			1480[33]	230[34]	SL
Grumman AF-2W Guardian	1315	145	2–150			6.9	23.8[12]			1565[35]	228[26]	SL
Douglas AD-5W Skyraider	1650	154	2–300			6.4	16.9				242[26]	SL
Grumman E-1B Tracer	900[36]	137[36]		4.63[37]	6.83[38]		11.3			1120	201[26]	SL
Grumman S-2D Tracker	1130[36]	144[36]					12.0			1040[39]	193[26]	SL
Grumman E-2C Hawkeye				4.02				20.0		2515[40]	306[26]	SL
Lockheed S-3A Viking	3368	346	2–300				6.3	12.0		4150	429	SL

[12]To 15,000ft. [13]Underwing. [14]Scout. [15]Total. [16]Bomb bay. [17]3130 combat. [18]Combat rating. [19]Military rating. [20]14.9 combat. [21]1830 combat. [22]4360 [33]2300 dash. [34]228 dash. [35]2200 dash. [36]Ferry. [37]At 5000ft; 4.19 at 10,000ft. [38]At 5000ft; 6.30 at 10,000ft. [39]1420 dash. [40]3290 dash.

High altitude			Combat radius (nm)	Dash		Service ceiling (ft/m)	Armament — Guns	Armament — Load	
Speed (kts)	At (ft/m)	Range/at (nm/kts)		Speed (kts)	At (ft/m)			Bomb load for given performance	Alternative loads
179.1	8000	534.8/111				19,800	2–0.30	1–500lb	2–100lb bombs
170.4	8900	470.4				24,500	2–0.30	1–500lb	2–100lb bombs
201.7	15,200	513				23,500	1–0.30 or 0.50	1–500lb	1–1000lb or 2–100lb bombs
195.7	9500	461/129				19,900	2–0.50, 1–0.30	1–1000lb	1–500 or 1600lb bomb; 2–100lb[13]
261.7	13,000	870/156				23,500	6–0.50	1–1000lb	2–500lb or 2 depth bombs
219.1	13,800	970/121	209			24,100	2–0.50, 2–0.30	1–1000lb	1–1600 or 500lb bomb, 2–100 or 325lb bombs or 8–5in AR
232.2	15,000	983/131	183			22,600	3–0.50, 1–0.30	1 torpedo	1–2000 or 1600lb or 2–1000lb or 4–500lb or 12–100lb bombs
268	16,000	1324/186	670/175	293	15,000	24,400	4–20mm	1–2000lb	3–2000 or 500lb bombs or 1 torpedo or 1–1000 or 2000lb mine, 2–11.75in or 12–5in rockets
277	20,400	395		280	17,900	25,200	11–0.50	2 torpedoes	4–2000 or 1600 or 1000lb or 10–500lb or 36–100lb or 1–4000lb bombs
		890/150	345/175	252	16,500	24,700	2–20mm, 2–0.30	1–1000lb, APS-4 radar	1–2000lb or 2–500lb or 3–100lb or 1 torpedo[16]; 2–1000 or 500 or 250 or 100lb or 8 HVAR[13]
256	16,000	1390/174	675/175	310	1500	28,000	4–20mm	1–2000lb	3–2000 or 500lb bombs or 1 torpedo or 1–1000 or 2000lb mine, 2–11.75in or 12–5in rockets
272	16,500	1252/150				24,500	7–0.50	2 torpedoes	1 or 2 torpedoes or 4–500 or 1000lb or 2–1600 or 2000lb bombs
300[23]	26,000	2190/234	1010/207	390	34,000	34,500	–	1–3025lb Mk5 nuclear bomb	1 nuclear bomb up to 7600lb (Mk 15) or up to 10,000lb total (eg 6–1600lb)
256	20,000	1170/197	540/184	303	20,000	23,500	4–20mm	1–2000lb store, 12–5in HVAR, 2–150gal tanks	Max 6500lb ordnance from ship, 9900lb from shore
485[26]	41,500	2360/459	1200/459	559	SL	39,100	2–20mm	2–2025lb nuclear weapons (high altitude attack)	Max 12,800lb bombs (eg 4–2000lb, 8–1600lb)
597	20,000	1750/487	685/487	1147	40,000	41,400	–	1–1885lb Mk 28 nuclear weapon (high altitude attack)	2 external stores up to 2000lb or 400gal tanks
515[29]	35,000	820/405	160/405	566	SL	39,200	2–20mm	SL delivery of 2025lb store	4–150gal drop tanks or up to 4300lb[13]; up to 3757lb[30]
533	9000	2794/454	1210/457	535	10,000	31,700	2–20mm	Deep strike: 1 Mk 28 nuclear bomb (2000lb) and 3–300gal tanks	2 500lb, 4 3500lb, 2 2500lb pylons
		2407/413	773/339	552	SL	37,700	–	1–2060lb nuclear weapon (hi-lo-lo-hi delivery)	Up to 18,000lb total (eg 28 Mk 81 Snakeye)
231	9200	799/144	320/144	239	4000	22,900	–	1 Mk 34 torpedo	4 depth bombs (max cap 3700lb)[13], 6–5in AR
230	9200	750/144	300/144	237	4000	21,200	–	–	4 depth bombs (max cap 3700lb)[13], 6–5in AR
251	18,900	1055/151	420/151	266	19,300	25,300	–	AEW radar	–
197	4000	875/142	150/142	207	4000	15,800	–	AEW radar	–
191	5000	800/130	320/130	200	4000	16,000	–	6 Mk 46 torpedoes	1 Mk10 depth bomb, 4 torpedoes, 2 HVAR
302	10,000		200	315	13,500	28,800	–	AEW radar	–
393	40,000	2628/356	458			39,800	–	2 Mk 57 bombs, 48 sonobuoys	4 Mk 46 torpedoes, 60 sonobuoys, external stores up to 2500lb

combat. [23]Piston engines only. [24]840gal bomb bay. [25]6250 dash. [26]Dash. [27]Same weapon. [28]33,900 dash. [29]Max. [30]Centerline. [31]5370 dash. [32]7150 dash.

Aircraft	Year	Engine	Normal	Take-off	Dash	Fuel capacity (gal)
JAPAN						
Fighter Aircraft						
Nakajima A1N1	?	1 × Jupiter 6	520[1]			
Nakajima A2N1	1931	1 × Nakajima Ju 2	580[1]			
Nakajima A4N1	1936	1 × Nakajima Hikari 1	730[1]			
Mitsubishi A5M4 ('Claude')	1937	1 × Nakajima Kotobuki 41	680		785[2]	93
Mitsubishi A6M2 Zero ('Zeke')	1939	1 × Sakae 12	925	940	950[2]	143
Mitsubishi A6M5 Zero ('Zeke')	1943	1 × Sakae 21	1130	1130	1100[2]	150
Mitsubishi A7M2 Reppu ('Sam')	1944	1 × MK9A	2200	2200		240

[1]Cruise rating. [2]Military rating. [3]27kts WOD. [4]Landing speed.

Aircraft	Year	Engine	Normal	Take-off	Dash	Fuel capacity (gal)
Attack Aircraft						
Mitsubishi B1M1	1925	1 × Napier Lion		450		100.3
Mitsubishi B2M1	1933	1 × Mitsubishi 'HI 600'		790		
Yokosuka B3Y1	1933	1 × Type 91	600	750		
Yokosuka B4Y1	1935	1 × Hikari 2	700	840		
Aichi D1A2 ('Susie')	1936	1 × Hikari 1	730			198
Nakajima B5N2 ('Kate')	1939	1 × Sakae NK1B	970	1000		304
Aichi D3A2 ('Val')	1942	1 × Kinsei 54	1300			264
Nakajima B6N2 Tenzan ('Jill')	1942	1 × Kasei 25	1680	1850		424
Aichi B7A2 Ryusei ('Grace')	1942	1 × Homare NK9C	1540	1970	2050[2]	371
Nakajima C6N1 Saiun ('Myrt')	1943	1 × Homare NK9H	1870	1990		358
Yokosuka D4Y2 ('Judy')	1944	1 × Atsuta 32	1340	1400		282
Yokosuka D4Y3 ('Judy')	1944	1 × Kinsei MK8P	1340	1560		282

[1]27kts WOD. [2]Military rating.

Source Notes

The notes which follow are limited to principal archival materials and to principal books consulted, and thus do not include many hundreds of magazine articles, which were particularly important for aircraft data.

Data on US Navy carrier design and design doctrine has been taken primarily from official manuscript sources, at the National Archives, the Washington Navy Yard, and the Federal Record Center at Suitland. Most US naval aircraft data is derived from the official Standard Aircraft Characteristics booklets, the chief exceptions being recent types for which data was derived from standard (and unofficial) published sources. In addition, some data was taken from G Swanborough and P M Bowers, *United States Naval Aircraft* (Annapolis, 1979); from L S Jones, *US Navy Fighters* (Fallbrook, 1978), and from W T Larkins, *US Navy Aircraft 1921–1941* (Concord, 1961). Two official published sources must also be mentioned: a BuAer history of naval air *matériel* development 1936–1946, compiled after World War II by the BuAer historian, Lee Pearson, and a series of articles on the development of individual aircraft types which Dr Pearson published in the BuAer Confidential Bulletin in the early 1950s, now

| Carrier compatibility | | | | | | | | | | |
| Dimensions | | | | | | Take-off | | | Landing | |
Span (full) (ft-in/m)	Span (folded) (ft-in/m)	Length (ft-in/m)	Height (folded) (ft-in/m)	Wing area (sq ft/m²)	Weight (lb)	Stall speed (kts)	Roll @ 0kts WOD (ft/m)	Roll @ 25kts WOD (ft/m)	Weight (lb)	Stall speed (kts)
31.8	–	21.3	10.7	283	3196					
30.7	–	20.2	9.9	212	3416					
32.8	–	21.8	10.1	246	3879					
36–1	–	24–10	10–6	192	3684					
39–4	–	29–9	10–0	241.5	5139	60.0	636	262[3]		60.0[4]
36–1	–	29–11	11–6	229.3	6494	68.0	777	295[3]		63.5[4]
45–11	–	36–1	14–1	332	10,384					70.0[4]
48.4	–	32.0	11.5	635	5905					
49.1	–	33.4	11.8	527	7009					
44.3	–	31.3	12.2	538	7053					
49.2	–	33.3	14.3	538	7937					
37.3	–	30.8	11.2	371	6171					
50–11	24–7	33–10	12–2	406	8378	61.0	741	279[1]		61.0
47–2	–	33–5	12–7	376	8375	67.0	689	279[1]		70.0
48–10	23–8	35–8	12–6	400	11,464	70.0	850	426[1]		72.0
47–3	24–7	37–9	13–5	381	12,563	70.0	820	426[1]		69.5
41–0	–	36–1	13–0	274	9808	71.2		407[1]	8287	65.2
37–9	–	33–7	12–3	254	8455	78.0	1050	410[1]		78.0
37–9	–	33–7	12–3	254	8276	79.0	1155	410[1]		

declassified. In addition the Naval Air Systems Command Historical Office holds manuscript material on the development of most postwar US naval aircraft.

For British carriers I have relied primarily on the manuscript official materials in the Ship Covers at the National Maritime Museum, Greenwich. Unfortunately I was unable to obtain material of parallel quality on British naval aircraft (only figures for the Swordfish, Sea Hurricane, Fulmar, Firefly I, Barracuda, Sea Hornet and Spearfish being official data based on flight tests), and had to rely instead on a variety of published sources, principally the Putnam aircraft series (volumes on Blackburn, de Havilland, Fairey, and Hawker aircraft); on E M Brown, *Wings of the Navy* (London, 1979); on J D Brown, *Seafire* (London, 1973); and F K Mason, *The Gloster Gladiator* (London, 1962). To some extent figures in these books have been checked against official Admiralty data in the wartime *Particulars of War Vessels and Naval Aircraft*. As J D Brown has pointed out, there is a real conflict between the 'brochure' figures which are usually cited and realistic figures describing aircraft already well worn in service, such as wartime types with rebuilt engines. To

some extent the US Navy figures do appear to reflect service conditions, but the test pilot reports often cited in the Putnam series probably came closer to the 'brochure' category; comparisons are, at best, uncertain. For a few of the late wartime prototypes I have used the figures undoubtedly official in origin, appearing in Volume 7 of *Aircraft of the Fighting Powers* and in Jane's 1945/46 edition. These are all, at best, unreliable data. Moreover, no complete figures have yet been released concerning the later postwar jet fighters such as the Sea Venom, Sea Vixen, and Scimitar, all of which have long since passed from service.

For British naval practice and naval policy there are several parallel sources. From the latter part of World War I onwards US naval officers were welcome in the Royal Navy, and the files of the US Office of Naval Intelligence are replete with their reports; they are referred to in the current text as the reports of US 'observers.' Captain Stephen Roskill has produced both a compilation of *Documents Relating to the Naval Air Service 1908–1918* (London, 1969) and a two-volume history of *Naval Policy Between the Wars* (London, 1968 and 1976). Interwar policy is

| | Performance | | | | | | | | | | | |
| | Range | | | | | Climb | | | | | Low altitude | |
	Max (nm)	At (kts)	With tanks (no-gal)	CAP loiter (hrs)	Mission time (hrs) or combat radius (nm)	To 5000ft (min)	To 10,000ft (min)	To 20,000ft (min)	To 30,000ft (min)	Initial rate (sea level) (ft/m per min)	Speed (kts)	(ft/m)
Fighter Aircraft												
Nakajima A1N1						7.3[5]						
Nakajima A2N1						5.75[5]						
Nakajima A4N1						3.5[5]						
Mitsubishi A5M4 ('Claude')	648	216	1–42			3.6[5]						
Mitsubishi A6M2 Zero ('Zeke')	1810	160	1–87				7.45[7]			*4517*		
Mitsubishi A6M5 Zero ('Zeke')							7.0[7]			*2800*		
Mitsubishi A7M2 Reppu ('Sam')			2–92				6.1[7]					

[5]To 3000m (9840ft). [6]Endurance (hrs). [7]To 6000m (19,680ft).

| | Performance | | | | | | | | | | | |
| | Range | | | | | Climb | | | | | Low altitude | |
	Max (nm)	At (kts)	With tanks (no-gal)	CAP loiter (hrs)	Mission time (hrs) or combat radius (nm)	To 5000ft (min)	To 10,000ft (min)	To 20,000ft (min)	To 30,000ft (min)	Initial rate (sea level) (ft/m per min)	Speed (kts)	(ft/m)
Attack Aircraft												
Mitsubishi B1M1												
Mitsubishi B2M1						12.0[4]						
Yokosuka B3Y1												
Yokosuka B4Y1						14.0[4]				150		
Aichi D1A2 ('Susie')						7.9[4]						
Nakajima B5N2 ('Kate')	1076					7.7[4]	13.8[5]					
Aichi D3A2 ('Val')						5.8[4]						
Nakajima B6N2 Tenzan ('Jill')	1644		1.79			5.6[4]	10.4[5]					
Aichi B7A2 Ryusei ('Grace')	1640						10.3[6]					
Nakajima C6N1 Saiun ('Myrt')	2730	210	1–192				7.6[6]				280.7	SL
Yokosuka D4Y2 ('Judy')	1945		2–87			4.6[4]	7.7[6]					
Yokosuka D4Y3 ('Judy')	1560					4.6[4]						

[3]Endurance (hrs). [4]To 3000m (9840ft). [5]To 5000m (16,400ft). [6]To 6000m (19,680ft).

also analysed in detail by G Till, in *Air Power and the Royal Navy* (London, 1979); Dr Till provides details of prewar British naval tactical policy through the examples of naval exercises. Wartime operational practice is described in J D Brown, *Carrier Operations In World War Two* (Volume I, London, 1968) and *Carrier Fighters* (London, 1975). For postwar Royal Navy policy I have relied on a Doctoral Dissertation prepared by Cdr W J Crowe Jr, of the US Navy, 'Policy Roots of the Modern Royal Navy, 1946–63'. Commander Crowe, a naval aviator, wrote at Princeton in 1965 just as it appeared that the Royal Navy had succeeded in its fight to modernize its naval air arm, with CVA-01 clearly in prospect. The postwar history of British naval aircraft is also described in detail in D Wood, *Project Cancelled* (London, 1975). Finally, my account of British wartime aircraft procurement policy, and particularly of the strike aircraft program, is based largely on the notes of a meeting between British and US naval air air representatives, held by the Ministry of Aircraft Production at Seaford House in London, 22 March 1944; my copy is held by the Naval Air Systems Command historian.

Japanese aircraft carrier design data has been taken primarily from the reports of the US Naval Technical Mission to Japan, which interviewed senior Japanese naval officials and naval constructors; from the semi-official publication *Shipbuilding In The Showa Era* (Volume I, Tokyo, 1977) prepared by the Japan Society of Naval Architects; from Japanese materials (both plans and statistics) obtained by the Naval Technical Mission and now held by the US National Archives; and, for the *Shokaku* class, from the *Maru Special* devoted to that class, which includes data apparently of official origin. For aircraft the basic source is a Japanese publication, *Taiheyo senso Nihon kaigunki* (Aireview's Japanese Naval Aircraft of the Pacific War, Tokyo, 1977) supplemented by R Françillon, *Japanese Aircraft of the Pacific War* (Putnam series, 1970), by US Navy test data incorporated in the Naval Technical Mission report on aircraft handling and aircraft-carrying ships and in wartime ONI reports, and, for prewar types, by a *Koku-Fan* special devoted to Japanese wartime and prewar naval aircraft (Tokyo, 1979). E Sekigawa, *Pictorial History of Japanese Military Aviation* (London, 1974) was valuable for background material. For the evolution of tactical doctrine I benefited greatly from a

| High altitude | | | Combat radius (nm) | Dash | | Service ceiling (ft/m) | Armament | | |
| | | | | | | | Guns | Load | |
Speed (kts)	At (ft/m)	Range/at (nm/kts)		Speed (kts)	At (ft/m)			Bomb load for given performance	Alternative loads
129	3000	3.5[6]				7440	2–7.7mm	–	2–66lb bombs
158	3000	221				9800	2–7.7mm	–	2–66lb bombs
190	3200	394				7740	2–7.7mm	–	2–66lb bombs
233.5	3160					9800	2–7.7mm	–	2–66lb bombs
279.5	4300	1200/160				10,000	2–7.7mm, 2–20mm	–	2–66 or 132lb bombs
302	6000	1284/200				11,740	2–7.7mm, 2–20mm	–	2–66 or 132lb or 1–550lb
339	5660	840/225				10,900	4–20mm	–	2–550lb bombs
113		2.6[3]					2–7.7mm	1 torpedo	1–529lb bomb
123		949					2–7.7mm	1 torpedo	1–1763lb bomb
118		4.5[1]					2–7.7mm	1 torpedo	1–1763 or 1102lb or 2–551lb or 6–66lb bombs
		847				6000	1–7.7mm	1 torpedo	1–1763 or 1102lb or 2–551lb or 1102lb total bombs
167	3200	502/120				6980	3–7.7mm	1–551lb and 2–66lb bombs	–
204	3600	551/142				7640	1–7.7mm	1 torpedo	1–1763 or 1102lb or 2–551lb or 6–132lb bombs
231	5650	567/160				10,500	3–7.7mm	1–551lb and 2–66lb bombs	–
260	4900	943/180				9040	1–13mm, 1–7.9mm	1 torpedo	1–1763 or 1102lb or 2–551lb or 6–132lb bombs
293	6200	1000/200				8950	2–20mm, 1–7.7 or 13mm	1 torpedo	1–1763 or 1102lb or 2–551lb bombs
342.8	6000	1687/210				10,800	1–7.9mm	–	–
313	5250	790/230				10,700	2–7.7mm, 1–7.9mm	1–1102 or 551lb, 2–66lb bombs	–
304	5900	820/200				9900	2–7.7mm, 1–13mm	1–1102 or 551lb, 2–66lb bombs	–

seires of lectures and notes prepared by Captain Minoru Genda of the former Imperial Japanese Navy.

For French carriers and their aircraft the standard source must be F Dousset, *Les Porte-Avions Français* (Paris, 1978), which appears to have been based entirely on official documents. Data on the *Graf Zeppelin* is taken from her designer's book: W Hadeler, *Der Flugzeugträger* (Munich, 1968). Finally, I am grateful to Giorgio Giorgerini of *Almanacco Navale* for access to an official report on the *Aquila* design by General Sigismondi, her designer (August 1945).

Norman Friedman

Overleaf: Fifty years of carrier air power – a Fairey Flycatcher posing by HMS *Eagle* in the late 1920s (top) contrasts with the BAe Sea Harrier hovering alongside HMS *Invincible* in 1980.